Applying Cognitive
Psychology to
User-interface Design

Applying Cognitive Psychology to User-interface Design

Edited by

Margaret M. Gardiner

HeptaCon Ltd.

and

Bruce Christie

City of London Polytechnic

JOHN WILEY & SONS
Chichester · New York · Brisbane · Toronto · Singapore

Library of Congress Cataloging in Publication Data:

Applying cognitive psychology to user-interface design.

(Wiley series in information processing)
Includes index.
1. Computer input–output equipment—Design and construction. 2. Cognition. I. Gardiner, Margaret M. II. Christie, Bruce. III. Series.
TK7887.5.A67 1987   004'.019   86–16004
ISBN 0 471 91184 4

British Library Cataloguing in Publication Data:

Applying cognitive psychology to user-
interface design.—(Wiley series in
information processing)
1. Electronic data processing 2. Computer
engineering 3. Man–machine systems
I. Gardiner, Margaret M. II. Christie, Bruce
004.2'1'019   QA76

ISBN 0 471 91184 4

Typeset by Inforum Ltd, Portsmouth
Printed and bound in Great Britain by Anchor Brendon

The Purist

I give you now Professor Twist,
A conscientious scientist.
Trustees exclaimed, 'He never bungles!'
And sent him off to distant jungles.
Camped on a tropic riverside,
One day he missed his loving bride.
She had, the guide informed him later,
Been eaten by an alligator.
Professor Twist could not but smile.
'You mean,' he said, 'a crocodile.'

Ogden Nash
I Wouldn't Have Missed It (1983)

(Reprinted by permission, André Deutsch Ltd.)

Contents

Contributors

Bruce Christie*, City of London Polytechnic[1]
Margaret M. Gardiner*, HeptaCon Ltd.[1]
Nick Hammond, University of York
James A. Hampton, The City University
Graham J. Hitch, University of Manchester
Julian Jones, University of York
Ken Manktelow, Sunderland Polytechnic
Chris Marshall*, Hewlett-Packard[2]
Catherine Nelson*, GEC Research Laboratories
Robert Scane, Southampton University

* Current or former member of the ESPRIT Project 234 Team
[1] Formerly with ITT Europe, ESC-RC, Human Factors Technology Centre
[2] Formerly with GEC Research Laboratories

Ideas from the Warwick University MMI Team were useful in the preparation of sections of Chapter 9.

Preface

The original idea for this book was born out of earlier work by some of the contributors on Project 234 of the ESPRIT Programme of the Commission of the European Communities.

The project was concerned with applying mainstream cognitive psychology to the problems of user-interface design in office systems, with particular emphasis on developing an automated tool for interface evaluation. In this book we build on and expand the achievements of that project, and adopt a broader perspective: we consider the design process and organizational approaches to human factors work, and address the wider field of human factors and the needs of an emerging discipline.

Cognitive psychology is a difficult discipline to write about at the best of times. From the scepticism we encountered early on in our work concerning the feasibility of applying cognitive psychology to user-interface design, we would not have been overly surprised had we ended up with a conspicuously slim volume. Having endured the exceptionally hard work of putting it together, we could perhaps be forgiven for trying to present a rosy picture of the contribution cognitive psychology can make to interface design. However, we emerge at the other end convinced that the discipline does have a lot to offer, and feel our objectivity has not been too badly crippled in the process. We also feel that cognitive psychologists could do a lot more than they do now to make their discipline better known and to increase its impact on the design process. To survive in the competitive field of information technology, psychologists will have to become at least as competitive. We hope this book inspires cognitive psychologists (both budding and well established) to think more carefully about their potential contribution.

We would like to acknowledge here the support we received on the early stages of this work from the Commission of the European Communities, ITT Europe, GEC Research Laboratories, the MRC Applied Psychology Unit, and Logos Progetti s.r.l.

PART ONE:
INTRODUCTION

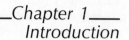

_____Chapter 1___
Introduction

Margaret M. Gardiner and Bruce Christie

INTRODUCTION

Research by cognitive psychologists has resulted in a significant body of know-ledge about the way humans process information. From early roots in philosophy through simple but historically important experiments such as those on human memory conducted by Ebbinghaus at the end of the last century, cognitive psychology has developed as a subdiscipline of psychology until the present stage, in which it can boast sophisticated models of the human information-processing system. This does not signify by any means that all the questions have been answered. As is typically the case with the development of a new area of science, continued research tends to raise more questions than it answers. This is true of those aspects of cognitive psychology that are the subject of this book, as will be clear in the chapters that follow. This is not a bad thing. It indicates that our understanding of the domain has been growing beyond the level at which simple answers may have seemed to suffice, or at which we did not have sufficient understanding to be able to pose the right sorts of questions.

During a similar period of time as the science of human information processing has been developing, there have been significant developments in the tech-nology of information processing by machine. It is now possible for sophisticated electronic information-processing machines to be made widely available at reasonable cost. At the time of writing this book, it is perfectly possible to purchase 'off the shelf' in any of several high street shops a very good word-processing system for less than £500, including monitor, printer and all the other necessary components. A wide range of other software covering such applica-tions as project planning, financial forecasting, database management, prepara-tion of visual aids, and many others, can be purchased to run on the machine for around £50 for each package. In the light of such continuing trends in the cost and power of the machines available, it is not surprising that many manufacturers are increasingly interested in developing electronic systems that meet the information-processing needs of the market.

The largest sector of the market for information-processing systems during the 1980s and 1990s will be the office systems market. It is in offices of one sort or another that most people in the developed nations will be employed. It is in this area that the competition for the market will be fiercest. And it is here that an understanding of the information-processing characteristics of the human may help manufacturers to design their systems to be the most readily accepted by the humans who have to choose which machines to use. Designing information-processing machines to be compatible with their human users means designing them to fit in with the way in which the human is built in regard to information processing. The human information-processing system is only one particular type of system. It does things in its own way (or within its own repertoire). It has its own particular strengths and weaknesses, which need to be taken into account in designing for human–machine compatibility.

Recognition that designing for human–machine cognitive compatibility can help to make a machine more acceptable and more useful to its intended users, and thereby help to win in the competition for the intended market, has led to an interesting trend in systems design which has only recently begun to become evident and which still has a long way to go before it reaches a plateau, and it is this: People who have wished to work with electronic information-processing machines of various sorts in the past have by and large had to do their best to fit in with the information-processing strategies of the machine. They have had to adjust their own behaviour at the interface to the machine in order to fit in with the characteristics of the 'basic machine'. We are now seeing a trend in systems design towards adding sophisticated 'user interfaces' to the 'basic machine' which effectively mean that the 'basic machine' can fit in better with what the human finds natural and easy to do.

The benefits of this trend are many. Less training is needed to use the machines, errors in using them are less likely, more complex operations can be carried out by more people, work can be done faster, and more interesting work can be done with little or no undesirable stress on the user.

The design adopted for the user interface is key to this trend. It is with the user interface that the user conducts the 'dialogue' by which the work is done. The user interface *is* the machine, as the user sees it.

This book is concerned with the relevance of what we know about human information processing to the design of the user interface, in order to achieve human–machine cognitive compatibility.

APPLYING COGNITIVE PSYCHOLOGY TO USER-INTERFACE DESIGN

Recognizing that cognitive psychology is that area of science especially concerned with human information processing, manufacturers of office systems have been increasingly using the services of cognitive psychologists in the design of user interfaces. Whilst this has been helpful in introducing cognitive psychology into the design process, and in raising awareness of what can be achieved, it has not proved adequate to the needs of the time.

Trained cognitive psychologists with experience in information technology are few and far between in industry and are certainly not available to most product designers 'on tap' to contribute to the design of specific products under development. Furthermore, progress in cognitive psychology research is proceeding at such a pace that few cognitive psychologists — even in the academic world — can claim a thorough acquaintance with more than one or two of the several areas of cognitive psychology research that are important for the design of systems. For this reason, there has been growing interest in the possibility of systematizing and packaging cognitive psychology knowledge in ways that mean it can be made more widely available more easily. Human factors specialists as well as other members of the design team could benefit from having available to them tools of various sorts that allow them to make some practical use of the results of cognitive psychology research in the design process.

One possible way of systematizing knowledge based on cognitive psychology research is in the form of design guidelines, such as are used to systematize other areas of knowledge relevant to the design process. As in other areas of knowledge, such guidelines would be expected to have both strengths and weaknesses as a way of making the knowledge available. This is discussed in later chapters (especially Chapters 2 and 8). But there are other types of tools as well. To the extent that it is possible to systematize the findings from cognitive psychology research at all (whether in guidelines or in some other way), then it should be possible to package them in software as well as on paper, the two being vehicles for knowledge rather than the knowledge itself. A key advantage of software over paper would be that the principles embodied could be applied in a more interactive, more dynamic way than is possible with paper-based guidelines or similar materials.

Such a software 'black box' in principle is appealing. It would not be as good nor as flexible as a human cognitive psychologist, but it would have two major advantages as a means of importing psychological knowledge into the design process: it would be available on tap, and it would cover more areas than an individual expert would be likely ever to be able to cover.

It is envisaged that such software 'black boxes', potentially of various different sorts, could be part of the design team's 'toolkit', along with more traditional 'tools' such as paper-based design guidelines. The availability of such tools could provide opportunities for design teams to review their methods of working in order to optimize their use of time and resources, and one can envisage developments in design methodology that could result from this process. These possibilities are discussed in more detail in a later chapter (Chapter 10), where special consideration is given to the possibility of a software-based design support environment, incorporating a number of different tools, including tools based on cognitive psychology research findings.

SCIENTIFIC FEASIBILITY

It is a relatively simple matter to systematize knowledge about how a particular type of machine processes information, for two main reasons: Such machines, at least today, are relatively very simple compared with the human information-processing system; and, even more to the point, we have the 'engineering diagrams' (because the machine was designed by humans). Conversely, the human information-processing system is extremely complex, and we do not have the 'engineering diagrams' (because it was not designed by humans) — indeed, cognitive psychology research can be considered as being about inferring what the 'engineering diagrams' are, given the behaviour of the system. This is somewhat akin to trying to write the 'engineering diagrams' for a particular word-processor by observing its behaviour under various conditions, and without 'taking the lid off'.

One school of thought is that human behaviour is so complex and so flexible that, especially since we cannot 'take the lid off' and do not have access to 'the diagrams', it is a hopeless cause to try and explain it scientifically. We do not accept this position. We believe that over the past 30 years or more, useful models have been developed in a number of different areas of psychology that demonstrate the feasibility of treating human behaviour scientifically. We are not claiming that these models represent the complete story or that they do not have significant limitations, simply that they have demonstrated the feasibility of developing models that have some practical use and which provide some theoretical insights. There is no doubt that it is still early days and much needs to be done to progress the development of the discipline further.

An early type of model, developed from about the early 1950s, was the 'mathematical learning theory' type of model. These models attempted to formulate hypotheses about human learning in terms of precise mathematical equations. Some of the models developed were able to predict, in quantitative terms, the degree of learning attained in defined circumstances, and could do so with very great accuracy (for example, to within 5% or better). In a different area, highly quantitative 'psychometric' models have provided the basis for psychological tests of various sorts (intelligence, personality, clinical abnormality, and so forth) which have proved to be of practical value in a variety of circumstances from selecting personnel for the war effort during the First World War through to personnel selection in modern business. Even in the social arena, quantitative models such as expectancy-value models have been used with some success to predict behaviour in a range of different situations from voting behaviour through to brand choice in the area of consumer psychology.

It would be unwise to regard these types of model as more than they are. They do not by any means represent a complete science in any area. Indeed, the limitations of the models are well-recognized by psychologists working in the areas concerned, both in terms of their theoretical limitations and in terms of their generally very limited 'boundary conditions' (the conditions under which they are theoretically applicable and/or can be expected to provide useful results). On the other hand, it would be equally unwise to dismiss them as of no value at all. At the very least, they have demonstrated the possibility in principle of moving beyond common sense in predicting human behaviour towards more quantitative, more theoretically based models. Equally important in the present context, they have demonstrated the possibility of taking often rather nebulous theoretical concepts about behaviour and translating them into well-defined models that have some applied value. They have shown that, armed with such models, it is possible in some (admittedly often limited) contexts to make accurate predictions about behavioural outcomes without having to rely on the (intuitive) judgements of an expert psychologist. The judgements of such an expert might add further information, help to define the boundary conditions more clearly, in some cases modify the predictions, or in other ways augment the predictions made by the models — but the models nevertheless help to make public and applicable the knowledge on which they are based, rather than relying solely on the private knowledge of 'the experts'.

A second school of thought is that, whilst some areas of psychology have developed to the stage where it has been possible to begin developing applicable models, the area of cognitive psychology is too young for this to be fruitful at this stage. More pure research is needed in order to develop the fundamental theory before it will be possible to start developing applicable models. A further, related point of view suggests that it will be a long time before pure research on cognitive psychology has much to offer of direct applicability to the design of systems, and that what is needed is more research of a clearly applied nature on specific design issues, so that a body of applied knowledge can be built up without waiting for developments in 'mainstream' cognitive psychology. It may even be, as has been the case to some extent in the past (see Chapter 3), the that applied work will stimulate and support developments in mainstream cognitive psychology.

At the time we started to write this book, we had an open mind about how much cognitive psychology has to offer to the problems of designing user interfaces. We felt that it would have something to offer, and we believe that the later chapters in the book support that view. Whether it is more or less than might have been expected at this stage in its scientific development is for the individual reader to judge. We have some sympathy with the view that more directly applied research could be done by cognitive psychologists working on specific design issues, and that this might facilitate the growth of cognitive psycholgoy in general. Certainly we feel that mainstream cognitive psychology could benefit from greater emphasis on the 'ecological validity' of the research done. This is a point we discuss further in Chapter 10.

THE STRUCTURE AND SCOPE OF THE BOOK

The book is divided into four parts.

Part One contains this introductory chapter and a chapter on the design context. The two chapters together introduce the notion of applying cognitive psychology to the design of user interfaces and consider the design context in which that needs to be done.

Part Two contains five chapters. The first provides a historical context, briefly outlining the roots of cognitive psychology and its development. This will be of most interest to non-psychologists who may find it helpful in placing the topics covered in the book in a broader disciplinary framework. The remaining four chapters each consider one particular aspect of cognitive psychology and compile a list of summary principles which may be derived from that area relevant to the design of user interfaces.

Part Three demonstrates the applied value of the psychology discussed. Chapter 8 takes the summary principles discussed in the previous chapters and interprets them into a set of design guidelines. A number of other sets of design guidelines concerning user-interface design have been produced before, but we believe this chapter is unusual in being based directly on a selective review of mainstream cognitive psychology by experts in their respective fields. The translation of the 'pure' principles into design guidelines has been done by specialists in applied cognitive psychology and ergonomics working within an industrial context on the design of user interfaces. This chapter will be of most interest to design teams concerned with the user interface. The second chapter in Part Three considers the types and 'ecological validity' of the work that will need to be done, as technology and techniques for human–computer interaction develop.

A major problem in applying cognitive psychology is that developments in the technology of office systems are running ahead of developments in our understanding of human information processing. Given the huge area that is covered by the term 'cognitive psychology', and the limits on the research personnel and resources available, it is important that research efforts are concentrated on the key issues, and not on peripheral or relatively trivial questions. There is a need — and we feel it applies to cognitive psychology research in general — for greater emphasis to be put on research in ecologically valid situations (that is, to research human information processing in situations that are directly relevant to real life, rather than the simple, contrived situations of the traditional cognitive psychological laboratory).

Part Four considers the next stages in applying cognitive psychology in the design process. Within this framework it outlines a 'design support environment' aimed at maximizing the effectiveness of cognitive psychology contributions to the design process, and lists research priorities that need to be addressed in order to improve the relevance and value of cognitive psychology within that design process. The chapter is concerned with both 'pure' and 'applied' aspects and should be of interest both to researchers (both 'pure' and 'applied') and to practitioners.

The aspects of cognitive psychology covered

The review of relevant areas of cognitive psychology presented in Part Two focuses on 'higher-order' cognitive processes. It does not attempt to treat any of these in depth. Its purpose is to identify key research findings that can be used both as a direct contribution to the development of design guidelines (presented in Chapter 8) and other software-based design tools (discussed in Chapter 10).

The areas reviewed have not previously received much attention from the applied field, and certainly guidelines for application of knowledge from the areas covered are not in common usage, if they exist at all. The selective review presented in Part Two is therefore a first step towards showing what these so far neglected areas have to offer to the applied field. Four key areas are covered:

— thinking and mental models (Chapter 4)
— episodic and semantic memory, and working memory (Chapter 5)
— skill acquisition (Chapter 6)
— language (Chapter 7).

The rationale for choosing these is as follows.

In interacting with an electronic office system, users typically think about what they are doing and how to use the system to best advantage. They may encounter a variety of problems, both routine and otherwise, in using the system, and they need to engage in various kinds of problem-solving in order to use the system effectively. The first area covered in Part Two is therefore thinking and problem-solving. Mental models have been discussed widely in connection with the use of electronic systems, and the chapter considers the nature and role of mental models in the thinking and problem-solving process.

Consideration of users' thinking and problem-solving highlights the importance of human memory in user–system interaction. Chapter 5 considers different aspects of human memory in this context. It considers theories which treat memory as a relatively 'static' entity, outlining its limitations and type of organization. It also considers a more dynamic and task-oriented view of memory as it obtains in complex environments.

Users of office systems are not the same at each point in time; in particular, they learn about the system and how to use it. The learning process is considered to some extent in the chapters on problem-solving and memory, and another aspect of learning — the acquisition of specific skills — is discussed in Chapter 6. That chapter brings together several of the different theoretical strands outlined in the earlier chapters and describes the types of processing changes that occur as a user progresses from beginner to expert. In some ways, the chapter qualifies some of the points made in the earlier chapters.

The last area considered is the linguistic aspects of communication between humans, including information about the expectations and social conventions that make language such an efficient medium of communication. Knowledge from this field can then be translated for application to the linguistic aspects of the 'dialogue' by which the human and the machine work together to accomplish the tasks that need to be done.

Topics not covered

The review does *not* specifically address the following areas of cognitive psychology, for the reasons given below:

- — perception
- — attention
- — developmental processes.

Perception and attention are not included because they have received extensive treatment in the classical human factors and systems design literature, particularly with respect to the physical ergonomics of screen design. Developmental processes cover the changes in processing strategies, and emphasis on certain processing functions, as an individual develops from infancy to maturity and old age; it is not of direct relevance to the area of office systems where the users can be assumed to be working adults of similar ages within a broad range.

COMPLEMENTARY BOOKS

There are a number of complementary books which the interested reader may wish to consult (see also references, p. 335). The following selection focuses on books which are directly concerned with the user interface, rather than on more general psychological texts.

Card, S.K., Moran, T.P. and Newell, A. (1983). *The Psychology of Human–Computer Interaction*. London/New Jersey: Lawrence Erlbaum Associates. This is now a standard text for researchers working on the cognitive aspects of user–system interaction. It presents the now well-known GOMS model and describes some of the research done within the framework of the model at Xerox Palo Alto Research Center.

Christie, B. (ed.) (1985). *Human Factors of Information Technology in the Office.*

Chichester/New York: John Wiley and Sons Ltd. This book was produced by the Human Factors Technology Centre of ITT Europe with contributions from various academic and industry associates. It considers cognitive aspects of user-interface design within a broader range of topics, from the history and functions of the office, through psychophysiological and other aspects of usability, to organizational and other aspects of introducing new office systems into organizations.

Christie, B. (ed.) (1985). *Human Factors of the User–System Interface: A Report on an ESPRIT Preparatory Study*. Amsterdam: Elsevier Science Publishers (North-Holland). This book presents an account of the work done for the Commission of the European Communities on an ESPRIT Preparatory Study in 1983. The book identifies key elements of user-interface research at that time, and identifies areas where research on cognitive psychological aspects and other aspects of user-interface design are needed.

Gale, A. and Christie, B. (eds.) (In Press). *Psychophysiology of the Electronic Workplace*. Chichester/New York: John Wiley and Sons Ltd. Distinguished researchers in psychophysiology from various countries contribute their views on what can be learned about user–system interaction from research on psychophysiology. The book includes a consideration of cognitive psychological aspects of user–system interaction and helps to place these in a broader psychophysiological context.

Monk, A. (ed.) (1984). *Fundamentals of Human–Computer Interaction*. London/New York: Academic Press. This is a wide-ranging, introductory book to the general area of user-interface design and evaluation. It takes the reader from the mechanics of setting up an experiment and selecting appropriate subjects, to the theory behind the psychology of thinking, memory, etc. It also considers the 'office of the future', and expert systems.

Oborne, D.J. (1983). *Computers at Work*. Chichester/New York: John Wiley and Sons Ltd. This is an overview of many facets of the use of computers at work, including organizational factors, the impacts of the introduction of new technology in the office, hardware and software considerations and principles of 'software psychology'. The book also includes a useful section on the use of computers in three areas of work: the office, education and medicine.

Sime, M.E. and Coombs, M.J. (eds.) (1983). *Designing for Human–Computer Communication*. London/New York: Academic Press. This is a useful book of readings by key researchers from the United States, Canada, Sweden, Scotland, and — mostly — England. The book is organized into two main parts, dealing with the user interface (issues such as natural language, 'user growth', database query) and the 'task interface' (medical consultation, air traffic control, and other application areas).

Wickens, C.D. (1984). *Engineering Psychology and Human Performance*. Columbus/Toronto/London/Sydney: Charles E. Merrill Publishing Company. This is a well researched and impressive book, covering many well-known areas of experimental psychology and human performance, and drawing conclusions from each one to the applied domain. The emphasis is on providing information which will be usable in teaching the many different facts of interacting with an electronic system, and the application domain extends beyond the office environment to domains such as command and control systems.

Chapter 2

The role of cognitive psychology in user-interface design

Nick Hammond, Margaret M. Gardiner, Bruce Christie and Chris Marshall

THE USABILITY PROBLEM

Office staff are little concerned with the technicalities of the machines they use. It is sufficient that a machine should provide the function that is needed and that its use should be easy to learn and to remember. This is, of course, just as true for computerized office systems as it is for the more familiar technology of the typewriter, telephone and dictaphone. The design of these devices, though, posed quite different problems from those now posed by the growing breed of integrated office systems. First of all, the function of these older technologies is, relatively speaking, simple and clearly defined, with only limited options for varying the interface between machine and user. Second, and more significantly, the nature of that function is quite different. Traditional office machines deal with the mechanical transfer of information from one form to another, whereas computerized systems manipulate information: the direct mapping between input and output is no longer preserved. People *communicate* with electronic office systems but merely *operate* traditional devices.

It is easy to forget how recently direct communication with office systems has come about. The high cost and the limited power of systems even 15 years ago meant that virtually all use was computer-centred; users seldom had access to the machine themselves, but had to deal indirectly through specialists such as keypunch personnel and computer operators. System designers were concerned with function provision in relation to optimum use of resources, concerns that left little room for the convenience of those using output from the system, a view that some argue is still all too prevalent (see, for example, Stibic, 1980). The change in user population from computer expert to non-expert* has been made

_____

* The term non-expert is used here to refer to a person with little or no computer expertise rather than to a person with no professional expertise.

possible by the ever-increasing computer power and decreasing costs resulting from rapidly developing hardware and software technologies. The most important consequence for usability of this increased computational power is the cutting of traditional ties between the underlying architecture of the system and the detailed design of the user interface. Design has escaped from computer-centricity, but the danger is that it is being replaced by a designer-centricity just as alien to the user.

The designer has available seemingly infinite possibilities for task, function and dialogue definition, a flexibility of choice that may be a two-edged sword when it comes to improving the ease of system use. On the one hand, more power means that some classes of interface problem can be finessed: a modern word-processor provides editing facilities far superior to those of a teletype-based line editor. On the other hand, increased power allows greater potential for functional and conceptual complexity at the interface, with concomitant risks of user misunderstandings. The more varied and complex the tasks a system supports, the greater the need for the system to be easy to learn and to use. Even with today's technology, a large number of additional office tasks could in principle be supported electronically (Helander, 1985); the problem is that there are means neither for determining how computerized tasks might best be organized so as to fit successfully into existing work and social contexts (Bjørn-Andersen and Rasmussen, 1980), nor for optimizing the individual's learning and use. Functionality is in danger of outstripping usability.

Just as significant for design as changes in computational power is the changing population of users. Now that decreasing costs have opened the door to direct interaction by the non-expert, ease of use has moved on from its role as an occasional rabbit pulled out of the designer's hat to being an essential marketing feature of a product. If there are plenty of inexpensive products in the market place, disgruntled users can vote with their feet. Users can no longer be expected to plough through lengthy manuals or to fight with incomprehensible dialogues; if the system demands overmuch time or effort then users will attempt to find other means of achieving their ends. Today's designer, therefore, is required to produce a system which not only processes widgets more efficiently than the competitor's system, but also does so in a way which is seen to support optimal user learning and performance.

A glance at advertisers' hype in many current business computer magazines might suggest that problems of learning and use have already followed the dodo; but why, then, does a scan of the same magazines reveal so many advertisements for training courses, workshops and other remedial services? Leaving aside the question of whether such advertising claims are in reality backed up by actual design actions and user performance data, the truth, of course, is that any complex system, however well-designed, poses certain difficulties for the non-expert. Learning to do new things is hard, and learning to do old things in new ways may be even harder, as discussed elsewhere in this volume (Chapters 4 and

6). In any case, it seems unlikely that current systems exploit fully their users' prior knowledge and their capabilities for learning. Certainly recent observational studies of system use provide evidence of considerable user difficulty in both learning (see, for example, Baker and Eason, 1981; Hammond and Barnard, 1984; Hammond et al., 1984; Mack, Lewis and Carroll, 1983) and in more experienced usage (Rosson, 1984; Wilson, Barnard and MacLean, 1985). Successful interface design is no longer a straightforward matter; there is no simple formula for ensuring that a system will be easy to learn and to use. Unless the tools of human factors are called upon, the evolutionary forces of natural selection in the marketplace may be the first and last indicator of failure.

It is a truism that an understanding of the usability of any but the simplest office system requires consideration of user characteristics as well as those of the task and system. Usability is a joint function of system and user. For a homogenous population of users, the determinants of usability — in the sense of the factors that the designer is able to control — of course lie within the system, but the point is that usability cannot be fully analysed, understood or predicted from consideration of the formal aspects of task and system alone. For instance, both the knowledge people bring to the interaction and the way in which they develop their understanding will influence the ease of use of the system. Less obvious, though, is the extent to which such influences are adequately captured by the existing methods of task and system analysis plus a modicum of 'common sense psychology' about user knowledge and behaviour. If everyday psychology fails to deliver systems that are easy to use, then is the more formal body of knowledge about human cognition, cognitive psychology, of any more use? Certainly some large commercial organizations — particularly in the United States — are looking more and more towards psychologists and human factors specialists for solutions, at least to judge by their employment policies. It is this general issue of the applicability of cognitive psychology to user-interface design that this volume addresses, and its background is the topic of the remainder of this chapter.

In the next two sections we consider some relevant aspects of cognitive psychology and design practice. We then selectively review existing approaches to the application of cognitive psychology to design, and conclude by summarizing the approach taken in the rest of the book.

USABILITY AND HUMAN COGNITION

Cognitive psychology

This book aims to explore some chosen areas of cognitive psychology and their implications for interface design. The focus is on *cognitive psychology* in particular rather than on *cognitive science* in general. Cognitive psychology broadly refers to the scientific study of the acquisition, storage and use of knowledge by the individual — knowledge covering not only consciously accessible information but also other internalized forms such as underlie emotional states or skilled actions. Such a definition is so wide as to be almost useless for providing insight into the relationship between cognitive psychology and interface design. Indeed, according to a recent survey, over three-quarters of academic psychologists in the United States consider themselves to be cognitive psychologists (quoted in Eysenck, 1984), a finding reflecting the diffuse usage of the term. Rather than try to hone down the definition of cognitive psychology, it is more useful for our purpose of setting the scene to consider where psychology is positioned within cognitive science and to discuss how it has been applied. Some of the historical roots of cognitive psychology are explored later in the book (Chapter 3).

Cognitive psychology and cognitive science

Cognitive science is a loose assembly of disciplines with a common interest in the nature of knowledge and how it may be processed. Principal amongst these are *artificial intelligence, linguistics* and *cognitive psychology*. Although these differ in their subject matter, theories and methods, they all revolve around the twin concepts of representation and process. Representation is concerned with what the person (animal, society, robot or whatever) knows and how such knowledge is organized, and for psychology it provides a theoretical platform for explaining human thought and action. In its narrow sense, though, representation reflects only static aspects of cognition; representations are developed, shaped and transformed by means of cognitive processes. As Mandler (1985) has pointed out, these two rocks, representation and process, are taken as axioms within cognitive science; the storms concern the nature of representations, of processes and of their interactions, not whether cognitive science should be about something other than representation and process. Psychology has, of course, been concerned with these two concepts, and particularly representation, for a good deal longer than the 25 or so years since the flag of cognitive psychology was first raised. In contrast with other schools of psychology, though, cognitive psychology is *primarily* concerned with representation and process; these have been the chosen issues and they underpin the central theoretical developments. They are also, of course, central to the study of human–computer interaction. As we will discuss below, both designers and users will form mental representations of the task and system, though often not matching ones. It is the nature of this mismatch which generates many of the problems in system usage.

Where, then, does cognitive psychology sit within cognitive science? The contrast most germane here is with artifical intelligence, partly because of the central position of artificial intelligence within cognitive science, but mainly because the differences in approach between artifical intelligence and cognitive psychology are mirrored in opposing views of interface design. There is a good deal of dispute over what constitutes the proper arena of artifical intelligence. It is certainly concerned with extending our insight into *possible* representations and processes underlying intelligent behaviour. In this respect, its goals differ from those of cognitive psychology, which is concerned with understanding *human* intelligence. Some (for example, Aitkenhead and Slack, 1985) suggest that the objective of artificial intelligence is the explanation of human cognition. However, it can be argued that the constraints from artificial intelligence on cognitive psychology at a theoretical level are only weak (see, for example, Miller, 1981; Morton, 1981). The dispute primarily concerns the relevance to cognitive theory of the outputs from the methods of artificial intelligence. Artificially intelligent behaviour can be achieved in quite different ways from that achieved by the human brain, although as a *simulation* of behaviour the match might be quite good. A case in point is the development of the early chess-playing machines, where the most successful machines did not attempt to imitate the human expert but relied instead on brute computing power. The same argument has frequently been used to question the psychological status of some formalisms within linguistics, such as transformational grammars (Chomsky, 1965), for example by Broadbent (1973). Researchers into artificial intelligence can reasonably argue that such cases are an exception and that many advances have been made by modelling what is known about human processes. But even so, the argument usually relies on plausibility rather than proof, or even empirical test; it is rare to be able to establish that no other possible model could achieve the same ends while accounting better for human performance data. A final argument of the artificial intelligence community is that if artificial intelligence does develop non-human kinds of intelligence, then the general principles generated could be helpful in understanding human intelligence (Pylyshyn, 1978), and there are many reasons for supposing that this is so.

While the goals of artificial intelligence and cognitive psychology are somewhat different, their proximity can hardly fail to bring some mutual benefit both conceptually and methodologically. Certainly many of the representational concepts that psychologists now juggle with — semantic networks, distributed memories, schemata, mental models and the like — would have been so much hot air without the benefit of exploration and instantiation by computer, and indeed many of these concepts originated in the artificial intelligence camp. The crucial differences between artificial intelligence and cognitive psychology lie in their methods and in the evaluation of their models and theories. The methods of artificial intelligence mainly involve building computer simulations of models of intelligent behaviour, and within the research domain these are assessed by criteria such as logical coherence, elegance or computational efficiency. This formalist (or rationalist) approach is primarily concerned with the internal structure of the model, not its relation to relevant evidence about human performance. Formalists tend to argue from first principles. In contrast, functionalists, mostly psychologists, are more concerned with ensuring that models of specific mechanisms or processes are compatible with experimental data, and they build up theoretical structures in order to account for observed behaviour in a way which the formalist might consider to be piecemeal and unprincipled. The formalist–functionalist distinction is, of course, more of a dimension than a dichotomy, and people tending towards either end of the spectrum can be identified in both artificial intelligence and cognitive psychology. This distinction is strongly evident in interface design methodologies, where, for example, functionalist psychologists argue that formal specification methods ignore the vagaries of human performance and are perforce of limited utility (see, for example, Carroll and Rosson, 1984). This point is taken up later in the chapter (p. 25).

Amongst its methods, though, artifical intelligence holds the computational tools to test internal aspects of cognitive models, rather as mathematics is the power behind the throne of the physical sciences. Artificial intelligence work has provided the possibility for complex cognitive models to be specified, implemented and tested for internal validity or indeterminacy. Further, the discipline brought by the implementation of a model shines a floodlight into dark corners that would otherwise remain hidden. Implementation focuses the mind. If a model is so vague that its postulates and principles cannot be implemented, then at least we can know this to be so, and we can work towards greater specificity.

Cognitive psychology and human factors

Whether simulated or not, models of human–computer interaction can exist at a number of levels. A psychological model of the user may be sufficiently specified to be implemented or to generate hypotheses testable against experimental data, but it may lack the generality needed to withstand the rigors of real applications. The issue here is one of scope: the model does not extend to contexts outside the laboratory. This may not matter to the scientist whose aim is to uncover and understand the fundamental nature of the particular phenomena under study. The criterion for the applied scientist or engineer — within the human–computer interaction field, the human factors engineer — is different, however. An applications model has to be broad enough to operate within the particular applications domain, although it may not specify the *minutiae* of human cognitive processes: the criterion here is operability. Since many of the findings of cognitive psychology are based on relatively simple and short artificial tasks conducted on homogeneous populations of subjects, they frequently are not directly applicable. The further a model is extrapolated to new situations, the more its assumptions are likely to be violated and the less determinate its predictions are likely to become.

Just as with other applicable sciences, this has led psychology to spawn a number of specialized applied disciplines, such as educational psychology, clinical psychology and, in the case of human interaction with machines, human

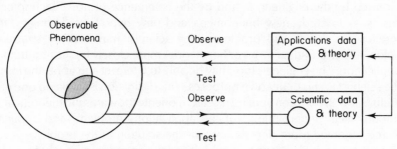

Figure 1.   Scientific and applied research: Differences and similarities.

factors, which aim to deal with the practical problems not otherwise addressed by the parent discipline. To a greater or lesser extent, each of these has its methodological and theoretical roots in experimental psychology. Human factors expertise has in fact developed largely independently of cognitive theory, although in its methods of observation, simulation and evaluation it calls heavily upon experimental psychology. Applications models have been derived not so much from the parent science as from direct study of user tasks and the problems of design.

Figure 1 illustrates some relevant relationships between science and application. Both scientific and applied psychologists choose to observe certain phenomena, generate hypotheses concerning their observations and then test these hypotheses by means of further manipulations and observations of the real world. The scientist and engineer ostensibly investigating the same domain may or may not sample the same phenomena; there were few shared observations between the army of researchers into human learning of nonsense material in the 1950s and educational psychologists working in the field. Nevertheless, while scientists and engineers apply different criteria and may sample different phenomena, their eventual goals may be similar. Engineers are concerned that their applications should work, but the risk is that each new problem may have to be tackled afresh. Human factors wisdom about one application, perhaps enshrined in constructs such as simple guidelines, may just not generalize to new applications. Scientists hope that, by uncovering knowledge about the underlying nature of phenomena, they will be able to hand engineers conceptual tools of wider predictive power which allow them to go beyond the specific evidence at hand.

In the ideal world there is a two-way dialogue between applications and science (see the line between the applications and scientific boxes in Figure 1). This communication acts at both the methodological and the conceptual levels. Each discipline may develop specialized techniques which can, at least potentially, be mutually beneficial. Human factors' greatest debt to psychology is probably for its methodological toolkit. At the conceptual level, the scientist may be spurred by the engineer — and by the emergence of novel technological domains — to study new phenomena and new hypotheses, bringing fresh theoretical insights to old problems. The scientist may also be spurred to develop, interpret and refine his or her theories more closely for the requirements of application. The engineer, too, may be able to interpret and apply the insights of the scientist for his or her own purposes. This distinction is similar to one made by Belbin (1979) between *applied* research, oriented towards the theoretical and methodological underpinnings of the applications problem, and *applicable* research, oriented more directly towards the solution of the problem.

The extent to which these approaches overlap depends to a large extent on the natures of the applied and scientific disciplines. In the study of human–computer interaction, the greatest overlap is methodological, as we have indicated above. Conceptual overlap is poor primarily because of the problems of interpreting evidence from studies of human–computer interaction and of drawing generalizations from it. Difficulties arise because typically many factors combine to determine how a user understands or learns a particular part of the interaction. Factors may well be interdependent, and a design solution which is adequate in one context may be poor in another, where some critical factor has changed. In addition, different measures of performance which might be employed in empirical studies — user preferences, time on task, error rates, memorability, use of help and so on — may yield contradictory answers, at least if results are applied too literally. While much of the underlying cognitive basis for user performance remains a mystery — and hence also the pattern of factors likely to determine performance — extrapolation of research findings will continue to be problematic.

Hammond *et al.* (1983a) discuss as an example three recent investigations concerned with the choice of command terms for text-editing operations. One study (Ledgard *et al.*, 1980) found that 'English-like' command structures were superior to 'notational' structures, one (Scapin, 1981) found 'computer-oriented' terms were superior to 'task-oriented' terms, while a third (Landauer, Galotti and Hartwell, 1983) found that choice of vocabulary made little difference. These findings are likely to be puzzling to the diligent designer who takes the trouble to seek out human factors literature: which finding should form the basis of a particular design decision? To the cognitive psychologist – the 'expert user' of such experiments — the fact that the results are, at an applied level, seemingly contradictory is not so surprising. The three studies used different measures of performance (for example, Scapin measured memorability, Landauer *et al.* measured time on task), tested subjects on different task conditions (for example, the Scapin study was conducted offline, the other two online; the number of commands differed widely across the three studies) and manipulated different variables. As Barnard (1983a) states, these findings form three pieces of a very large behavioural jigsaw puzzle, and one might add that the picture on the puzzle is unknown and that many of the pieces are missing. The studies can only be fully interpreted by means of cognitive theories dealing with the representation of users' knowledge and the processes performed on those representations; the aim of the studies is more to advance theoretical understanding than to provide direct human factors recommendations. The issue is discussed further in Barnard (1983a) and Barnard and Hammond (1982).

The argument, then, is that if the applied discipline of human factors is to broaden its activities to allow tighter prediction of user preference and performance, then it needs to call upon more powerful and more specific psychological theories. In Figure 1, the route from the scientific box to the applied box needs to convey more in the way of interpretive tools. Historically, psychology has a poor record of applying its scientific insights, with some notable exceptions. Psychologists have tended to study quaint and esoteric phenomena in the hope of gaining general theoretical insight, failing either to probe phenomena which might have led to more applicable theories or to shape their theories for the purposes of the psychological engineer. (One might add that many such failures resulted not from lack of trying but from the intractable natures of some applied problems.) Even when psychological theory might have something to offer, the engineer may either not know about it or may be ill-equipped to interpret it appropriately. Worse, a theory may appear applicable but may in fact be quite misleading when removed from its constrained laboratory setting as, for example, in the simplistic application of learning theory derived mainly from animal studies to the classroom situation. However, the current climate in psychology (scientific as well as financial) strongly favours a shift towards ecological validity, and the study and modelling of phenomena occurring naturally rather then those artificially induced in the laboratory (see Baddeley, 1982, for examples in the area of human memory). The study of human–computer interaction by psychologists is an instance of this shift, and is resulting in, amongst other things, far more vigorous attempts by psychologists to provide useful cognitive theory for the human factors community. The best known example is the work of Card, Moran and Newell (1983). Some of these developments are mentioned in a later section of this chapter. At least in this area, psychologists, human factors specialists, computer scientists and designers are now studying similar phenomena and are engaged in constructive dialogue.

Much of the research into human–computer interaction, both applied and scientific, is problem-driven; starting with a particular goal in mind, be it applied or theoretical, the researcher brings relevant conceptual and methodological tools of psychology to bear on the problem. A potential danger of this approach is that it can lead to parochial conclusions; the researcher fails to see the links with other problems or the wider cognitive issues, and small-scale data repositories or local mini-theories of dubious generality proliferate. In terms of Figure 1, the local evidence encompassed by the circle in the scientific box fails to be integrated into more general theory. One might criticize some of the work on choosing command names, cited above, for falling into this trap. It may be the case, though, that general psychological theory cannot provide the necessary framework, in which case parochiality has to suffice until integrating theories are developed. One aim of this book is to explore whether existing areas of cognition can serve this integrative function rather more than they do at present. However, the aim is not only to provide a framework for interpreting research findings, but also to identify potentially applicable areas of theory and data, perhaps leading to insight into where future research might be most fruitfully directed. There are dangers in this approach too. The main ones relate to potential failures in extrapolation from other domains of study to human–computer interaction, and particularly so where this is masked by a surface plausibility. Other dangers are incompleteness and irrelevance: since so little cognitive theory is based on the observation of human–computer interaction, then many important issues in human–computer interaction may not be addressed. However, in so far as the theoretical base for explaining and predicting human–computer interaction is so sparse, even the possibility that cognitive theory has little to offer interface design would be worth exploring if it yielded insights into why this should be so.

USABILITY AND DESIGN

The end users of human–computer interaction research are the designers* of interactive systems. However firmly human factors recommendations might be based on the theoretical rocks of psychology (and however sound or shaky these rocks), they will be useless if they fall upon deaf ears: the products of human–computer interaction research must not only be relevant and true, but also 'user-friendly' to the designer. One solution is for the entire user interface of the system to be designed and implemented by human factors specialists; Gould and Boies (1983) discuss some of the advantages of this route. This approach is unlikely to be adopted widely for some time, even if only for the pragmatic reason that there are too few people with suitable skills in the industry. In any case, it is probably not a practicable approach for many types of system. It is important, therefore, to explore how designer decision-making influences the final usability of the interface, with a view to organizing and directing recommendations so as to have the greatest impact. This section looks at some relevant features of design practice.

Studies of decision-making in interface design are surprisingly rare. Generally speaking, it seems that the development history of commercial products is confidential, or at least not openly discussed. The exceptions, though, are very instructive. There have been a number of questionnaire studies of the way designers conceptualize the organizational and job roles of users (for example, Dagwell and Weber, 1983; Hedberg and Mumford, 1975), but these give little

---

* By designer, we mean anyone making decisions about the user interface, whether planner, analyst, developer or programmer.

insight into the way design options are formulated or decisions actually reached. There are several reports by designers of the philosophy behind the development of their own products (see, for example, Botterill, 1982; Gould and Boies, 1983; Ingalls, 1981; Smith *et al.*, 1982; Woodmansee, 1983) and some informal interviews with designers about particular products (see, Morgan, Williams and Lemmons, 1983). There are only a handful of investigations — by interview or questionnaire — directed specifically at how designers reach decisions about the user interface (for example, Gould and Lewis, 1985; Hammond *et al.*, 1983a; Mosier and Smith, 1986; Smith and Mosier, 1984a). Finally, a few studies have required designers to make decisions about interfaces to artificial systems and to comment about their choices (see Hammond *et al.*, in press; Jørgensen *et al.*, 1983).

Organizational influences on design

Even from the few studies listed above, it is clear that the determinants of interface design are both manifold and complex. A common theme is that design of the interface is seen as an increasingly important aspect of development, and the time and money spent on interface-related aspects of system development can represent a large proportion of the total development resource. For instance, respondents in Smith and Mosier's survey (1984a) estimated that on average 35% of operational software was devoted to implementing the user interface, and that for some systems this figure was over 80%. Organizations have not always been able to adapt their structures to accommodate this change in emphasis. For example, the organization often requires different facets of the user interface — the software, the workstation, the documentation, the training procedures and so on — to be designed separately by different groups of people. It is quite common with large projects for the interface software to be split between development groups in different geographical locations. Constraints of this sort result in the ossification of the interface early in development so that the different groups have a fixed point of reference from which to proceed (Gould and Lewis, 1985), and it may be very difficult to counter the fragmentation of any subsequent design effort on the interface (Morgan, Williams and Lemmons, 1983). Early ossification of the interface, of course, will make later modification a difficult and expensive enterprise, and so user testing and prototype refinement is less likely to take place.

Other organizational constraints influence decision-making about the interface more directly. Lack of time and other resources within development is a common complaint in designer interviews (Hammond *et al.*, 1983a). Organizations build up in-house design standards, traditions and work practices. Too often, standards develop more through the dictates of fashion, or even accrue largely by opportunism or chance, rather than being soundly based on distilled design experience on human factors expertise or on feedback from users.

Finally, the scope for innovation may be limited by the requirements to maintain compatibility with existing products. If constraints such as these are followed, then, according to designers interviewed by Hammond *et al.* (1983a), the number of decisions based on usability is reduced: 'As much as I complain about compatibility, compatibility makes the job a lot easier. If I have to keep things compatible I have a lot less decision-making to do.' 'If you stick to existing conventions, formats and so on, the options beyond that are not large in number.'

This may be all well and good, at least if the conventions are sound and the designer is able to interpret them in the context of the particular design problem; but even if a standard serves one family of systems well, it will not necessarily be optimal for another. Designers who do break the conventions may be putting their head on the block. If the innovation is a failure, the blame is theirs alone. It is the role of human factors to ensure that both organizational structure and design practice help rather than hinder the development of usable interfaces.

Designers' models of users and their tasks

Even if organizational constraints do limit the designer's scope, many decisions concerning interface specification remain. Designers can be extremely variable both in the decisions actually made and in the way they are arrived at (Hammond *et al.*, in press; Jørgensen *et al.*, 1983). This variability results from the fact that the design of interface software is a very different sort of activity from the design of software with no external interface. The internals of the system are amenable to rational and formal analysis, and well-proven design methods support the building of a clean internal architecture; good design of internals relies on sound analysis and detailed planning. In contrast, the human is an information processor of unknown characteristics and somewhat unpredictable behaviour and, once coupled to the computer system, puts paid to the philosophy of perfect design from first principles. In consequence, there are few formal methods for analysing interfaces and predicting human performance, and Carroll and Rosson (1984), amongst others, argue that those that have been proposed are of only limited utility. To supplement prior analyses, whether formal or informal, human factors experts commonly recommend empirical testing of simulations and prototypes by potential users as a part of the iterative development of the interface (see, for example, Gould and Lewis, 1985). In any event, analytical methods are very much at the research stage and are not in common use. External design wisdom is usually embodied in *ad hoc* guidelines, a form of advice which, according to a recent survey (Smith and Mosier, 1984a), only the minority of designers consult in any case. Of course the reasons for this may be as much to do with the way designers design, or have to design, as with the inherent value of a guidelines approach.

In this light, it is not surprising that designers fall back upon their own and their colleagues' experience, or reason from 'common sense' user psychology. Just as in other areas of expertise, many decisions may not be deliberately considered at all. Evidence from interviews with designers supports this: when tackled on specific interface decisions, phrases such as 'by intuition', 'seat-of-the pants decision' and 'it seemed the best choice' abound (Hammond *et al.*, 1983a). Even when designers do give reasons for their decisions, these may sometimes reflect more of a *post hoc* rationalization than a principled motivation. For instance, Hammond *et al.* (in press) asked designers to choose argument orderings for a set of commands taking two numeric arguments, one of which referred to a common entity for all the commands. *Consistency* was invoked as a reason almost as often by designers who generated positionally inconsistent argument systems (that is, designs with the common argument sometimes placed first and sometimes second) as by those who generated positionally consistent systems.

It would be misleading to infer from such findings that major decisions are made without deliberate consideration. A good deal of careful planning is likely to go into the critical decisions, and particularly when innovative interfaces have resulted (Gould and Boies, 1983; Ingalls, 1981; Morgan, Williams and Lemmons, 1983; Smith *et al.*, 1982; Woodmansee, 1983). The information used is likely to be varied and complex, and space precludes a full discussion here. We can, however, indicate some key points. First, virtually all development will start with some sort of analysis of user tasks, whether formal or informal. A formal description of putative user tasks is usually seen as a prerequisite for a functional specification. A specific contrast made by designers in interviews is that such an analysis focuses on the logical·structure of the task domain rather than on how users themselves might view the problem domain or structure their goals: 'In general, not much explicit consideration was taken of users and users' tasks.' '. . . what they actually did was they just ignored the customers' requirements they took hundreds of thousands of newspapers and they analysed the end result and they said "How would we construct a system that would produce this end result?" '

Rational analysis of tasks is an important design step, but relying on reason alone, ignoring the way users might naturally tackle the task, has its dangers. Any complex design task is intrinsically evolutionary; it involves the discovery of new goals as it proceeds. Carroll and Rosson (1984) and Wright and Bason (1983) discuss these issues further.

Second, interface design involves a good deal more than task analysis. Implicitly or explicitly, designers must make a host of choices based on what they assume users will know or be able to learn. In retrospective interviews, these assumptions tend to emerge as 'common sense theories' of users (Hammond *et al.*, 1983a), although the extent to which such theories contribute to decisions rather than merely justify them is not clear. Some of these designer theories operate not on specific decisions but on the design philosophy. For instance, a common view is that users benefit from a consistent model of the system, as this will support learning. They are akin to high-level principles proposed by computer scientists and psychologists, such as *understanding ability* (diSessa, 1985) or *predictability* (Harrison and Thimbleby, 1985) which, at least their instantiations, also embody theories of user cognition. Abstract design principles have the laudable aim of bringing some order to the chaotic world of interface design. Their proof is not so much in the psychological validity of the principles themselves, but in how they are mapped onto design decisions; for example, a system based on a conceptual model which is consistent and predictable in formal terms may still appear alien to users if it fails to relate to their knowledge or to their ways of thinking. Furthermore, these principles only address certain sorts of issues and may, for example, have little to say about interface presentation.

Designers also appear to call upon more specific 'user theories', for instance, to reach decisions about the presentation of the interface. Should pointing, digit selection or letter selection be used for menu choice? When should icons be used? How should selected text be marked in a word-processor? Examples of beliefs which underlie questions such as these are given in Hammond *et al.* (1983a), and at times they include assumptions about specific aspects of human cognition about which empirical evidence exists. Designers cannot generally be expected to know about such evidence nor how it should be interpreted. In fact a striking feature about these sorts of 'user theories' is that they tend to be stated as broad generalizations, not subject to variation over tasks or users. Designers' theories may well be insufficiently sensitive to context; studies of human–computer interaction typically find that the way system factors determine ease of use is strongly dependent on the nature of users and their tasks.

Input from human factors

Interface design is not conducted in a vacuum; designers seek out, or have thrust upon them, information and advice from many external sources. The nature of this information and how it influences design will depend largely on the policy of the organization for whom the designers work. There is little evidence on the extent to which external sources of information are used in interface design, but what evidence there is suggests that human factors recommendations have less impact on design than many in the discipline would hope for. The small sample of designers (five) interviewed by Hammond *et al.* (1983a) had little or no familiarity with human factors literature and, despite the fact that they all worked at sites where there were human factors departments, reported making only little use of their services. In some cases, human factors specialists were consulted only to 'put out fires' when unforeseen problems arose which the designers themselves were unable to resolve. This picture is broadly consonant with other evidence. Smith and Mosier (1984a), in a survey of over 200 designers from a range of organizations (mainly in the United States), found that, of the 43% of their sample who answered questions about guideline usage, 63% did not use guidelines at all. It is likely that an even higher proportion of those who chose not to answer the question also failed to use guidelines. Gould and Lewis (1985) asked 447 designers (attending a human factors talk) to 'write down the major steps one should go through in developing and evaluating a new computer system for end users'. Despite the bias built into the context and even into the request, they found that three seemingly common sense principles about the collection of evidence from users were mentioned surprisingly rarely. Although 62% mentioned early focus on users and tasks, only 40% mentioned the possibility of any sort of empirical testing or evaluation and a meagre 20% mentioned the use of iteration, that is of modifying the system on the basis of user tests. Only 16% of designers mentioned all three of these principles.

From this evidence it would appear that external human factors advice, whether in the form of guidelines or in the form of exhortations to focus on users and their problems, has only modest impact on design. This evidence should be treated with caution, though; it is indirect, and even if it is generally the case that human factors has only a small input to design, it may be that its input is focused on just those innovative systems where its impact will be most effective. There are plenty of instances of productive cooperation between human factors specialists and designers.

There are probably several interrelated reasons why human factors advice is not sought as much as it might. We have already discussed how organizational constraints can limit design choice, and hence reduce the perceived need for external consultation. In addition, where no user consultation or testing takes place, then the designer may just not recognize that problems exist. A third reason may lie in the type of advice typically offered, or at least in the way the designer construes the advice. A commonly expressed view is that human factors advice is too local in scope, dealing only with such matters as the detailed presentation of information: 'My view of the help I've got from HF is that it's been way too narrow. It looks only at the problem at hand, it seems to have little appreciation of the overall integrity.'

The same is generally true about published guidelines, and although the aspects they address may be more important to the interface than designers typically admit, such advice fails to meet the hopes of the designer for more structured, integrated or formal tools. In consequence, advice will be sought less often.

These points relate to a fourth possible reason, which is that many current guidelines in particular and some human factors advice in general may make only intermittent contact with the body of knowledge that designers actually call upon to make their decisions. As in many other spheres of expertise, decisions may in part be reached intuitively by reference to a set of complex internal knowledge structures (schemata, see Chapter 4), the details of which the person is normally not aware of. For example, an experienced doctor is likely to reach a correct diagnosis without laboriously considering the possible implications of every symptom of the patient, and indeed might be unable to articulate just why the diagnosis has been reached. We have already seen that some design decisions do seem to be made intuitively; in these cases, guidelines, however relevant, will only influence the decision if the designer has internalized the knowledge that they embody. On at least some of those occasions when decisions are considered explicitly, they may be based upon beliefs or theories about user cognition, as discussed above. Many guidelines may be expressed in a form which does not materially influence these beliefs; the guidelines may, for example, be too prescriptive. To the extent that this is so, one would expect that the designer would find them of little utility.

These are some of the problems which the design guidelines presented in Chapter 8 attempt to address. Apart from dealing with a wide range of issues in user-interface design, these guidelines were developed within a framework which attempts to take into account the whole design process, and the different problems faced at different stages of that process. Chapter 8 does not claim to present a completely developed, tried and tested human factors tool. But it does take steps in the direction of acknowledging that besides being theoretically sound, human factors tools need to be at least as 'user-friendly' as the interfaces they help to design.

Human factors input is not limited to the provision of guidelines and prescriptions; for example it may be involved in initial specification, such as defining the task domain and setting usability criteria, in the development and evaluation of system simulations or prototypes or in a final evaluation of the completed product. Much of this activity involves the collection of information from users, and it is notable that user evaluations of one sort of another featured prominently in the development of a number of interfaces considered to be highly innovative (see, for example, Gould and Boies, 1983; Morgan et al., 1983; Woodmansee, 1983). The scant evidence from interviews and surveys (Gould and Lewis, 1985; Hammond et al., 1983a) suggests that this is the exception rather than the rule. Gould and Lewis (1985) argue persuasively that iteration should be used at many stages of design, whereby evidence collected from users is repeatedly fed back into the design process. They discuss some of the reasons given by designers for not collecting user evidence; these include excessive faith in the power of reason, the belief that evaluations are prohibitively protracted or costly and belief that they will not provide useful information anyway. In many cases, it may just be that the organizational structure does not permit such activities, however empirically minded the designer, and that a suitable budget for human factors inputs is simply not built-in from the start of system development.

In this section we have attempted to illustrate that the final form of an interface results from a myriad of causes, some organizational and some individual, some deliberate and some fortuitous, some analytical and some empirical. By impli-cation we have also pointed to some of the perceived shortcomings of human factors in the eyes of designers. Some of the constraints on interface design are essentially organizational and some are technical; others, though, fall within the remit of cognitive psychology, whether in terms of design knowledge, of design process or of the 'marketing' of cognitive psychology as such. In the next part of the chapter we consider in more detail the ways in which cognitive psychology has been applied to these problems.

APPLYING PSYCHOLOGY TO DESIGN

Routes from psychology to design

Psychology is multifaceted, its subject matter covering techniques and methods, findings and phenomena as well as theoretical explanations. The successful application of psychology to a practical problem may call upon any of these sorts of information. The decision between the use of a menu-driven or a command-driven interface might benefit from the application of techniques for gathering *new data* about user performance and preference. In contrast, the designer of display hardware might refer to *existing data* about the relative sensitivity of the eye to different colours. For many decisions, *existing theoretical understanding* might suffice; if a system requires novice users to memorize 20-item menus, then a theory of short-term memory would predict the general nature of users' difficulties without any need to collect evidence with the specific material in question. Such understanding might be embodied in a full-blown scientific theory or in a local principle of restricted scope.

There are therefore a number of routes by which psychological knowledge can influence design, and in this section we exemplify — rather than review — some of these. At the outset it would be unwise to claim that any one of these was the 'correct' approach. The most productive route will depend at least on the details of the application problem, on the extent of available psychological knowledge and on the resources that can be expended in solving the problem. It is also important to note that while method, data and theory can be treated separately for many purposes, they are closely intertwined. The generation of evidence is prompted by theory, implicitly if not explicitly, and constrained by available methods, while the development or use of a particular methodological instrument reflects the theoretically based quest for observation of one set of phenomena rather than another. Evidence, once generated, is of little use if it is kept in a vacuum: to be applied, it has to be interpreted. For some applications, perhaps, one can argue that the interpretive theory is no more than common design sense, and that the main dearth is of good evidence, not of good theory. Even in such cases, it makes good sense to be explicit about one's working explanations and assumptions; it might be possible to improve upon them. However, an atheoretical stance would be hard to maintain for all, or even for the majority of, application problems within human–computer interaction. The designer hopes that hard-learned experience about user behaviour with one system will generalize to seemingly similar situations; experience tells that such generalization can fail.

The intertwining of method, evidence and theory is evident in existing approaches to the application of theory to design. Empirical methods are typically not proposed independently from the phenomena thought to be worth observing, nor from ways of interpreting the evidence gained. Formal methods of interface analysis necessarily embody assumptions about human cognition, at least once the analysis is mapped onto a design decision, and such methods may go hand in hand with admonitions to collect supportive empirical evidence. The following sections are therefore organized in terms of the major routes for applying psychology to design which already exist. *Empirical routes* involve the collection of user-based information about possible interfaces, such as along the lines of classical and error ergonomics. *Analytical routes* involve the analysis of potential interfaces and their consequences for users and users' tasks. Generally speaking, these can be divided into *representational tools*, which attempt to make explicit the detailed structure and content of the interface, and *predictive tools*, which aim to predict how users will perform when faced with the interface. Probably the most commonly trodden route is the application of *pre-existing recommendations*, such as principles, guidelines, standards or design rules. Finally, psychology can offer some suggestions about *organizational routes*, whereby organizational change can enhance decision-making interfaces. In practical situations, of course, many design decisions will receive interrelated evidence along several of these routes.

The empirical route

Design is by nature a dynamic process: during development, new goals will come to the fore and others will recede; solutions seemingly robust at an intermediate stage may not be present in the final product. The empirical approach acknowledges that design is more than a formal science, and rather than to prescribe design, it aims to provide an input to the decision process alongside those provided by, for example, engineering, art and tradition. The approach advocates the collection of information about users, their tasks and their reactions to the interface at every feasible stage along the design path. This information is fed back into the design process, so that usability grows as an integral part of the design. Although the idea of collecting user evidence and factoring it into design is not a new one (see, for example, Chapanis, Garner and Morgan, 1949; Dreyfus, 1953), a systematic and integrated empirical approach to computer-interface design has been paid little more than lip service. We have already discussed some of the possible reasons for this above.

It is, of course, the case that information collected about a particular system can serve two masters: it has a direct application role, addressing some specific issue about the system in question, and it may also help towards the formulation of a theoretical framework or model accounting for user behaviour more generally. While these activities have traditionally been kept somewhat separate, there is a growing body of work, particularly from research wings of large business organizations in the United States, which successfully marries applications and scientific approaches. In some respects, then, use of empirical methods spans a continuum between the scientific and the applied, with the emphasis on one or the other dependent on the realism of the system and the task under study and on the goals of the investigation. In this chapter we can sample only a section of this continuum, and only some of the many empirical methods available. We shall focus on the more applied issues, since many of the theoretical issues are tackled elsewhere in this book.

Empirical methods can serve as *studies* or as *tests*, to use the terminology of Bailey (1982). Studies are used to collect information before a decision is made, whereas tests help to evaluate a design following the decision. If the design is iterative, then a single empirical investigation can be both a test for a decision and a study for its further refinement. Use of empirical methods has been advocated at all stages of design, from exploration of the task domain right through to evaluation of the final product (Gould and Lewis, 1985). Techniques available range from questionnaires, interviews and other observational techniques, through performance testing on prototypes and simulations, to fully fledged laboratory experiments investigating critical system components or issues.

The task domain

Investigations of the task domain, prior to any formal design work, can help identify how people organize their goals and activities, and thus throw light both on the sorts of facilities a system might provide and on the acceptability of the compromises required by computerization. An example is provided by Malone (1983), who studied how people deal with information kept on their desks and in their offices. His findings illuminate not only how existing tasks and requirements might be supported by a computerized system, but also potential ways of alleviating the difficulties inherent in the non-computer environment. One strong finding was that the organization of people's desks not only helps them to look for information, but it also serves to remind them of things to do and when to do them. A system which failed to provide this reminding function might prove less than ideal. Furthermore, the requirements of classifying and filing information by hand can result in major difficulties: choosing the best category, the mechanics of filing, adding new categories and finding filed information may all pose problems. A computerized system may well be able to help with these, for example by allowing multiple access routes and more flexible organization schemes. Malone's study is discussed in more detail in Chapter 5.

A second example comes from Gould, Conti and Hovanyecz (1983), who used an experimental methodology rather than field observation (see also

Chapter 9). They were concerned with issues in the use of a 'listening typewriter', a device which produces printed (or displayed) copy from spoken input. Although the speech recognition technology does not yet exist for such a device, Gould *et al.* simulated it using a human intermediary, unbeknown to the subjects in their study. Thus, they could not only compare the listening typewriter with existing technologies, but were also able to explore systematically the acceptability of a degraded speech recognizer. For example, a requirement on users to produce speech as isolated words rather than continuously, as normal, was not a great disadvantage provided the vocabulary size of the recognizer was large. Simulation techniques of this sort provide the only way of exploring a domain before the technology is actually available, and may also be a cost-effective means of exploring a task domain even where the technology exists but is expensive or inflexible.

Interface specification

The above studies tackle questions about the task domain. Empirical methods can also be important in the more specific role of defining user and task characteristics as a preliminary to a formal requirements specification. Early decisions about system requirements and constraints will colour the whole development process, and so can strongly influence how easily the final system can be learned and used. Simply knowing in formal terms what the system has to do is not enough; the designer must also know who will do the work and how they are likely to set about it. Textbooks on system design (see, for example, Bailey, 1982) stress the importance of identifying user characteristics, their needs and tasks. Of course relevant information will not be restricted to the psychological; sociological, anthropometric or physiological characteristics of users might be important.

   One use of empirical methods at this stage is to allow the designer and client to identify together both task requirements and putative design solutions. Carroll, Thomas and Malhotra (1980) argue that typically a designer does not know in advance the detailed goals of the design problem, and indeed may not even know the initial problem state. Potential users of systems may also be unable to specify requirements at a level of detail appropriate for design, and even if they can, they may not realize the full consequences. Discussion between designer and client, as exemplified by Carroll, Thomas and Malhotra (1979), allows the design requirements, and pointers towards solutions, to emerge in a cyclical fashion. For details of this use of empirical testing, see also Malhotra *et al.* (1980).

   The sorts of tests and studies we have discussed above can be seen as feeding into both the *functional specification* for a system (what it enables users to do) and the *usability specification* (which users, and how they will learn and use the system). Usability specifications can be phrased in terms of task performance, such as: '80% of secretaries with no prior word-processing experience should be able to type in and print out a standard letter in 20 minutes, using only the instruction manual'.

Specifications such as this can serve a number of purposes. One is to help in the definition of benchmark tasks (Card, Moran and Newell, 1983; Roberts and Moran, 1983; Whiteside *et al.*, 1985), standard performance tasks (much as in the above example) which can be used both to determine whether the system meets usability criteria and to compare different systems or prototypes. The better the available information on users' tasks and on users' organization of the domain, the easier it will be to choose relevant and discriminating benchmarks. The usual dependent measure in benchmark testing is the time to complete the task, although MacLean, Barnard and Wilson (1985a, 1985b) have questioned the validity of tests using unitary performance measures. They demonstrate that, where alternative means exist for completing a task, user preferences (and what they actually do) can deviate widely from the most time-efficient method, possibly because users attempt to minimize mental effort rather than time taken. Ogden and Boyle (1982) also found strong user preference (form-filling dialogue over command dialogue) even when performance differences were minimal. Therefore the sole use of time as an evaluation metric may have hidden costs in terms of user acceptance.

Benchmark tests are all very well, but in themselves they do not direct or constrain design; they do not specify how the usability specification is to be achieved. A second use of usability specifications, discussed by Carroll and Rosson (1984), is to facilitate further usability testing on components of the interface so as to influence decision-making more directly. Carroll and Rosson propose taking the usability and functional specifications one step further by defining *user subskill specifications*. These define the user skills which are required in order for a given usability specification to be met. For instance, taking the example above, a user must be able to understand relevant parts of the instruction manual and relevant information displayed on the screen, and must be able to choose between and act upon options needed for carrying out the task. The identification of subskills is in itself an analytical technique (discussed below) which results in empirically testable propositions about the interface. The intent is not only that detailed subskill specifications (and associated empirical tests) serve as more detailed benchmarks but also that the actual testing should suggest design solutions to problems in the interface.

Advocation of methods such as benchmarking and subskill specification is recent; they are not widely used in design practice and so remain unproven. Although some encouraging indications of their use can be found in the articles referred to above, possible criticisms are not hard to come by. Some of these are discussed in the following section.

Prototyping and iterative design

As we have pointed out, a major aim of subskill specification is to promote a continuous process of evaluation and modification during the development process. This strategy is strongly endorsed by, for example, Gould and Lewis (1985) and some evidence for the success of iterative design in commercial systems can be seen in Boyle *et al.* (1984), Gould and Boies (1983) and Savage, Habinek and Barnhart (1982). For example, in a cycle of design, test, redesign, retest on a menu-driven interface, Savage, Habinek and Barnhart (1982) measured how accurately and quickly different classes of users completed benchmark tasks. Results from the first test were used to modify the design of the menu panels and the routing between them. From the first test to the second, end users improved their mean times from 6.3 to 2.9 minutes and their success rates from 81% to 95%. Equivalent improvements were found with other groups of users, namely programmers and computer operators. By quantifying the size of the improvement in a way which could be directly related to the productivity of the interface, Savage, Habinek and Barnhart (1982) were able to justify the extra resources required for the empirical work. It is likely that this sort of exercise creates a better organizational climate for empirical testing in general. It is also worth noting that if the system is designed from the start to permit both user testing and flexible modifications to its interface, then the additional resources required for testing may not be all that large. This point is dicussed further by Gould and Boies (1983).

On what aspects of the design should iterative design focus? It would clearly be impractical to conduct fully blown experimental studies on every screen displayed and on every page of the documentation. The choice can be narrowed down by means of appropriate analytical methods, hopefully directing the investigator to possible problem areas in the interface. Empirical tests themselves can also help: observation of subjects using the system as a whole (or as much of it as is available) can be very revealing. Informal studies with small numbers of subjects, perhaps using the 'think aloud' technique (Ericsson and Simon, 1984) may not be scientifically watertight, but can be excellent in drawing attention to areas of the interface in need of refinement (Hammond *et al.*, 1984; Mack, Lewis and Carroll, 1983). It is not necessarily the case that large numbers of users have to be tested: Hammond *et al.* (1984) found in a study of five users of a word-processor that of 330 difficulties observed, 75% were shared by at least two users. A central core 28% of difficulties were observed in all five users, and many of these appeared to be the ones having the greatest impact on performance. While the extent of overlap will obviously vary somewhat from system to system, it is encouraging that user performance was not so divergent as to invalidate the use of small samples.

Use of think-aloud methods has the additional advantage that users' comments about *why* they have difficulties can provide hints towards possible solutions, at least partly countering one critism of empirical methods, that they fail to suggest remedies for the problems they identify. Users' comments are useful not, of course, because users have any special design insight but because their comments provide designers with the users' perspectives on the interface, a view not otherwise available. This point is acknowledged by Morgan, Williams and Williams (1983), who give instances of design solutions based on specific comments collected during usability testing.

A further criticism raised against prototype testing is that it focuses on low-level details, such as interface presentation or selection and performance of individual commands, rather than on more architectural aspects of the task and its representation in the system. There may be some substance to this as far as observed difficulties are concerned. Hammond *et al.* (1984) compared evaluations of a word-processor by human factors experts alone with one where an expert observed novice users learning the system. The evidence from user testing did indeed centre more on low-level issues, users themselves providing little or no overview. While it is important to realize that this is the case, it is hardly a crippling criticism of the method; no one claims that prototype testing does the complete job. Evidence from user testing must always be interpreted, and the interpretation may well reflect more architectural issues; in addition, the aim of testing at earlier stages, as we have indicated above, is to provide insight into just such issues.

Finally, we can point to a benefit of empirical testing over and above immediate design iteration, and one that designers themselves have noted (for example, Boyle *et al.*, 1984; Hammond *et al.*, 1983a). This is that extended feedback from users provides designers with a much richer view of users and of the sorts of difficulties they encounter. This can only be generally beneficial; not only are usability questions likely to move closer to the forefront of designers' minds, but once attention is focused on a usability problem, designers will be armed with better knowledge to think about it. As Eason (1982) states, design is an evolutionary process which develops from one release of a product to the next, and from one product to another; even if empirical testing does little to help the present product, it may result in more careful scrutiny of the design of the interface of the next.

The analytical route

Analytical tools provide the means for representing, more or less formally, aspects of the interaction *before* the interface is actually built. The properties of alternative interfaces can then be evaluated for their ease of learning and use by means of predictive tools. The analytical route therefore differs markedly from the empirical one in terms of philosophy, at least when taken in isolation. It assumes that, through the power of reason, an optimal, or at least a good design solution can be found. It further assumes that design is a relatively linear process of requirements specification, system specification and system implementation rather than the 'radically transformational' process described by Carroll and Rosson (1984). Finally, it assumes that the predictive tools have sufficient psychological power to do the job. Of course, in practice analytical methods are unlikely to be used in isolation; they can and do happily mingle with other means of design decision-making.

The term 'analytical' actually covers a variety of approaches, with diverse aims and techniques. In this section we can only indicate some of the major directions. Since an interaction consists of a *user* performing a *task* on a *system*, then most analytical tools embody information concerning these three entities. Tools do differ in their emphasis, however. Some focus on the logical structure of tasks with little explicit reference to user knowledge or process (for example, Gibbs and Tsichritzis, 1983), some on user activities and task knowledge (for example, Johnson, Diaper and Long, 1984), some on the structure of the interface (for example, Jacob, 1983) and others on the relationship between possible system and user representations of the task (for example, Kieras and Polson, 1985).

Different techniques also differ in their purposes. Some aim to represent and clarify the structure of an interface, aiding comparison between alternatives (for example, Moran, 1981; Reisner, 1983). These techniques — and others too which are not strictly representational but go further than conventional guidelines (for example, Harrison and Thimbleby, 1985) — also serve to generate decisions about the interface rather than just represent them. Little or no psychology is involved explicitly in many of the formal methods; for example Dix and Runciman (1985) describe a mathematical model of editors which relates internal structures to interface constraint. Techniques such as these may have implicit psychological assumptions, particularly if they aim also to evaluate design. Evaluation is a second major purpose of analytical tools, and involves prediction of user preference or performance. In many cases, this consists of appeals to principles such as understandability, consistency, predictability and the like, without detailed consideration of the mappings between interface design and user behaviour. There are, though, a number of more psychologically based approaches applicable to restricted design issues (for example, Bannon *et al.*, 1983), and one well-articulated set of application models intended to predict user performance for a wide range of interfaces (Card, Moran and Newell, 1983). The division between representational and predictive tools, while certainly not a dichotomy (Payne, 1984, for example, spans both camps), provides a convenient way of slicing up the analytical cake.

Representational tools

We can consider here only a few examples in order to make some general points. As we have indicated, representational tools attempt to make explicit the most relevant characteristics of the task, the system and the user's knowledge of these. Conceptual analysis of the task domain can lead directly to interface decisions, even when there is little explicit consideration of user cognition (see, for example, Gibbs and Tsichritzis, 1983; Tsichritzis, 1985). Indeed, as we noted in an earlier section, this would seem to be a common design route. Other methods of task analysis take more consideration of the user. For instance, Johnson, Diaper and Long (1984) describe a technique ('task analysis for knowledge descriptions' — TAKD) which identifies and classifies constituent task actions and task objects, and then specifies the knowledge required to perform the task. An example of the application of TAKD is given in Johnson (1985). A rather similar approach to task analysis is taken by Smolensky, Monty and Conway (1984). These techniques are particularly useful in helping define the requirements and functional specifications.

Other methods more directly address the mutual interactions between tasks and how they are supported by the interface (for example, Bannon *et al.*, 1983; Kieras and Polson, 1985; Moran, 1983; Riley and O'Malley, 1984). The most ambitious is that of Kieras and Polson (1985), who present notations for representing user knowledge of the task, as a production system, and for representing the 'notional device' underlying the interface, as a generalized transition network. Good correspondence between these two representations is taken to reflect a good task-to-device mapping, in other words a good interface in respect to functionality. While this approach goes a long way towards formalizing aspects of the interaction, it has yet no published evaluations, and it can be criticized on a number of counts. Just as with Moran's command language grammar (1981; see below), the task representation method assumes a user with 'ideal' knowledge and rationality. Furthermore, Kieras and Polson do not consider learning in any significant way. In this respect, analysis of the relationship between task and device representations which assume fixed task knowledge is questionable, since many detailed aspects of task knowledge might well derive from direct observations of the behaviour of the device. Certainly the examples presented by Kieras and Polson are less than entirely convincing. Nevertheless, their method provides a sufficiently thorough analysis to constitute a psychological applications model which can be evaluated against empirical data. The method can also serve as a *predictive* tool.

Finally, other representational tools focus primarily on the interface, encompassing only the minimum of information. Best known are techniques put forward by Jacob (1983), Moran (1981) and Reisner (1983). Jacob represents the interface in terms of state transitions, Moran as hierarchical command-language structure and Reisner in terms of Backus Normal Form (BNF) notation. Both Moran and Reisner attempt to incorporate aspects of user cognition into the representation in order to build some evaluative component into the methods, but their success in so doing has been seriously questioned by Carroll and Rosson (1984). Jacob (1983) makes no explicit attempt to take user knowledge or process into account, but his method includes the provision of an interpreter to generate a working simulation of the interface. This, therefore, can be used as a flexible tool for empirical evaluation and iterative design. Apart from having explicit psychological assumptions, these approaches also necessarily have hidden ones embodied in their structures and notations. For instance, both Jacob (1983) and Moran (1981) stratify the interface hierarchically in a way which makes it difficult (though not impossible) to capture interrelationships between different levels. Certainly user performance can be determined by strong interactions between levels (Hammond and Barnard, 1984), and it can be argued that such interactions are the rule rather than the exception, at least for novice users.

A problem with applying many of these approaches at an early stage in design is that they are cumbersome; they require detailed consideration of fully articulated interfaces. It is therefore implausible to suppose that a wide range of designs would be submitted to their scrutiny for representation and subsequent evaluation. Furthermore, and despite their unwieldy nature, all the methods are incomplete (though some more so than others) in terms of the levels at which a user might represent the interface. This is particularly so for novice users, for whom problems are the most acute. In view of these problems, it would certainly be premature to claim that representational methods can in themselves lead to optimal design. That said, they do focus the designer's activities onto the interface in a more principled and directed way than might otherwise occur. Any but the most perverse of methods should be an improvement on the haphazard accretion so much a characteristic of unplanned design.

Predictive tools

The case of predictive models of user performance is argued persuasively by Card, Moran and Newell (1983); without models, the designer is unable to predict user performance, will be unlikely to consider performance requirements and the whole design effort will de-emphasize usability issues. Armed with general, accurate and applicable performance models, the designer would certainly be in a strong position to meet usability requirements; nevertheless, even without general predictive models the position is not entirely bleak. We have already argued that the iterative methods espoused by proponents of the empirical route, combined with more local interface and task analyses, provide a means for achieving usability specifications. General predictive models do, however, provide a complementary approach, and their promise is that, by constraining design at an early stage, they block expensive usability failures and reduce the need for usability testing. In some situations it may also be possible to run predictive models 'in reverse' so as to generate design ideas from the characteristic strengths and weaknesses of human performance.

Predictive models are *psychological* models of the user which specify user performance contingent upon the characteristics of user, task and system. Several of the general representational methods discussed above are sufficiently detailed to fall into this category (Kieras and Polson, 1985; Payne, 1984), and their assumptions are amenable to experimental test. There are also a number of more specific models which address particular issues, such as the migration of knowledge when a person transfers from one system to another (Moran, 1983; Singley and Anderson, 1985). However the most general approach of this sort is that of Card, Moran and Newell (1983). They propose a set of *calculational* models, that is, models which permit direct computation of significant aspects of user performance. Starting with a summary of the state of knowledge about human information-processing architecture, they develop a general predictive performance model, GOMS. The model deals specifically with error-free performance, and is explored mainly within the domain of text-editing. GOMS (an acronym for goals, operators, methods and selection rules) provides a general theoretical overview, spanning from the users' task goals through to details of interaction methods. In itself it is inappropriate as a design tool, and so Card, Moran and Newell derive a number of more specific applications models from GOMS. One, the keystroke-level model, relates user performance to the detailed interaction sequence of the dialogue. A second, the unit–task–level model, is concerned with the system's functional specification rather than with interaction details.

These models are prime examples of applications models rather than scientific models, and in order to remain general and relatively straightforward to apply they make strong simplifying assumptions about human cognition. They are, for example, strongly decompositional. While acknowledging they have a number of limitations, Card, Moran and Newell claim that they are sufficiently accurate, robust and flexible to be applied in practical design and evaluation. However, according to Allen and Scerbo (1983), such claims and premature, at least for the keystroke-level model. Allen and Scerbo first of all demonstrate that the keystroke model provides only a modest fit to performance data collected on a general-purpose line editor. They criticize the model on several technical grounds, such as the ambiguous or arbitrary nature of some of the rules for categorising activities, and assumptions that users will choose methods in terms of minimizing keystrokes. This latter issue was discussed above in relation to benchmark testing. Their most serious criticism, though, is of the simplifying assumptions about the cognitive processes of users, assumptions which they consider vitiate much of the model's effectiveness. Allen and Scerbo advocate an approach which examines the components of the cognitive system, such as short-term memory, in more detail. This suggestion, although not developed, is much in accord with the approach taken in this book, where the focus is on the detailed characteristics of the human cognitive architecture and its diverse processes. A predictive tool based on this approach is discussed in a little more detail in Chapter 10.

Principles, guidelines and standards

Guidelines are usually stated as short and simple recommendations, perhaps with examples, exceptions and cross-references to other guidelines. Much effort has been expended in their compilation: one recent report (Smith and Mosier, 1984b) runs to 679 guidelines for the software interface, spread over 448 pages. They may vary widely in generality ('know the user' versus 'compose sentences in the active voice rather than passive voice'), but all are based upon findings or beliefs about human performance. The intent is that they should capture some psychological principle which is sufficiently invariant across a range of contexts for the guideline to remain useful. In this section we will merely consider some of the strengths and weaknesses of the guidelines approach. Chapter 8 expands this discussion along a number of different dimensions, in the context of a proposed framework for guideline formulation which attempts to take account of some of the weaknesses in the guidelines approach identified in this and preceding sections.

Guidelines differ from *design principles* on the one hand and *design standards* on the other. (*Note*: the usage of the term *principle* here is different from its usage in the theoretical chapters of this book, where *summary principles* are used to present, in concise form, the key findings reported in the chapter concerned.) Design principles are generally taken to be more abstract recommendations, often posed in psychological or conceptual terms rather than as design action. For example, Shneiderman (1984) identifies the principle of *direct manipulation* — the visibility and direct and immediate control of objects of interest — as the driving force behind the interface of many successful systems. One recent approach (Harrison and Thimbleby, 1985; Thimbleby, 1984) advocates the use of *generative principles* which serve the dual purpose of providing a basis for user understanding (the colloquial version of the principle) and of formally constraining design (the formal version of the principle). Compared with guidelines, design principles require much more interpretation within the context of a particular problem in order to support decision-making, a process which may have both advantages and disadvantages. Interface design standards, on the other hand, are intended to be as unambiguous as possible, and are stated as requirements for the interface. They may be imposed on design in some formal way, such as by contract or even by legislation. There already exist such standards for interface hardware which are starting to encroach into software design. However, there are strong arguments for supposing that rigid standards for software would be not just premature but also misguided in principle (see, for example, Smith, 1986).

Some reasons for the inappropriateness of imposing standards can be seen from consideration of the use of guidelines. We have already discussed Smith and Mosier's (1984a) survey which demonstrated somewhat equivocal usage of guidelines by designers. A more recent, and more selective, survey (Mosier and

Smith, 1986) provides information on the use of a particular set of guidelines by 130 professionals, about half of whom were human factors specialists. On the whole, the guidelines were considered to be generally useful for establishing requirements in advance of design, as a decision aid and for evaluation purposes. However, this survey revealed some shortcomings of guidelines. First, respondents were not always able to find relevant information even when it was present, and could spend a good deal of time reading irrelevant material. The estimate of average search time for information actually found was 14 minutes. Second, the guidelines were sometimes seen as irrelevant, sometimes as too general to apply or, occasionally, as too specific. Third, respondents had difficulty in determining tradeoffs amongst conflicting guidelines. Finally, respondents often felt that guidelines were not sufficiently helpful in supporting decisions about new technology: guidelines lag behind the times. Despite these criticisms, it would seem that guidelines do provide a practical aid particularly for decisions about interface presentation and dialogue. The impression is that guidelines are taken not so much as prescriptive rules but rather as sources of information about user performance and about alternative design options, information to be evaluated in the design context along with other evidence. Strict standards would not fit well into this method of decision-making.

Guidelines are applications aids; practical efficacy rather than scientific truth is the criterion for their use. However, some guidelines are more efficacious than others, and in some situations it can be argued that they are actually misleading (for example, Barnard, 1983b). It is therefore worth considering briefly their scientific basis. As we have discussed above, human behaviour is contextually determined; in general it cannot be fully described by a number, even a large number, of simple independent propositions. Since guidelines are simple statements about user behaviour, they, too, cannot fully describe the interaction between system and user. If behaviour results from an interplay of factors, so will the ease of use of an interface. These interdependencies are hard, or even impossible, to capture in simple statements. A guideline which is true in one context may well be misleading in another. While for many purposes it would seem that guidelines do provide a useful simplification, the more complex the interface, the less plausible it is that guidelines will help.

Used in isolation, as the sole source of design decisions, guidelines may therefore be better suited to physical aspects of the interface and to simple presentation issues than to the more cognitive aspects of the interaction. Problems arising from conflicting guidelines, as noted by Mosier and Smith's respondents (1986), may be resolved by empirical test or by the designer's judgement, but they also reflect the need for more integrative principles of design (MacGuire, 1982) or more realistic approaches to the design process. Guidelines are only one of the tools in the human factors toolkit and, just as one would not build a house using only one tool, so interfaces need to be built through the combined use of different tools. This means that guidelines may have their own important role to play in specific facets of the design process, and should be used within that application boundary. They may, for example, be excellent vehicles for guiding the *human factors* expert in the initial stages of team work on a particular interface development: current thinking and research on cognitive psychology is so broad and spans so many different areas that it is logistically impossible for one person to be fully acquainted with everything that all the different research domains have to offer. Guidelines may bypass the need to traverse personally the full route from scientific research to potential design application. Similarly, within the context of a design team which benefits from cognitive psychology inputs such as those described in the next section of this chapter, guidelines may provide a useful interim source of information which can be disambiguated as necessary by those who have expertise in the discipline.

Organizational routes

Depending upon the particular organization concerned, cognitive psychologists can make contributions to the design and evaluation process in many ways, within two broad categories:

— directly, as members of design team or as consultants to a design team;
— indirectly, by transferring cognitive psychology knowledge or design aids based on cognitive psychology knowledge to others.

Within the first category — direct contributions — cognitive psychologists are increasingly found on the design teams responsible for product developments and where this is not the case often make inputs on a consultancy basis.

Direct application routes

The cognitive psychologist as an expert on the design team Design of office systems is normally done by teams, not by individuals. The teams concerned are multidisciplinary, and psychologists are playing an increasingly important role in such teams. Three important shifts are discernible in connection with this over the last several years:

— The psychologist concerned is increasingly likely to be invited to join the team as a full member, on a par with specialists from other disciplines (such as, computer science, electronics), rather than to be used as a consultant who is only brought in occasionally for specific purposes, and who has less influence than the rest of the team.
— The person concerned is increasingly likely to have a background in cognitive psychology. This person will often be expected to provide

     inputs that are different from and complementary to those made by specialists in traditional ergonomics who may be used on a consultancy basis to contribute primarily to the physical ergonomics of the workstation.

— Design inputs from psychologists are increasingly likely to be sought early on in the design process — often at the very earliest stages when the product is only defined in the most general terms — rather than being sought only after the critical design decisions have been made.

This style of working is especially rewarding and challenging. It is rewarding to see psychological advice having a tangible influence on key design decisions right from the outset of a particular product development, and it is challenging in the degree to which it requires the psychologist concerned to 'come off the fence' and be prepared to make a mistake by saying something definite based on his or her best judgement at the time. Although many decisions could benefit from specific research, the design cycle is often too short and the budget too limited for the necessary research to be done, and so decisions have to be made on the basis of existing knowledge and best judgements.

The cognitive psychologist as a consultant to the design team This style of working is still widely used and is likely to remain important for two related reasons; it means that a relatively large number of product developments can have access both to a relatively limited number of cognitive psychologists, and to the facilities (such as prototype testing facilities) which the psychologists may need to use.

The effectiveness of this approach requires identifying those areas where relatively specific inputs from a cognitive psychologist to relatively well-defined questions can have a useful influence on the design. Where there is a psychologist working in the design team who is responsible for identifying such areas and the consultancy is seen as providing supplementary inputs on specific points, this approach is likely to be more successful than where there is no psychologist on the team and the areas for psychological consultancy are identified by people from other specialisms. In the latter case, important areas may be overlooked, and questions may be posed in inappropriate ways. In such cases, the onus is partly on the psychologist concerned to try and identify the problem and talk it through with the client; unfortunately, the timescales involved and the limitations on the budget as well as other factors (for example, filtering of information in accordance with what the design team considers to be relevant to the problems identified) may combine to make this rather difficult to do effectively. The cognitive psychology team in such instances may find themselves working on inappropriately specified problems that are relevant to only a very restricted part of the overall design.

Constraints on direct application routes

Budgeting for cognitive psychology The need to work within the budget available for the product development concerned has been mentioned above. It is a particular problem for the involvement of cognitive psychologists in the design process because in many organizations those concerned with agreeing the budget (not necessarily involving the design team at all) do not normally write in an explicit budget for cognitive psychology or even think about it at the time of drawing up the budgets. Even when a budget for human factors and/or industrial design is included, the intention is more often to fund work on the physical aspects of the design than work on the cognitive aspects. This situation may improve as some organizations recognize the need to build in an allocation for the cognitive aspects of the design right from the start, but significant improvements in this regard depend upon cognitive psychologists marketing their skills and knowhow much more effectively than in the past.

The problem of timescales The time allowed for cognitive psychology (or any other) contributions to a product development has two aspects:

— the overall level of effort (the number of person-months; for example, four people working full-time for three months and one person working full-time for twelve months both amount to an overall level of effort of twelve person-months); and
— the calendar time available (for example, the contribution is required three months from now, no matter how many people need to work on it in order to achieve that). The overall level of effort is clearly related to the amount of money allocated. The calendar time available is related to other factors, especially the 'market window'.

The 'market window' is the period of time during which market conditions are right for the launch of the product concerned. If it is launched too early, the market may not be ready for it. For various reasons, people or organizations who might have bought the product later do not buy it now. One reason may be that they have an existing generation of equipment that has still not been fully depreciated — it is still being paid for, and the organization concerned cannot afford new equipment. Another reason might be that the new product is too sophisticated. This relates to the concept of 'user migration'. Products which 'migrate' (in terms of their sophistication) faster than their users fail because they are 'before their time'. This can be a problem for cognitive psychologists. If they are *too* innovative in their design recommendations, they may have a hard time convincing the marketing department that the product is not too 'way out' for the current population of users. (The response from some conservative sectors of the market during 1985 to the use of a mouse in the user interface — even though other sectors were taking to it enthusiastically — was an example of this.)

A more serious problem for the cognitive psychologist is likely to be the need to launch the product before it is too late — before it is overtaken by some new development in technology or a change in market conditions. For a number of years, the 'market window' in regard to information technology products has been shortening. In some cases, there is a critical six-month period in which a product must be launched if it is to be successful. A product which is 70% right and is launched within that window may well make money, whereas a product that is 80% right but is launched late will probably lose money. The moral is that it is often better to launch a product within the critical 'market window', even if it could clearly be improved, than to delay its launch in order to make the improvements.

The important implication which this has for cognitive psychology is twofold. First, it is necessary to adopt methods which can result in positive contributions within the rather short timescales that often apply. Relying exclusively on methods which require longer periods of time will often significantly reduce the value of the eventual results — it may simply be too late to incorporate them into the design in time to meet the product launch date. This may point to a need to develop new methods, and adapt old methods to new circumstances. Secondly, it means that contributions from cognitive psychology will be much more welcome if they help to reduce the design cycle, or at the very least do not make it longer, than if they slow down the development of the product. This means, for example, that running evaluations of the design of a user interface as it is developed will have to be justified very hard if the evaluations are seen to be slowing down the process; they will be accepted much more readily if they can fit in with the existing timescales, helping to improve the quality of the final product without delaying its launch.

Organizational marketing of cognitive psychology The successful marketing of cognitive psychology within an organization normally needs to be done in a highly competitive context in which others are competing for the available funds. A necessary condition is that cognitive psychologists have some 'success stories' to be able to show, in terms of product developments which can clearly be seen to have benefited from cognitive psychology. Generic designs, perhaps embodied in illustrative prototypes (discussed below) have a part to play in this. But although this is a necessary condition, it is not sufficient. Building on this base, it is then necessary to 'advertise' the existence of a cognitive psychology resource within the organization, and what that resource has to offer. As we discussed earlier, it is far too often the case that many product developments proceed without inputs from cognitive psychologists because those concerned did not appreciate that some of the design problems involved were of a cognitive psychological nature, were not aware that a cognitive psychology resource was available in the organization, and/or were not aware of the kinds of services that the resource could provide.

Some of the necessary raising of awareness can be done through the distribution of in-house newsletters, organization of in-house symposia, and so forth. In addition, it is necessary for the appropriate communication channels to be set up. This can be a long process at the formal level because it represents a disturbing influence on the way the organization has operated in the past, and is one reason why cognitive psychologists more than some other specialists often may depend largely upon the informal contacts built up over a period of time by the individuals concerned.

The professional image of cognitive psychology The particular image which cognitive psychology has within any given organization will often depend to a large extent on the particular contributions made to particular product developments. This by itself may be a constraining influence on what cognitive psychologists are invited to do in the future, but there are other difficulties as well. It seems to be an unfortunate fact that bad design is more obvious than good design. Gross errors of judgement in the design are (almost by definition) easily spotted, and it is often relatively easy to make a plausible suggestion concerning how the design could be improved. This helps to reinforce the feeling which is still prevalent that good design is common sense. It also means that when cognitive psychologists do make errors of judgement, the criticisms which are likely to follow may well reinforce any feelings there might be that cognitive psychology is too 'academic' and that real design work should be left to those who have the necessary practical experience. Good design, in contrast, often goes unnoticed; it is taken for granted that the product should be easy to use, and no special comment is called for when it is found to be so. The image of cognitive psychology as being a specialism which can make a positive contribution to the design of real products will improve as general organizational awareness of the subtleties of the cognitive aspects of product design is enhanced through the professional promotion of the specialism — not just through the 'advertising' of the specialism discussed above or the quality and importance of the direct contributions that cognitive psychologists make, but also through the various indirect contributions which enhance awareness of what the specialism has to offer.

The direct contributions that cognitive psychologists can make to product developments are necessarily limited by the number of such people employed in the relevant industrial contexts. It is therefore important to complement the direct contributions that are possible with indirect contributions aimed at transferring cognitive psychology knowledge, and design aids of various sorts derived from such knowledge, to a wider population of specialists involved in the design process. In this way, product developments generally should benefit to varying degrees from what cognitive psychology has to offer, and cognitive psychology specialists can make especially significant contributions to selected developments where their special expertise is of most value.

Indirect application routes

There are many vehicles by which cognitive psychologists can make indirect contributions within the organizational context, especially: through training programmes, design guidelines, provision of generic designs, contributions to standardization activities, and provision of design and evaluation aids. The next few sections consider these in more detail.

Training programmes One of the most valuable services a psychologist can perform in relation to office systems design is to make relevant concepts and methods available more widely through appropriate training programmes for the non-psychologist members of design teams. Many organizations encourage their human factors experts to prepare and teach formal training courses which are aimed at raising designers' awareness of the different types of problem involved in 'good' interface design. Cognitive psychology has a part to play in these courses as it becomes an increasingly important part of the human factors effort generally.

Design guidelines We noted earlier that the successs of design guidelines has been mixed, but it is certainly the case that in some organizations the design teams welcome concise statements of important 'do's' and 'don'ts' relating to the design of office products. These can be at their most successful when they are provided as concise 'manuals' rather than as texts on psychology or ergonomics. The fast-moving and often frenetic context of product development to meet a tight deadline is not the time to try to educate designers in the niceties of the psychological principles involved. There are other, more appropriate contexts in which the training role of psychologists will have its full benefits. However, the design team often appreciates having a document which it can use as a reference book, rather than a text to aid in learning about human factors or psychology. Guidelines may be most likely to succeed when they are presented as a set of recommendations to follow, complementary to rather than as a vehicle for training. The design team is then more likely to use them in a similar way to standards, whilst recognizing their more tentative status and using them accordingly (that is, as *guides* rather than rigid rules).

Generic designs Generic designs provide concrete illustrations of how to apply design guidelines. They show by example. Such a design includes design concepts that have a useful degree of generality, so they can be incorporated into many particular designs used across a range of products. The concepts incorporated into a generic design might include, for example: particularly good ways of allowing the user to scroll through a document, particularly interesting windowing techniques, particularly helpful ways of allowing the user to edit voice messages, and so forth.

In the organizational context, generic designs are often provided in the form of a leading-edge prototype office product, but they need not always be an actual product or prototype. They can be conceptual and yet have an important influence on user-interface design. The conceptual WIMP interface, for example (windows, icons, mouse, pull-down/pop-up menus), has influenced the design of many products. Readers familiar with modern office systems will see the strong influence of WIMP concepts on such products as the Xerox Star, Apple Lisa and Macintosh, GEM, Tapestry, Taxi and other products.

Standardization activities The similarities one can observe between many different products on the market often represent a kind of *de facto* standardization. Users learn what to expect from products in a given category because previous such products have chosen to incorporate particular features in particular ways — even if the result has been suboptimal from a psychological point of view. An example of what is meant by a psychologically suboptimal solution in this context is provided in the hardware domain by the QWERTY keyboard, which has become a standard which would be very difficult to displace despite the fact that it was designed to meet non-psychological criteria and that ergonomically better designs have been proposed. The same kind of problem will arise in the software domain unless cognitive psychologists and other human factors specialists work energetically to propose standards based on adequate research before *de facto* standards become so well established that they are as difficult to displace as the QWERTY keyboard.

Psychologists are represented on some of the key standardization bodies operating in industry but it must be said that they are currently hampered in their work by the paucity of directly relevant and applicable research. This is an area where the psychological research community must recognize that product developments will not slow down to await the results of psychological research — indeed, the product development cycle has been shortening — and if psychologists wish to influence such developments they need to develop methods of research that are suitable for producing applicable findings within the timescales that apply. Recently, a European wide programme of research has been launched which, amongst other issues, addresses this problem specifically. Under the COST programme, attention is being given to producing standards for user-interface design within an industry-led framework involving a number of European academic institutions.

Design and evaluation aids Guidelines, generic design concepts and standards help to provide the designer with a framework within which to work. However, an infinite number of possibilities exist within that framework and designers increasingly turn to psychologists for particular advice on the cognitive aspects of the particular products on which they are working. In some cases it is appropriate for the psychologist to become a member of the design team or to provide advice to the team on a consultancy basis. However, there are not enough psychologists in industry to be able to cover all product developments adquately in this way. Another organizational route to applying cognitive psychology which attempts to address this problem is setting aside resources for the development of design and evaluation aids, or tools, which can be shipped out to the designer when the psychologist or human factors expert is not available — at least for some of the more routine aspects of design.

In the older field of workstation ergonomics, an approach that has proved useful to design teams has been to provide a 'black box' that can accept descriptions of proposed layouts and provide feedback concerning their appropriateness in terms of ergonomic considerations (see Pulat and Crice, 1985, for several examples of such design aids). Even where these require a trained ergonomist to interpret the results, they can be useful in automating some of the routine aspects of the work, thereby increasing productivity and releasing some of the ergonomist's time for other, higher level work.

Less work of this sort has been done in relation to the cognitive psychological aspects of the user interface to office systems. We saw in a previous section that there exist a number of psychological models which can serve as tools for clarifying and representing particular facets of the *psychological* side of the interface equation. These invariably require a psychologist to apply them, and they often are seen more as research devices leading to a better understanding of human–computer interaction, than as tools which designers can use to solve specific design problems. Within the organizational context, their influence is largely restricted to human factors specialists. Moves have now started towards applying these psychological tools more widely, within the framework of automated design aids that require no significant knowledge of psychology or human factors, and which can be ported to the design team who needs them, even in the absence of a psychologist. One such design aid is currently being developed through the work on the ESPRIT project which was the initial triggering motivation for this book (see Gardiner and Christie, 1985). It is described in more detail in Chapter 10.

Such design aids, as well as helping to assess given designs in terms of their 'cognitive compatibility' between human and machine, have a contribution to make in the training area as well. They provide a structured environment within which designers can be shown formal specification techniques, can see the effects of different modifications to a particular design, and can have their attention called to the reasoning behind particular evaluations. The degree to which such design tools will be useful as vehicles for training (either in industry or in academia) depends to a large extent on how well designed their *own* interfaces and ancillary documentation are, so that, for example, the task of describing an interface for evaluation does not obscure the real purpose of the design aid, which is to evaluate the interface description from the point of view of users' cognitive capabilities and limitations. Obviously, this entails a certain degree of commitment from industry in carrying further and expanding the basic work currently being done in this area. Equally obviously, it entails commitment from academia to provide the applicable research that will make using those tools, in whatever capacity, worthwhile. This is, once again, an instance where industry and academia ought to be talking much more than they do at present.

Developments in design methodology

Both the direct and the indirect contributions that cognitive psychologists can make to the design process need to be considered in the context of a changing environment. It has been noted above that increasingly the 'market window' for a new product may be quite short, and there is increasing pressure to shorten the design cycle. This suggests a need for developments in design methodology to take account of these emerging requirements. For the cognitive psychologist, this represents an opportunity. Contributions from cognitive psychology will be welcomed if it can be shown that they can help to maintain or improve the quality of the final product whilst also helping to shorten the design cycle. This implies, for example, that cognitive psychologists could usefully consider how evaluation of products for usability could be integrated into the design process in such a way that usability evaluations could be conducted in parallel with the specification and production of software, rather than these being seen as sequential stages in an iterative process. Possibilities relating to this are considered later in this book.

CONCLUSIONS

The population of users of electronic systems has been changing. Decreasing costs have opened the door to direct interaction by non-computer specialists, opening up significant new markets. Ease of use is becoming a significant marketing feature of a new product. A key market sector in this regard is the office. Office staff are little concerned with the technicalities of the machines they use. What is important is that the machines should provide the functions that are needed, should be easy to learn, and easy to use.

In designing office systems to meet these criteria, the designer needs to take account of the relevant characteristics of the intended users, the tasks to be supported, and the relevant system parameters. Within this framework, the designer has available seemingly infinite design possibilities. This flexibility of choice may be a two-edged sword, however, and increasingly designers are looking to cognitive psychologists (and other human factors experts) for guidance.

Cognitive psychology, aiming as it does to understand the information-processing capabilities of the human, would seem in principle to have much to offer the designer of systems concerned with supporting human information processing (in the office, and in other areas). In practice, however, the overlap between the 'applied' and the 'scientific' fields of endeavour in this area has been largely in terms of methodolgy. Conceptual overlap has been limited largely because of the problems of interpreting evidence from relevant studies and drawing conclusions with sufficient generality. This situation may improve in the future. But if the applied discipline of human factors in this area is to broaden its activities to allow tighter prediction of user preference and performance, then it needs to call upon more powerful and more specific psychological theories. The other side of this coin is that theory development needs to be oriented in appropriate directions.

One of the impediments to general progress in this area has been that much of the research, both applied and academic, has been driven by very specific practical or theoretical problems. Whilst this has had the advantage of focusing efforts, it has tended to work against the development of useful linkages between different problem areas and the development of a broader, more integrated conceptual framework. One result of this in the applied context is that it has tended to be self-perpetuating; because practitioners do not have a solid, general and applicable theoretical base to draw on, they are forced to take a problem-driven approach to addressing the immediate design problem. This tendency is reinforced by the severe limits of time and resources within which practitioners must operate. The practice of applied cognitive psychology within the field of office systems design would therefore benefit in the longer term from work by the scientific community on the development of a broad, applicable theroretical base. This does mean, it needs to be repeated, that to be useful to the practitioner the theoretical work must be oriented in an appropriate direction — to address the relevant and pertinent issues. Whilst there may be a place for more 'freewheeling' theoretical work as well, such work is less likely to be of value in the applied domain — or at least to be taken up readily in that domain.

If one problem facing the practitioner has been the lack of a solid theoretical base from which to work, another has been the difficulty of making a significant impact on the design process. The two are related, of course — it will be easier to make a significant impact when the science (both pure and applied) is stronger — but there are other considerations as well. However firmly recommendations might be based, they also need to be 'user-friendly' to the designer if they are to have an impact. What little evidence is available suggests that human factors recommendations in general have less impact on the design process than many in the field would hope for, and cognitive psychology is not an exception to this.

A number of factors are involved. Even though the amount of effort devoted to the user interface can represent a significant proportion of the total development costs for a product, lack of a sufficient allocation of time and resources to cognitive psychology inputs is a key factor limiting the extent and kind of inputs that are typically made. This often reinforces the criticism of human factors that the advice given is often too limited in scope. Improving the situation requires marketing cognitive psychology more effectively.

Effective marketing depends, amongst other things, on relating cognitive psychology to the design process in ways that are helpful. This involves both contributions on an individual basis to particular product developments, and a more general transfer of capability from the specialist cognitive psychologist to other design practitioners.

A number of possibilities concerning the transfer of cognitive psychological capability have been discussed in this chapter. However, no matter how good the tools, to be effective they need to be applied within an appropriate design context — which to a large extent does not yet exist. Cognitive psychologists have a role to play in contributing to methodological developments in this area, if they can make their contributions relevant and constructive.

THE NEXT CHAPTER

The previous two chapters have set the scene for the rest of the book: a structure and justification for the work covered and the approach adopted were discussed in Chapter 1; Chapter 2 then put the application of cognitive psychology within the wider design framework, reviewing application routes both from the point of view of an applied discipline of psychology — human factors — and from the point of view of the organizational structures and *mores* through which human factors work is channelled to the design process. The cognitive psychology principles which from the basis for such application work will now be reviewed. Part Two contains five theoretical chapters which address areas of cognitive psychology research which have direct relevance to the study of human–computer interaction. Chapter 3 starts this presentation by tracing the roots of many of the ideas which are discussed in detail in these theoretical chapters, providing the context in which cognitive psychological thinking emerged and developed into what it is today.

PART TWO:
KEY AREAS OF COGNITIVE PSYCHOLOGY

A historical perspective

Robert Scane

INTRODUCTION

As a discrete field of study, cognitive psychology has been in existence for some 20–25 years, although its basic concepts can be traced back much further than this. Even in this short space of time, it has exerted considerable influence in other areas of psychology.

Fundamentally, cognitive psychology is the study of knowledge and of how people use it. It deals with how we gain information from the world, how it is represented and transformed as knowledge, how that information is stored, and how that knowledge is used to direct behaviour. The whole range of mental activities and the use of language is subsumed under cognitive psychology.

A formal definition is given by Mayer (1981): 'Cognitive psychology is the scientific analysis of human mental processes and structures with the aim of understanding human behaviour.'

Some of the terms used here require elaboration:

— Cognitive psychology, above all, is scientific — only scientific methods may be used, and so employing solely feelings or intuition to examine knowledge representation is not appropriate.
— The domain of study is human mental life, and study focuses on two domains:
  • process (what occurs internally); and
  • structure (the way knowledge is stored).
— The aim of cognitive psychology is to understand behaviour by providing clear and accurate descriptions of internal cognitive events in order to predict behaviour.

The prime concern of all science is to establish cause and effect relationships in order to gain understanding of the significance of observable phenomena. These relationships, and facts impinging upon them, are formalized in terms of theories which are then testable by experimentation. The importance of the theory-driven approach in science is that it enables predictions to be made concerning future events: if a particular theory has predictive power, then it is of value.

THE ROOTS OF MODERN PSYCHOLOGY

All modern scientific disciplines have emerged from a broad stream of philosophical speculation which had its origins with the classical Greeks, and which has flowed forward through the history of Western civilization. This philosophical tradition was concerned with the nature and meaning of all phenomena that influenced human experience.

Associationism

In time, interest in human experience itself grew into a separate field of study as, for example, interest in numbers had earlier developed into the discipline of mathematics. The corpus of philosophical study which gave rise to scientific psychology is known as *associationism*.

Associationism began with the writings of Aristotle (*'De Anima'*) who formulated three basic Laws of Association as a reaction to the concept of *eidola* proposed by Plato. *Eidola* were alleged to be the building blocks of memory, faint perceptual copies of objects, which entered the mind directly. Aristotle asserted that memories were generated by association between concepts, by virtue of the following laws:

— similarity,
— contrast, and
— temporal and spatial contiguity.

For example, the image of 'hot' often gives rise to that of 'cold', through the operation of contrasting associations.

The Aristotelean Laws of Association remained essentially unaltered until post-Renaissance times. From this point onwards, they were expanded and reworked by a succession of eminent, generally British, empiricist philosophers (such as, Hobbes, 1588–1679; Hume, 1711–76; Hartley, 1705–57; and John Stuart Mill, 1806–73).

Locke and others

The most prominent of those was John Locke, whose *'An Essay Concerning Human Understanding'* (1690) represented a fundamental change of direction within philosophy.

During the 17th century, innovations in science, amounting almost to a revolution, were sweeping through Europe. The medieval concept of a God-centred universe was gradually yielding to notions of the world as a giant machine which obeyed laws discoverable through mathematics and science. The works of Isaac Newton contributed substantially to this new view of the world; and Locke was a contemporary and admirer of Newton.

Locke brought the empiricist approach of science to philosophy, stressing the paramountcy of observation over metaphysical speculation. He was concerned with *how* knowledge is represented in the mind, and came to the conclusion that all ideas derive from experience. Perhaps the best known theme of Locke's philosophy is the empiricist principle of the *'tabula rasa'*: the mind, at birth, is a blank sheet, onto which all knowledge is projected through experience.

Experience Locke held to be of two kinds:

— sensations derived from external objects, and
— reflections upon the internal workings of the mind.

It was thus possible to observe the mind in operation by introspection. The major points of Locke's thesis may be summed up as follows:

— processes of sensation: the senses are the gateways through which passes knowledge of the world.
— elements: simple ideas, such as 'brightness', 'redness'. These are the building blocks from which all complex ideas are constructed.
— associations: the way in which the more complex ideas are constucted.
— consciousness: all mental processes are conscious and accessible to introspection.

Locke himself was not a practical scientist; he did not attempt to experiment to test these hypotheses. Nor was there total consistency in his writings. However, he can be seen as preparing the way for the scientific study of the mind, by dispensing with the metaphysical elements of philosophy, and by emphasizing the importance of observing events.

Locke's successors within the associationist tradition attempted to build on his ideas. They attempted to use the experimental methods propounded by Newton to investigate how sensory elements became combined, through the principles of association, to form more complex structures.

Hume, for example, developed a tripartite classification of association:

— resemblance,
— contiguity,
— cause and effect,

and used it as a theoretical tool to examine some basic phenomena. Hartley distinguished between two types of association (which, incidentally, are echoed in the learning theories of the 20th century):

— successive: where a chain of elementary sensations regularly follow each other in time, and so become a permanent structure, or idea.
— simultaneous: where sensations regularly become associated at the same instant, and in consequence become associated.

Hartley also attempted to account for the physiological basis of associations and sensory elements.

However, although these and other associationist philosophers attempted to follow in the empiricist tradition, their endeavours cannot be regarded as truly scientific. Certainly, the necessity to make observations was acknowledged; but these were not made in any systematic manner, and neither was any kind of experimentation undertaken.

In fact, it was not until the second half of the 19th century that there arose a tradition of experimentation to test empiricist principles in the area of mental functioning; with the work of men such as Weber and Fechner, psychology at last began to have an identity distinct from philosophy.

Fechner, a physicist by training, realized that conscious processes could be accessed by controlling the environmental stimuli available to an individual. Weber, a physiologist, had been the originator of a method of getting subjects to discriminate between stimuli of different magnitudes, but it was Fechner who performed the first controlled experiments using this method (Fechner, 1860). By varying experimentally the difference in magnitude between two qualitatively similar stimuli, and by varying the absolute magnitude of the two stimuli, it was possible to ask a subject to say if (s)he could discriminate between them. Sensation could then be measured in terms of the strength of the stimuli presented. Fechner was able to produce a mathematical law relating the magnitude of a stimulus to the strength of sensation.

Another experimental technique devised at around this period gave an impetus to the development of psychology as a new discipline: that of mental chronometry, or the measurement of reaction time. If a subject is presented with a stimulus and required to press a key in response, it is possible to obtain a measure of the elapsed time: simple reaction time. If a task (say, of a discriminant nature) is presented along with the stimulus, reaction time is typically extended as a function of the time needed to perform the task. Thus the simple reaction time subtracted from the time taken to perform the task give a quantitative, temporal measure of the inferred mental processes involved in the task.

Another prominent worker who helped to prepare the way for an ex-perimental psychology to emerge from philosophy was Ebbinghaus, who in-vestigated associationist principles in the area of memory and learning by carefully controlling variables to study their effects on remembering and forgetting. However, the first modern experimental psychologist is generally held to be Wilhelm Wundt, and his contribution to psychology will be discussed in the following section.

Structuralism

Most major developments in psychology have been identified with various schools of thought, which have embodied particular approaches in terms of subject matter, methodology and a general body of theory. Historically, the first such school to arise was structuralism.

Scientific psychology is generally held to have been born when Wundt established the first psychological laboratory in Leipzig in 1879. The new science incorporated elements of associationist–empiricist philosophy, together with data emerging from contemporary German physiology, and Wundt himself is widely acknowledged as the founder of experimental psychology. The subject matter of the infant science was conscious experience, which Wundt considered was analysable into elementary sensations. A fair analogy for the structuralist endeavour is with chemistry; as chemists analyse complex compounds into chemical elements, so Wundt attempted to analyse complex experiences into sensory elements. Having accomplished this, the next move was to determine how these elements were connected, and so discover general laws of connection. This concern with structure gave the movement its name.

These aims could only be achieved by investigating immediate experience as it occurred. In addition, as experience could only be reported by the individual undergoing the experience, it had to be treated as objectively as possible. Wundt proceeded to derive a method suitable for gathering the necessary objective data: that method became known as classical introspection.

Classical introspection is a form of self-observation, in which the meaning of the experience was to be ignored in favour of the component sensations. Thus, to see a 'large red book' was an error (a stimulus error, according to Wundt). The appropriate report should be of the form 'a red-coloured trapezoidal shape' (see Gilhooly, 1982).

There were a number of problems associated with classical introspection as a research technique:

— subjects were required to be articulate adults, and it took a great deal of time to train them to report experience objectively;
— it was difficult to reconcile conflicting reports from different studies;
— it focused narrowly on laboratory studies, and so the results were not generalizable to human experience in a wider context; and
— it was not truly scientific in that it was impossible to validate introspectionist report.

The structuralists concentrated almost entirely upon sensation, since higher cognitive functions were not amenable to investigation by introspection. Inevitably, opposition to structuralism arose because of the inherent sterility of its subject matter and research technique, and structuralism as a movement within psychology died an early death. For all its faults, structuralism is acclaimed as pioneering experimental psychology. Although this view is undoubtedly correct, it can also be argued that its narrowness of approach disinclined many future psychologists from studying cognition: in rejecting introspection as an appropriate experimental technique, they also rejected cognitive functioning as a valid area of study.

Reactions to structuralism

William James The principles formulated by James constitute a significant contribution to psychology although they never gave rise to a major school of thought in the way that Wundt inspired structuralism. Rather, they facilitated the transition from structuralism to other ways of looking at experience and behaviour.

James considered psychology to be the science of mental life, encompassing both individual experience and relevant biological processes. Cognitive functioning was intimately related to the adaptive biology of the organism: cognition had evolved to enhance the capability for survival.

The proper area for study was then the totality of experience: by this he meant physiology, emotions, events and the meanings of events, not just sensations isolated from the context in which they arose. He held that the structuralists' basic elements were artefacts, existing only in psychological abstraction, and not as real entities.

In many ways, his views on different aspects of cognition foreshadow modern cognitive psychological approaches. He asserted that:

— sense organs responded to only a particular range of stimuli;
— perception was an elaboration of the sensory processes within the central nervous system, and was mediated by both past and present experience;
— higher mental processes such as believing, reasoning and remembering were higher-order elaborations of perceptions.

Thus attempts to isolate and label these functions were a distortion of the dynamic nature of cognition.

In addition, James anticipated the later concept of different stages of memory: those of short-term and long-term memory (see a later section of this chapter, and also Chapter 5, for a further discussion of the two-store approach to memory). He distinguished between primary memory, which lasted only a short term, and secondary memory, which was knowledge of events after they left consciousness.

James' theories were incomplete, and he himself was not greatly involved in experimentation to confirm them, preferring after a few years to abandon psychology for philosophy. However, his writings set the scene for the development of Western experimental psychology, and provided a framework for the study of cognition as a series of dynamic processes. According to Reynolds and Flagg (1983): 'Cognitive psychology was conceived with James' *Principles of Psychology* in 1890.'

Functionalism

Structuralism had taken root in the United States when Titchener, a student of Wundt, set up a psychology department at Cornell University in 1892. In the same year, psychology was established at Chicago University, but the theoretical orientation of this group of workers was markedly different from that of the structuralists. This movement came to be known as functionalism, and came into existence entirely as a reaction to the straightjacket of structuralist theory and methodology. As such, it did not attain the status of a formal school within psychology, and its own theoretical constructs remained rather vague. However, drawing its inspiration from the writings of James and others, the functionalist movement had great influence on the development of American psychology.

As the name suggests, the movement was more concerned with studying the *function* of mental activity, rather than its *structure*. The concept had a number of different meanings: for example, function could be envisaged as all of the following:

— synonymous with a mental-activity category such as 'perception';
— the biological utility of an activity;
— a contingent relationship (in a mathematical sense) between two entities.

As these different meanings were not held by functionalists to be contradictory, the way was opened for a fundamental change in emphasis within psychology: since it was asserted that behaviour was a function of mental activity (in the sense of the latter two categories above), the study of behaviour itself could be incorporated into psychology.

By so broadening the scope of psychology, the range of possible subject-matter greatly increased; it now became legitimate to study children, the mentally impaired, and those from different cultural and societal groups (in marked contrast to the structuralists' trained adult subjects).

Even the study of animals became justifiable. Evolutionary theory had shown that the physiology of humans and certain animals was closely related, so it seemed quite probable that the study of animals would throw light on the nature of human psychology. There was also the pragmatic consideration that it was somewhat easier to justify experimental control over animals (see Dickinson, 1980, p. 2).

Another benefit was that methodological innovation flourished. Methods of data collection now being employed included questionnaires, various psychometric instruments (the Stanford–Binet intelligence test was produced by Terman in 1916), and descriptions of behaviour.

However, functionalism did not, by and large, address itself to the study of cognition. This was mainly because functionalists, in reacting to structuralism, saw no need to reinterpret an area which the latter had not greatly studied. Perversely, in moving away from the structure of consciousness towards its utility, they overreacted and ignored both structure and process in cognition.

Behaviourism

For some workers, the effects of widening the science of mental life to include a science of behaviour were so marked that they felt encouraged to do away with the mind entirely. J.B. Watson was the foremost proponent of this view (see Watson, 1913), and his pioneering influence, together with the earlier work of the functionalist Thorndike, led to the establishment of behaviourism as the dominant movement within American psychology from about 1920 onwards.

Behaviourism rested on a few basic principles:

— Overt behaviour, rather than conscious experience, should be the data of psychology, since individual experiences was necessarily vague and difficult to describe accurately.
— Introspection as a method of data collection should therefore be discarded and measures of behavioural response should replace it.
— The study of mental events (sensations, thought, etc.) should be replaced by the study of behaviour. Further, behaviour could be analysed in terms of the connections between various stimuli and the responses made to them.

For Watson, the concept of mind simply did not exist. Everything 'mental' was ultimately reducible to stimulus–response associations within the nervous and endocrine systems; consciousness itself, therefore, was purely a mentalistic convention for describing behavioural events. Thinking, for example, was conceived of by Watson as implicit speech, a laryngeal habit. The fact that certain individuals who did not possess a larynx demonstrated evidence of thinking caused Watson some problems in reconciling data with theory. In spite of such apparent reductions *ad absurdum*, behaviourism as a psychological system flourished in the United States until well into the 1950s.

The major research tool of behaviourism was adapted from Pavlov's famous work on conditioning dogs: the stimulus–response link. All complex behaviour, it was asserted, was built up from an array of simple stimulus–response bonds. From this, it followed that learning, rather than thought, was the appropriate topic of study for psychology. Behaviourism provides a clear illustration of an empirical, bottom-up approach to research, with the data themselves leading to theory construction.

Later behaviourists (neo-behaviourists as they were called) followed Watson's line in ignoring mental activities, although some of them attempted to account for their apparent existence in terms of behavioural concepts such as intervening variables between stimulus and response. An exception which must be mentioned here is the work of Tolman and his concept of cognitive maps (for example, Tolman, 1948).

Much of Tolman's experimental work was carried out using rats in mazes. He contended that, rather than learning a number of specific stimulus–response connections, corresponding to each choice point in the maze, the rat forms an internal representation of the maze as a whole — a cognitive map.

This view seems not dissimilar from the gestalist position; and in fact it anticipates the information-processing approach, in that Tolman argues that incoming stimuli are elaborated by the mind into a different representation.

However, despite Tolman, behaviourism all but eliminated serious research in cognitive processes for around 40 years. Behaviourism flourished for a number of reasons:

— It was scientific: a large body of knowledge was amassed concerned with how organisms learned.
— The research methodology was clear-cut: specific stimuli could be presented, and resulting behaviour accurately measured.
— It was powerfully predictive: a certain piece of behaviour could be accurately predicted on the presentation of a particular stimulus regimen.

It ultimately foundered because its field of study was too narrowly focused; much of the research was involved with how animals such as rats behaved in controlled laboratory studies, and the results were not easily generalizable to humans in much more complex environments. (An exception here is behaviour therapy, a body of therapeutic techniques which grew out of behaviourism, and which is used very effectively in adaptively changing the behaviour of those suffering various neuroses and psychoses.)

Gestalt psychology

Gestalt psychology developed in Germany between the two world wars, largely in opposition to structuralism. Like the functionalist movement in America, it objected to attempts to reduce the mind to elements, emphasizing rather the patterning or organization of sensation.

Gestalt psychology paralleled the development of behaviourism in the United States from about 1920 up until the end of the 1930s. Its practitioners were as fiercely critical of the behaviourists as they were of the structuralists, albeit for different reasons. The scientific stance adopted by Watson's new discipline was seen as acceptable; what was not was the neglect of variables intervening between stimulus and response. Gestalt psychology insisted on the validity of studying the perceptual organization of organisms.

The term 'gestalt' means, broadly, 'shape' or 'form', and it underlines the concept that the basic data of consciousness are organized and structured 'wholes'. Perhaps the central theme of gestalt psychology is that the whole is something more than solely the sum of its constituent parts.

Gestalt psychologists were chiefly interested in the nature of sensory experience, perception and thought, and the new approach was both experimentally fruitful and methodologically innovative.

Sensation, for the gestaltists, was not merely raw data. Stimuli as they impinged on the sensory organs *were* unorganized, but order was imposed upon them both by the sensory organs themselves, and by the first-level reception areas in the brain, to produce a gestalt. Processes higher up in the nervous system then further modified gestalts by comparing them with past experience.

Thinking was conceived of as grasping relationships in the perceptual field, and as such it was synonymous with insight. Insight was therefore an integrated reaction to the whole perceptual situation, not a number of particular responses to individual stimuli. It involved:

— the acquisition of new concepts;
— retaining these concepts; and
— applying them to novel, but analogous, situations, thereby facilitating learning.

There are parallels in gestalt psychology with James' writings; and gestalt psychology can be seen as a link between the earlier experimental psychologies and modern cognitive psychology. Cognition in gestalt psychology was implicitly recognized as a dynamic process, combining the stream of sensations into patterns which, restructured by past experience, could initiate and direct behaviour.

As a formal school, gestalt psychology split up in the political climate of Germany in the late 1930s, its more prominent members moving to the United

States. There, their views became gradually absorbed into the mainstream of experimental psychology.

THE RE-EMERGENCE OF COGNITIVE PSYCHOLOGY

Introduction

In the late 1950s there began a reawakening of interest in the study of human cognitive activity. The various threads which contributed to this resurgence will be pulled together in this section, but above all there was one hugely significant factor: the development of the digitial computer.

As computer science developed after the Second World War, there was a growing awareness amongst psychologists that the activities of computers were similar in certain ways to human cognition. For example, computers accept information as input, act upon it by transforming it into an appropriate internal representation, store and retrieve it, and produce an output of some kind. Whether humans and computers performed these functions in the same way was seen to be secondary: the point was that here was a likely model for looking at the way humans dealt with knowledge representation. The computer legitimized a return to the study of cognition.

While a number of contributions to the development of cognitive psychology arose from within the mainstream of scientific psychology, several others can be identified as developments in other disciplines. The more prominent of these were:

— information and communication theory,
— linguistics,
— computer science.

These are discussed in more detail in the sections that follow.

Contributing factors to modern cognitive psychology from areas outside psychology

Information and communication theory: the information-processing approach

The concept of the human as a processor and transformer of information grew out of two broad areas of study:

— human factors work, and
— information theory.

Human factors refers to the application of research in human skills and performance. This area was given a substantial impetus in the Second World

War, when a pressing need was identified to determine how best to design systems and machines so as to optimize the interaction between these and their operators. In this respect, the emergent new area of psychology received from the technological field as significant an input as it later tried to feed back into it. And it benefited greatly in these early stages from this input, in terms of theory development, guidance for reasearch and immediate applicability of research work. Indeed, some would suggest that the technological field should now, once again, make its inputs to cognitive psychology research, as a 'naturalistic' test-bed for the theories developed within cognitive psychology.

Information theory stemmed from communication theory (a body of work concerned with attention, signal detection and cybernetics), and offered the means of measuring learning in terms more abstract than the highly specific stimulus–response relationship. From cybernetics, in particular, came the important concept of self-regulation through informational feedback. Organisms could be envisaged as mechanical control systems which take in information via the senses, transform it internally, and produce an output in terms of behaviour. The behaviour is then capable of regulating the input and subsequent transformation of information. This change in emphasis, from measuring changes in response to studying units of information, was fundamental to the inception of cognitive psychology.

Ideas from these two fields were integrated by Broadbent (for example, 1958) to develop an information-processing approach to cognition and learning. Initially, this approach was applied to studies of perception and attention, but the model quickly came to be seen as useful in other areas. The central assumption of the information-processing approach is that human cognitive capabilities can be regarded as analogous with the functioning of computer systems. This approach remains the dominant theme within cognitive psychology, and has stimulated a huge body of research in both academic and applied fields.

Information-processing theories will be examined at greater length in a later section of this chapter.

Linguistics

In parallel with the information-processing approach, it soon became clear that, as computers functioned by means of internal symbol manipulation, so much of human cognition was mediated by the manipulation of verbal symbols. Significant proportions of the information accessible to humans are auditory and visual signals in the form of the spoken and written word, and it followed that there must exist internal linguistic structures to transform and process them.

However, no concepts existed within psychology at this time to aid in the construction of a formal taxonomy of language, something that was urgently required within the developing information-processing approach (an exception being neuropsychology — the study of how localized brain lesions affected different aspects of language in particular, and cognition in general). Language had traditionally been regarded within psychology as something of a side issue, but it was increasingly becoming regarded as central to information representation and the higher cognitive processes.

Linguistics, the formal description of the structure of language, was seen at this point as possessing the necessary conceptual tools to describe the structure and process of language. Stemming from the work of Chomsky (for example, 1957a and b), linguistic analyses were incorporated into studies of cognition and contributed greatly to cognitive theory and research.

Chomsky's transformational grammar posited a hierarchical structure to language; interactions between structures at different levels were mediated by transformational rules. The major themes of Chomsky's work can be summed up in the following points:

— Surface structure refers to the parts of actual sentences which can be identified in terms of verbs, nouns, articles, etc. Deep structures are envisaged as containing the essential meaning of the concept to be articulated. By the operation of transformational rules, the linguistic concept is capable of appearing in a number of syntactically different sentences, with different ordering of surface structural elements. Hence the same deep structure may code the production of two different sentences, which implies that meaning is more closely related to deep structures than it is to surface structures.
— Language is a generative, dynamic phenomenon.
— Deep structures contain elements common to all languages, and may embody principles of cognitive organization which are innate and universal.

Chomsky proceeded to describe the structural organization of language and to detail the particular transformational rules governing the manner in which one structure metamorphosed into another.

As these tools were adopted in the information-processing paradigm, a new discipline emerged: psycholinguistics. This area of study fused structural descriptions of language with broadly functional concepts of how language is cognitively represented, and it has stimulated an enormous proliferation of research. This research has led to an understanding of both the nature of the process whereby people use language effectively in interpersonal communication, and of how the brain deals with the transformation of linguistic information to enable individuals to interact effectively with their environment.

Computer science

A number of developments in computer science also contributed to the growth of cognitive psychology. As mentioned in the introduction to this section, the advent of the digital computer allowed psychologists to build a theoretical framework of human cognition on the basis that the mechanisms involved in both computer and cognitive functioning might be similar. In particular, studies from the area of artifical intelligence allowed psychologists to look again at the basis of storage and processing in memory, as well as the nature of language processing. Thus both structure and process in cognition became open to investigation.

Stochastic models led to memory being thought of in terms of transformational states, rather than connections or associations. Although distinctions between short-term and long-term memory had been made before (for example, by James), the adoption of the computer metaphor showed that the construction of theories about memory states (and indeed about processes) was both feasible and scientifically respectable. In addition, the metaphor stimulated research into measuring the *capacity* of memory states; although for most practical purposes long-term memory capacity could be seen as limitless, short-term memory possessed a finite and limited capacity. This distinction is still an important one in present-day research into memory (see Chapter 5).

Computer simulation studies opened up new ways of thinking about process in cognition. The precise analogy here was that the computer programme drives the behaviour of the machine in the same way that cognitive processes order human behaviour. By varying the nature of the programme, it becomes possible to understand the nature of the computer's behaviour. Similarly, experimental manipulation of cognitive variables leads to differential behaviour in human subjects, allowing modification and refinement of theory in an interactive process. Ultimately, a theory is produced which is sufficiently robust to explain the data in cause and effect terms, and which enables accurate prediction of behaviour.

Contributing factors to modern cognitive psychology from within psychology

Concept attainment

The work of Bruner and his associates in the early and mid 1950s (see, for example, Bruner, Goodnow and Austin, 1956), which focused on the functionality of thinking, represented one of the first attempts by psychologists interested in cognition to break free from the behaviourist view of the world.

The theory of concept attainment started with the premise that concepts, laws and categories had no objective existence, but rather were invented to impose order upon the environment. To form a concept was to become aware of the possibility of grouping entities according to the nature of their attributes:

— those entities which had attributes in common led to the formation of *conjunctive* concepts;
— those entities which had a mutual relationship to something else formed *relational* concepts; and
— those entities which possessed features which made them equivalent, although they were not alike, led to the formation of *disjunctive* concepts.

In order to group or attain a concept, individuals must employ a cognitive strategy to test whether entities fall into a particular category. Bruner stressed the notion of the human as an active hypothesizer; on the basis of what particular information was already available, various hypotheses could be constructed and tested, so as to gain further information. Successful hypothesis testing then allows individuals to establish general laws which direct further attempts to solve similar problems.

On the basis of their research, Bruner, Goodnow and Austin identified a number of general types of strategy used in concept attainment:

— Simultaneous scanning: an individual starts with all possible hypotheses, and gradually disposes of those shown to be in error.
— Successive scanning: a single hypothesis is chosen, and maintained if it is successful. If it is shown to be incorrect, another hypotheses is selected on the basis of past experience.
— Conservative focusing: a hypothesis is set up, and attributes examined one by one, leading to the re-evaluation of the hypothesis. When all irrelevant attributes have been discarded, the hypothesis is in its final, accurate form.
— Focus gambling: again, attributes are studied but sometimes more than one at a time is varied. This gamble then may lead to a quicker solution.

It was found that conservative focusing tended to be the most effective strategy, scanning and gambling yielding only variable degrees of success.

Bruner's work stimulated further research into concept attainment, and led to greater understanding of the strategies used in problem-solving. In time, these studies were subsumed under the information-processing approach (see, for example, Chapter 4, for a more detailed discussion of strategies in problem-solving). However, Bruner's work can be seen retrospectively as having greatly helped to legitimize the study of thinking and cognitive strategy.

The gestalt tradition
Gestalt psychology, though it ceased to exist as a formal school from the late 1930s, nevertheless maintained a tradition of research into aspects of cognition

throughout the behaviourist era. Influences from gestalt psychology were prominent in two areas in particular: those of *perception* (which was often studied through the medium of visual illusions; see, for example, Kohler and Wallach, 1944) and *problem-solving*.

An interesting example of the gestalt approach to problem-solving is provided by the work of Luchins (1951) on what was termed the *Einstellung* effect. This roughly translates as mental set, or cognitive rigidity. Luchins devised an experimental paradigm based on 'water problems'. These were a series of arithmetic problems concerned with the (mental) manipulation of volumes of water between differently sized containers in order to obtain a specified target volume.

The problem series started with a number of cases in which the target volume could only be obtained by adopting a particular, moderately difficult algorithm. After solving these, a certain mental set was induced in the subjects, inclining them to adopt the same approach in succeeding cases.

However, these subsequent cases could be solved both by using this initial algorithm or by using a much simpler one. Measures of cognitive rigidity could then be obtained on the basis of how long it took subjects to grasp the easier solution; or, in other words, to break the set.

The *Einstellung* effect relates to the gestaltist notion of the sudden acquisition of insight into solving a problem; that is, the various elements falling into place to form a 'whole' or a gestalt.

There are obvious parallels here with schematic memory in that the breaking of mental set can be seen in terms of switching between schemata (see Chapter 4); and with knowledge compilation (see Chapter 6).

As in other areas of psychology, data generated by gestalt-inspired research was incorporated and reinterpreted within the information-processing approach. The tradition still persists today, albeit in a less influential fashion.

Studies of memory

Research into memory was never totally abandoned in the period of behaviourist dominance in psychology, but it dealt largely with restricted studies of learning 'nonsense' syllables, following the Ebbinghaus tradition. This work, although it generated a fair body of empirical data, had no broad framework of theory to guide it, and possessed little that was generalizable outside the domain of the psychological laboratory.

There were two prominent exceptions to the above: one was the work of Bartlett in the 1930s (see, for example, Bartlett, 1932), and the other was interference theory.

Bartlett Bartlett's work differed from the tradition of learning nonsense syllables in some important ways. He opposed its essentially artificial nature and emphasized the need for what would today be called 'ecological validity' — the need to use experimental materials which are relevant to the real-life experience of subjects (Baddeley, 1982).

Bartlett's experimental work was based on the presentation of a passage of text in the form of a story. He then tested for recall of the story at various time intervals (for example, after 15 minutes, 2 months, 2½ years, etc.). The recalled versions of the story given by subjects were both abbreviated, and transformed in such a way as to be compatible with the individual subject's own knowledge and experience. Typically the general theme and a few dramatic details were remembered; these were used as a framework to reconstruct the passage.

On the basis of this experimental evidence, it became clear to Bartlett that memory was not a matter of, for example, looking up internal registers, but rather a synthesis, a schematic process. Schemata, therefore, were active organizations of past experience.

Bartlett's work was not followed up to any great extent until the 1960s. Then the concept of schema was taken up again by the neocognitivists, and its use as a metaphor of internal functioning was greatly developed (see also Chapters 4 and 5).

Bartlett's work can be regarded as foreshadowing modern theory in memory and thinking in two ways: first, by providing a theoretical account of process which is as germane and fruitful today as it was when Bartlett suggested it; and, second, by shifting the emphasis away from narrowly focused laboratory studies, thus helping to legitimize the application of cognitive psychology to real-life, applied situations. Baddeley (1982) addresses both these points in greater detail.

Interference theory   The influence of interference theory was felt primarily in the 1940s and 1950s, particularly in regard to studies of verbal learning. According to the theory, all learning consisted of establishing associations between stimuli and responses, the degree of learning of these associations being described in terms of *associative strength* (AS).

The main concern of interference theory was to account for changes in recall (interpreted as changes in AS) over time. Two basic mechanisms were proposed for failures in recall:

— response competition and,
— unlearning.

Briefly, response competition was seen to arise when a stimulus element had two or more associations. When a subject attempts to recall one of these associations, the other(s) compete for attention and interfere with recall.

Unlearning was said to occur when a *newly learnt* association reduced the associative strength of a *previously learnt* association.

Gradually, interference theory was subsumed under the information-processing framework, where later research cast serious doubts on its usefulness; however, it has historical importance as an attempt to derive a theoretical account of associative memory which instigated much fruitful research into memory in general. (For a fuller account of interference theory, see Wickelgren, 1979.)

Piagetian theory

The work of Jean Piaget in Switzerland from the 1920s onwards represents a theoretical orientation which contrasts markedly with that of behaviourism. His research interests were wide-ranging, but his work was particularly influential in the area of cognition, and especially in the nature of knowledge acquisition by children.

Piaget proposed that children went through several distinct periods of cognitive development, each period being characterized by qualitatively distinct modes of cognitive functioning. Thus, a child was born with a few elementary schemata, used here in the sense of simple action patterns such as sucking or grasping. Gradually, as infancy proceeded, schemata became more complex, evidencing a kind of thought abstracted from muscular activity, until in adolescence the individual became capable of propositional thought.

Piagetian theory had great impact in both psychology and education in the 1960s and 1970s. The concept of developmental stages had useful heuristic value, and the theory stimulated a large number of research programmes by other workers.

Again, information-processing approaches have moved into the area of developmental processes, although their perspective is somewhat different from that of Piaget. However, each has made important contributions to understanding cognitive growth and development.

Social psychology

Social psychology, the study of individuals in social contexts, is a subfield of psychology roughly contemporaneous with behaviourism, but still thriving today. It has never developed a unifying paradigm and has tended to be widely eclectic in its approach and subject-matter. However, its very eclecticism allowed it to make use of mentalistic terms, such as belief and attitude, to explain behaviour, although these were used in a rather loose, everyday sense.

Apart from this ready acceptance to explore these mental concepts, and maintaining this tradition throughout the behaviourist era, social psychology contributed little which directly influenced the inception of the discipline of cognitive psychology. A prominent exception was the work of Festinger (1957) on cognitive dissonance, a theory which became quite influential for a time.

Briefly, cognitive dissonance occurs when an individual holds two conflicting beliefs about an event. Dissonance is a state of cognitive and affective tension, which must be reduced by an appropriate change in behaviour. Festinger and his associates performed and inspired a substantial body of research with the aim of predicting behaviour change, once dissonance had been induced in subjects.

This, then, was a genuinely cognitive theory; beliefs were regarded as mental constructs capable, on their own or by interaction, of controlling behaviour.

Festinger's work undoubtedly contributed to the growing climate of change in the late 1950s which subsequently legitimized the study of cognition.

The demise of behaviourism

For several decades, behaviourism had exerted a stultifying hold over the development of psychology. In retrospect it is difficult to see how it could have adopted a non-mentalistic paradigm and maintained it for so long. Just because introspection had proved so inadequate as a research technique should not have meant that other methods could not have been found to study cognitive processes and structure, as indeed they were.

Behaviourism insisted that mentalistic concepts were not necessary to understand human behaviour, a stance still adopted now by such radical behaviourists as Skinner. However, an appropriate theory of mental functioning would have made understanding humans easier, as the success of cognitive psychology over the last two decades has shown.

Once established as a major force in psychology, however narrowly focused it had become, it was not likely that behaviourism would be ousted from its position except by the arrival on the scene of a fundamentally new way of looking at behaviour and experience. Kuhn's notion of paradigm failure is apposite here (see, for example, Kuhn, 1970): a body of theory does not simply wither and die of its own accord, however inadequate, but will survive and perpetuate itself until a rival paradigm arises to replace it. (Incidentally, this is precisely what occurred when behaviourism itself supplanted structuralism around 1920.) Behaviourism still persists today, but its practitioners (apart from the radical behaviourists, under the aegis of Skinner) have tended to become more eclectic in their approach; and it no longer retains its stronghold over innovation in theory and research.

THEORETICAL APPROACHES IN MODERN COGNITIVE PSYCHOLOGY

Introduction

As can be seen from the preceding subsections, a host of disparate influence came together in the 1950s to provide a new perspective for the study of human cognition. The most important was the digital computer, which directly shaped the concept of the human as a processor of information.

The development of the new discipline of cognitive psychology was guided by a number of important publications. Those which can be seen as seminal are briefly considered below.

The magical number seven . . . Miller (1956)

Miller summarized the early neocognitive research into memory and discussed in detail the relevance of information theory to psychology. This paper directly encouraged the development of information-processing models by others (see Chapter 5 for a more detailed description of Miller's work).

Syntactic Structures Chomsky (1957a)
Review of Verbal Behaviour by B.F. Skinner Chomsky (1957b)

Chomsky's contribution to the development of psycholinguistics has already been discussed. *Syntactic Structures* and his subsequent debate with the empirical behaviourist Skinner aroused great interest amongst psychologists, and stimulated new approaches in the study of the functions of language.

Plans and the Structure of Behaviour Miller, Galanter and Pribram (1960)

The concept of plans has been one of the most fruitful within cognitive psychology. Plans make a direct analogy with top-down computer programming, comprising a hierarchically ordered arrangement of subroutines and procedures aimed at directing behaviour towards particular goals. And important property of plans is their dynamic structure; they are capable of modification by feedback from the resulting effects of behaviour on the environment.

Cognitive Psychology Neisser (1967)

Neisser built on the framework of Miller, Galanter and Pribram and provided an integrated summary of the research in cognition up to that point.

The main theoretical contribution of this book was Neisser's description of a general information-processing model which proved to be an adequate framework for a large volume of subsequent cognitive research. This latter publication gave a new legitimacy to the field. In the words of Reynolds and Flagg (1983): 'Cognitive psychology was born with Neisser's *Cognitive Psychology* in 1967.'

In 1976 the journal *Cognitive Psychology* was founded, which became instrumental in giving definition to the field. Subsequently, the volume of publications has burgeoned almost exponentially, and cognitive research has both impacted on most other areas of psychology, and provided a host of valuable insights into human experience and behaviour.

The dominant paradigm in cognitive psychology today is the information-processing approach, and although other paradigms exist (see Leahey, 1980, Chapter 13), they will not be considered here.

Cognition refers to the processes by which all sensory input to an individual is transformed, elaborated, stored and used. The information-processing view assumes that cognition can be analysed into a number of stages through which incoming information has to go, being systematically transformed by the actions of different processes invoked at each stage. The following is an example list of some of the processes which are assumed to be invoked, singly or in combination, at each stage of information processing:

— sensation,
— perception,
— attention,
— imagery,
— memory,
— thinking and problem-solving.

Early information-processing models regarded this stage-transformation as linear and unidirectional: information was seen to be initially transformed during the lower-level stages of sensation and perception, it was then identified and consolidated by calling up the memory stage, subsequently it became available to the higher-level processes of thinking and language analysis. However, such simple models have in many cases now been superseded by models which assume multiple and complex connections between components.

In order to study the processes and structures involved in cognition, information-processing approaches have found it helpful to formulate cognitive models. These can be defined as metaphors, based on observations, which describe and provide a structure for the transformations that information undergoes in its progression through the system.

Models are useful as frameworks for directing research. They are not immutable; if they lose their predictive power, they quickly tend to be refined or abandoned. Cognitive psychology has largely been concerned with the production of cognitive models which possess sufficient sophistication and rigor to provide both understanding and accurate prediction of not yet observed events.

Information-processing models

Construction of cognitive models is based on the metaphor of the digital computer. Hence, early information-processing system models assumed the then prevailing Von Neumann sequential architecture. A complete model therefore involved:

— a sensory (input) system,
— memory,
— a central processor, and
— a response generator for output.

However, with the advent of truly concurrent computer systems, more recent information-processing models have tended to adopt the metaphor of parallel processing, thereby dispensing with the requirement for a central processor. Information-processing models attempt to depict the processes involved in cognitive functioning in terms of system flow diagrams. Information flow is represented by arrowed lines, and stages where information is transformed into a different 'code' are represented as blocks containing or associated with the relevant processes that need to be called up in order to effect the transformations.

Figure 1 shows one such, very primitive, cognitive model. It is easily noted that the model lacks so much detail as to be incapable of adequate description of process, let alone hypothesis construction to test behaviour. In many ways, it is not far removed from behaviourist concepts of psychological processes. Largely for this reason, cognitive psychology models tend to concentrate on somewhat smaller-scale integration of a number of functions, or on representing in detail the contents of a specific block or blocks, and pointing to possible connections between these and other blocks or functions that also critically affect cognition. It is an advantage of the information-processing approach that it allows this modular development of larger-scale models as and when data and theory allow such development.

An example of an early neocognitivist model which deals with a particular aspect of cognition — memory — was derived by Waugh and Norman (1965). It described three memory storage systems:

— a transitory sensory storage buffer,
— a short-term memory store (STM), and
— a long-term memory store (LTM).

Material was said to be maintained in short-term storage by rehearsal; if not rehearsed, it was quickly forgotten. The model then suggested that information was transferred from STM to LTM for permanent storage and could be retrieved from there when required. Output was generated from material organized in STM.

This model does not completely describe human memory, but it does fulfil the required criteria for hypothesis construction and prediction. For example, both

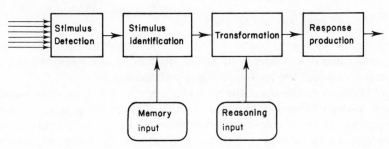

Figure 1. A simplistic information-processing model.

rehearsal and forgetting can be empirically investigated using the model as a framework.

Cognitive models have developed substantially in terms of complexity in the last 25 years, which reflects not necessarily the preoccupation of theorists with building models for their own sake, but rather the very nature of human cognition. The more detailed models are, the more accurate the predictions they can engender.

In the early stages of cognitive psychology, information-processing models tended to be involved with unravelling of the lower-level processes, such as perception and attention. As the principles underlying these processes began to become better understood, so the emphasis has moved to the study of thought and language. In recent years, there has been a growing interest in how studies of these higher-level processes impact on human–machine communication. That this is the case seems particularly apposite: as computer science originally prompted interest in cognitive processes, so the wheel has turned and cognitive psychological principles are applied now to the optimization of aspects of computer design.

Broad theoretical strands within cognitive psychology

Since the inception of cognitive psychology, there have been attempts to derive a meta-theory of cognitive functioning, in order to unite the various theoretical orientations which emerged. This has not yet been achieved. Although desirable, the lack of such a unifying super-theory has not however prevented the models which arose from generating valuable insights into cognition and behaviour.

Two particular general theoretical dimensions can be identified within the information-processing framework:

— data-driven versus goal-directed theories, and
— faculty versus unitary theories.

Data-driven and goal-directed theories

Data-driven, or bottom-up cognitive theories assume processing modes which are automatic and driven directly by the information input to the individual. As an example, consider the analysis of visual information.

Visual signals impinge upon the individual as retinal images. The analysis proceeds through various stages of perceptual transformation to locate such characteristics as lines, colours and movements. Increasingly sophisticated analysis leads to the patterning of pertinent combinations of features, until the input becomes fully recognizable. In this approach, the individual is seen to be entirely controlled by the environment.

Goal, or concept-directed, top-down theories postulate instead that cognition is driven by expectancies or conceptualizations of the incoming information. It is assumed, using the same example of visual information, that higher-level processes have an anticipation of an object's presence in the visual field. Intermediate and lower-level processes are then directed to hunt for particular features of the object, which are hypothesized to exist, on the basis of past experience and context. Once the directed search reaches the lower cognitive levels, individual perceptual subsystems are primed to be receptive to specific visual features, such as edges and contours. Hence, rather than being at the mercy of the environment, the individual is capable of imposing a conceptual structure on the world to help to decide what is there.

Both theoretical standpoints have attractions, but they also have problems in accounting for all the data. Bottom-up approaches fail to account for the fact that pattern recognition would be immensely difficult without direction from higher processes; both the sheer volume of processing which would be required, and the regular occurrence of unreliable data from the environment argue against this view.

Top-down approaches rely on the higher cognitive processes consistently formulating large numbers of correct hypotheses, something which seems unlikely given the complexity of information in the environment. It seems probable, therefore, that individuals employ a combination of these strategies, or favour one over the other, depending on the particular context in which they find themselves. It seems likely that as a person becomes more familiar with a particular situation or environment, the tendency will arise to pursue goal-directed, rather than data-driven strategies. Data do exist which support this view (for example, Larkin, *et al.*, 1980). These two theoretical stances within cognitive psychology need not, therefore, be seen as irreconcilable.

Unitary and faculty approaches

A second dimension along which cognitive theories can be broadly categorized is that concerned with unitary and faculty approaches.

Unitary theories hold that cognition can be accounted for by a single, universal set of principles. Piagetian theory, although outside the general information-processing framework, is an example of a unitary view of cognition. Piaget's notion of the development and integration of schemata has led to a discrete theoretical system which attempts to explain the diversity of intellectual processes in terms of a few universal organizing principles.

Information-processing models, by contrast, tended to adopt a pluralistic view of cognition, at least in the early stages of development of the information-processing approach. The mind was conceived of as containing a number of heterogeneous processes, each one almost a 'faculty' in its own right, which did not necessarily follow the same rules. For example, the processes involved in memory were seen as quite distinct from those operating in attention; the various mental faculties were assumed to possess qualitatively different architectural principles.

Recently, some information-processing models have been constructed on the basis of a unitary approach, particularly with regard to higher order cognition: the same organizational principles are seen to be responsible for controlling these higher-order functions (such as memory, problem-solving and language). An example is Anderson's work on a series of ACT models (ACT standing for adaptive control of thought; see Anderson, 1980, 1984).

Unlike data-driven and goal-directed approaches, the unitary–faculty dimension is at present still markedly polarized.

CURRENT TRENDS

The preceding sections have highlighted key contributions to the development of modern cognitive psychology. The aim was to set the scene for the chapters that follow, and which consider how modern-day cognitive psychology can contribute to a particular applied domain: user-interface design. Current trends in cognitive psychology continue to show strong links with the historical roots that we have just finished tracing. In addition, there is a growing interest in establishing research approaches and methodologies which bring the discipline closer to a realistic and applied domain. We will now conclude this historical introduction by outlining three key trends in current cognitive psychological thinking which have particular relevance for the topic of this book.

Ecological validity

A major concern in recent years has been with the concept of 'ecological validity'. Many of the earlier cognitive psychological studies focused on fairly artificial laboratory studies which, although rigorous, threw little light on behaviour and experience in the outside world. Leading advocates of the need to apply research to real-life events are Neisser (1976, 1984) and Baddeley (1982), but it is an issue which also received the attention of such earlier workers as Barlett (for example, 1932) and even William James (for example, 1890).

Methodological changes

Allied to considerations of ecological validity is the trend for changes in emphasis in methodology. The point was made earlier that the decline of structuralism was in part attributable to the inadequacy of its major research tool: classical introspection. Recently, introspection, in the form of self-reports and verbal protocols, has made something of a comeback. It is accepted that these data are limited in value, both because they cannot tap unconscious processes, and because their reliability is difficult to establish; however, they can usefully support more 'objective' types of data and point to areas where further experimentation may be fruitful.

Automatic and controlled processing

Finally, there is an increased awareness of differences in automatic and controlled processing. Practice enables many processes to become automatic, and these then make few, if any, demands on working memory (see Chapter 5). Controlled (attentional) processes operate under conscious control, are more capable of modification, but exert a cost in terms of high mental load. This distinction, between automatic and controlled forms of processing, has important implications for many real-world tasks, particularly in the area of user–system interaction. It is examined at greater length in Chapter 6.

THE NEXT CHAPTER

This chapter provided a broad overview of the many strands that, together, contributed to the methodologies and approaches prevailing in today's cognitive psychology theories. The next chapter now discusses how one area of modern cognitive psychology — the psychology of thinking — can contribute to the design of more effective and 'cognitively compatible' interfaces to electronic office systems. The chapter adopts a broad-brush approach to describing the psychology of thinking, and illustrates its implications for system design by drawing on one particular theory — mental models — and outlining its potential applicability.

Chapter 4

Principles from the psychology of thinking and mental models

Ken Manktelow and Julian Jones

INTRODUCTION

When people approach an information system — a computer, a word-processor, or, come to that, a recipe book or a 'hole-in-the-wall' automatic bank till — they are presented with a problem. They need some knowledge of the system, what it can and cannot do, of the task, and of what they need to do with the system to accomplish it. That knowledge is variable in all cases; people come equipped with knowledge which may or may not be useful, accurate or available. The *extent* of these pieces of knowledge will determine the amount of *thinking* in which the user must engage to perform the task successfully: the more novel the situation, the more thinking will be required. Indeed, as we shall see, this requirement may exceed the capacity of the individual and he or she will fail. Paradoxically, as familiarity increases, the amount of thinking may decrease, until in highly familiar situations people can be said to be hardly thinking at all, and this can also result in failure.

By 'thinking' we are referring to the active manipulation of knowledge. The *nature* of knowledge and the way it is manipulated will also determine the user's performance. For many researchers in cognitive ergonomics (fitting the mind to the job, we might say), this question is seen in terms of the *mental models* of the system and task which people are presumed to have inside their heads. The user's mental model does not necessarily take account of the fine detail of the system, but it does take account of the system's perceived modes of function, in that the relations and structure of the symbols in the mental model parallel those of the system itself. Hence a mental model is functionally similar to the system it parallels.

Research on human–computer interaction has provided two prompts to consider the user's cognitions in these terms. Firstly, researchers came to realize that users do not passively respond to a system, they are normally actively involved in the interaction: they have goals and expectations, they make inferences and predictions. It is as if users are interacting not with the system directly, but with their model of the system. Thus one of our goals in this chapter will be to account for the knowledge that constitutes the user's mental model. Secondly, it has often been found in human–computer interaction research that users make errors which cannot be explained as random, or as merely due to the limitations on working memory or attention (Chapters 5 and 6 explore these factors in detail). Many errors can best be accounted for in terms of an inappropriate mental model from which people make inappropriate inferences and predictions. If one can understand not only the kinds of knowledge which are used to construct mental models but also the ways in which these models are invoked and used, then one can go some way towards invoking these processes in the design of human–computer interfaces. Our second goal is therefore to account for both the evolution and action of mental models.

Our third goal is to apply these ideas in order to make some specific points about the design of user–system interfaces, not only by using the theories to explain and predict some clear and avoidable shortcomings, but also to set out some prescriptions about the nature of thinking and learning and what these mean for the nature of user–system interaction. We shall be confronting some pervasive misconceptions along the way about, for instance, the question of the conscious awareness of thought processes, the notion of formal and psychological equivalence of logical constructs, and the role of verbal instruction.

Thinking and mental models have been studied from a number of perspectives over many years, for instance by the gestalt school, in the work of Piaget, and in recent times by the cognitive science movement, as in the case of Newell and Simon (1972). Influences attributable to these sources will become apparent in the following pages. Rather than provide a broad survey, however, we shall concentrate on two major areas in detail: the psychological study of reasoning, and the related theory of mental models recently expounded by Johnson-Laird (1983). In doing so, we hope this chapter will make up in coherence what it might lack in breadth. In one recent review of mental models and software human factors, Carroll (1984a) concluded that 'the field is still really in an era of pre-theory in which no "whole" views yet exist'. This chapter is partly a response to the challenge laid down in that statement: we hope to show that current work on thinking in general and Johnson-Laird's theory in particular provide the foundations for the 'whole view' which Carroll is seeking.

CONTENT AND FORM IN THINKING

The major concern in this section will be on the interplay between the content of problems, that is what the problems are about semantically, and their form or logical structure. It should be noted at the outset that, while we shall be concerned primarily with the study of logical thinking, there are other areas of thinking in which similar relations between content and form are apparent, for instance in probability judgements, which have a mathematical expression. It is proposed that similar broad conclusions are possible across all areas of thinking. The study of logical thinking is particularly well suited to the purposes of this book both because of the large volume of research in this field, and because of the relevance of the resulting theoretical developments for user-interface design.

Thinking and logic

The study of human reasoning has undergone something of an upheaval in recent years, and to appreciate this state of affairs a brief account of the major historical developments in research is called for.

Since ancient times, theorists have appreciated that certain categories of problem are in principle the same regardless of what they are concerned with, and can therefore be expressed in terms of their form. The development of formal descriptions of logical arguments is generally assumed to have begun with Aristotle and his expression of syllogisms in the form, for example, 'All A are B; all B are C; hence, all A are C.' We shall be more concerned here, initially, with arguments involving conditional statements. Here is a conditional syllogism:

> If A then B
> A
> ———————
> Therefore B

This argument is valid whichever specific terms are substituted for A and B, and whether or not the argument makes sense in its relation to known facts: its validity is given by its structure.

Logical formalisms have been employed as theories of thought, and this is one of the major misconceptions we wish to attack here, both because of its inability to explain the findings of research on thinking and because of the errors which it is liable to spawn. Before considering empirical evidence, one can see some immediate problems with logic as a theory of thought. For example, people are disposed in ordinary discourse to draw conclusions from premises such as these:

> If A had happened then B might have happened too
> There is a good chance that A did happen

The problem here is that it is difficult, if not impossible, to express such arguments formally. Another problem lies in the fact that it is perfectly possible for a person to arrive at a formally correct answer to a problem without *using* any formal processes at all. One might simply guess, or recall the answer from memory. This is a central point, and worth labouring with a simple example. Consider the case of arithmetic. People still report that at school they were taught the 'times tables' — the chanting of rote-memorized multiplication tables, usually up to the number 12. Thus if you are asked what is 2 × 2, or 7 × 8, or 9 × 11, you will probably produce the answers quickly, from memory, that is without using an arithmetical procedure to compute them. Times tables are very handy, but suffer from the restrictions that they do not apply to numbers greater than 12, and do not of themselves promote an understanding of the *formal* principles of multiplication.

This example may seem trivial, but it contains many of the elements of the argument set out below: that logic is not necessary for logical thinking, and that the nature of thought is defined in people's memories for particular domains of knowledge. In the next section, we consider evidence for the content-dependency of human thought; the final point to be made here is the difference which needs emphasizing between two senses in which the term 'logical thinking' can be used. It can mean a conclusion in accord with a formal analysis, or it can refer to the thought processes used when reasoning. We argue that the former sense is unobjectionable, but that the latter sense is inappropriate; and that theorists and designers ignore this distinction at their peril.

Content-dependency in thinking

Background

The finding that people's reasoning is influenced by the content of arguments is an old one: Wilkins (1928), for example, using mostly Aristotelian syllogisms, found that more logically correct answers were given to problems containing familiar materials than to problems containing unfamiliar materials. An interesting variant of this is the 'belief-bias' effect demonstrated by Janis and Frick (1943), who found that subjects were more likely to accept as valid syllogistic arguments which accorded with their beliefs, irrespective of formal validity.

The debate about the role of content has become particularly lively in the area of conditional reasoning, the area on which we shall concentrate. The field is dominated by research on a single logical problem: the selection task devised by P.C. Wason in the early 1960s. The problem often strikes people as rather inconsequential, but we shall see that it is far from that; it has led to a tremendous amount of research and theory. Wason (1969) has captured its scientific attraction nicely in the phrase reffering to its 'structural simplicity and psychological complexity'. It presents a classic case of the production of large answers from small questions.

First, a description of the problem (readers are invited to provide their own solutions as we proceed). Imagine that you are sitting at a desk, and an experimenter has placed on it four cards. Each card has a letter of the alphabet on one side and a number on the other. You are given the following rule about the relation between letters and numbers on the four cards:

> If there is a vowel on one side then there is an even number on the other side.

The cards on the desk in front of you look like this:

| E | D | 4 | 7 |

Which cards would you need to turn over to establish whether the rule is true or false?

Now consider this problem. You are a cashier in a large department store. You have been given the following rule about receipts for the purchase of goods:

> If a purchase exceeds £20 then the receipt must be signed on the back by the manager.

There are four receipts on the table in front of you: one for £30, one for £10, one signed on the back, one unsigned. Which would you have to inspect to see whether this rule has been broken?

People who have not seen these problems before, even, legend has it, academic logicians and highly qualified mathematicians, are likely to produce the following answers (see Griggs, 1983; Mantkelow, 1981; Wason, 1983, for detailed reviews). In the abstract problem about letters and numbers they will tend to select the E card, either by itself or with the 4 card; in the thematic cashier problem, they will tend to choose the £30 receipt and the unsigned one. This typical profile is the basis of a mass of experiments and some profound conclusions about the nature of rational thought. This is because the problems are logically identical, differing only in content, but the typical answers to them are logically different. Only in the second case, with the cashier problem, is the typical solution logically correct.

This is the solution to the problems. Both are presented in the form of a conditional rule which can be written in the general form 'If P then Q'. The cards in each case show, in order of presentation above, a value representing the P statement, one representing not-P, one representing the Q statement, and one representing not-Q. To test whether the rule is being broken, consider each card in terms of what might be on the hidden side, and that will indicate whether it need be inspected. First the P card. this can have a Q or a not-Q value on its reverse. A Q value (an even number or the manager's signature) allows the rule to stand, but a not-Q value (an odd number or no signature) clearly violates the rule: we therefore must examine the P Card. Equally clearly, we need not examine the not-P card, since the rule does not concern consonants or small bills and it does not matter what is on the back of these: in any case, the rule would stand. The Q card could have a P or a not-P value on the back, neither of which would affect the rule, so we do not need to look at this one. However, the not-Q card or receipt might have a P value on the other side and as this combination, a vowel with an odd number or a large unsigned bill, is a clear violation of the rule, we must check the not-Q card.

Thus, for both problems, we need to inspect those items which could show P and not-Q values occurring together: the P and not-Q cards. If we return to the typical response profiles, we see that they are in the first problem with letters and numbers P alone or P and Q, and in the cashier problem, P and not-Q. So only with the cashier problem do most people produce the logically correct solution; looking back over the history of research on the abstract problem, only 9% of subjects have produced the correct solution (Manktelow, 1981). The greater degree of logicality with realistic content, demonstrated by the cashier problem above, is inconsistent: with some contents there is no such effect at all. These findings, that there is an effect of content and that it is variable, are the nub of the change which has come over explanations of human reasoning in recent years, and we consider them in detail in our examination of logic-based and non-logical theories of thinking below.

Thinking with logic

As we noted above, various attempts have been made with various formalisms to invoke logic as a theory of the thought processes used in reasoning. We shall outline their general form in this section before proceeding to the alternative body of explanation, in which the status of logic as a theory of thought processes rather than a description of their outcomes is disputed.

Probably the most famous exponent of logic-based explanations of thinking is Piaget, whose account of the acquisition of intelligence in the course of an individual's development is one of the most influential of all psychological theories. (This is not the place for a detailed exposition of Piagetian theory; see Gross, 1985, for a recent account.) Intelligence is conceived of by Piaget as an essentially biological process of adaptation to the environment, hence the term 'intellectual evolution' to describe the acquisition process (Piaget, 1977). A person is said to pass through an ordered sequence of discrete stages, acquiring a system of mental *operations* by interacting with and reflecting on the evironment. The culmination of this process is the attainment of the stage of *formal operations* in early adolescence (Inhelder and Piaget, 1958).

An adolescent at the formal operational stage becomes able to 'reason about a proposition considered as a hypothesis independently of the truth of its content' (Beth and Piaget, 1966). The formal operational thinker will approach a causality problem, for instance, by ascertaining whether fact X implies fact Y; in doing this (s)he will express the proposition as an 'If P then Q' statement, then search for a counterexample, that is, P and not-Q (Beth and Piaget, 1966). However, Wason and Johnson-Laird (1972) emphasize that this is an accurate account of just what subjects typically *fail* to do when confronted with the abstract form of the selection task. The increased level of logically correct performance with realistic contents such as the cashier problem does not solve the problem but compounds it, because formal operational thinking is supposed to have the prime characteristic of independence from content. The findings of selection task research are simply irreconcilable with the theory of formal operations. The late modification of the theory proposed by Piaget (1972), in which formal operational ability was restricted to an individual's 'area of specialization', effectively undermines the theory's testability. Any deviation from formal operational performance could always be explained by absence of the necessary expertise. This is a problem for all memory-dependent explanations of thinking.

Another influential attempt to explain reasoning by recourse to logic is that of Henle (1968), who studied performance on classical syllogisms presented in a realistic format. Solutions not in accord with the prescriptions of formal logic are accounted for by Henle by proposing that subjects misinterpreted the premises of the problems, or added premises which were not explicitly stated. Henle argues that if these interpretive factors are noted, it appears that subjects were reasoning logically about different versions of the problems from the ones set, thus only appearing to be in error. The problem, of circularity is present here too: do we assume logical thinking in order to unravel the subjects' interpretations, or vice versa? (cf. Smedslund, 1970) A similar problem besets an explanation of selection task performance by Johnson-Laird and Wason (1970a). This model accounts for initial performance on the abstract task by positing three states of insight into the logical relation underlying it: no insight, partial insight, and complete insight. The problem of circularity arises because these states are inferred from the performance they are supposed to underlie (Evans, 1977); the independent evidence required to support them — subjects' introspective reports — turns out to be a double-edged weapon, as we shall see later.

In this section we have dealt with some of the reasons why logic-based theories of thinking run into difficulties. Before proceeding to the positive evidence from selection task research and mental models theory for non-logical thinking, one or two further points are in order. First, there is the practical consequence of assuming a logical competence underlying thinking performance, as Chomsky proposes a distinction between linguistic competence and performance (see Chomsky, 1968). Apart from the problem of describing that competence — it is no more possible to specify a *priori* performance-free contexts for thinking than it is for language — there is the problem of designing situations on the assumption that obstructions to rationality can be removed, thus allowing human logical competence its full rein. This is a mistake: as we saw above, if we can ask whether arithmetic principles are necessary to produce correct answers to arithmetic problems, we can ask the same question of logic and logical problems. The answer is no in both cases, and the rest of this chapter is aimed at providing evidence for this assertion and at tracing its practical implications.

Thinking without logic

The earliest explanations of performance on the selection task proposed that the error of selecting the P and Q cards was due to people being *illogical*: they were failing to appreciate the need to falsify the rule and were instead searching only for items that could prove it true (Johnson-Laird and Wason, 1970a; Wason, 1968). 'Theory maintenance' of this kind has been observed with another of Wason's problems, the 2–4–6 task (Wason, 1960), and has since been recognized as a pervasive and powerful bias in thinking (Nisbett and Ross, 1980). In their model of selection task performance, Johnson-Laird and Wason (1970a) also propose that people in the state of no insight fixated on the values named in the rule: P and Q. The curious point about this argument is that it is not necessary to propose both verification bias and fixation on named values to explain the typical pattern of performance: the latter by itself accounts for the selection of P and Q and the omission of not-P and not-Q. Is it possible then that people were not even doing something as sophisticated as attempting to verify, but were simply responding to the stimulus of the named values? This possibility was addressed by Evans and Lynch (1973). They introduced negatives into the conditional rule to allow the separation of the naming of items from their logical value in the task. For instance, by inserting a negative into the second component of the abstract rule given as an example above, we change it to:

> If there is a vowel on one side then there is *not* an even number on the other side.

Note that in the original case the named items also verified the rule, but here they *falsify* the rule: a vowel card with an even number on its reverse is inconsistent with the negated rule. Evans and Lynch systematically varied the presence of negation in this way and revealed that fixating on the named values, which they termed matching bias, was the most significant determinant of performance, generalizing across all rules. There was no evidence at all for a verification bias when the items were not named in the rule.

These results provide the first element of a non-logical explanation of reasoning performance: errors with abstract problems appear to be due to a fixation on named items. However, we saw with the second example problem — the cashier problem — that varying the content of the problem can abolish the preponderance of error; with the cashier problem, the typical performance is to get it right. We now need to consider research on the role of content in thinking.

The study of content effects was contemporaneous with the study of matching effects. Wason and Shapiro (1971) used a version of the task in which rules about abstract properties such as letters and numbers were replaced by a thematic format concerning journeys. The rule defined a journey's destination ('Every time I go to Leeds') and a mode of transport ('I travel by train'), with cards showing alternative towns and conveyances. The correct selection — a card with Leeds on it and one with a mode of transport other than train — was produced by over 60% of the subjects.

Corroboration of this finding emerged in several studies, most impressively in the case of Johnson-Laird, Legrenzi and Legrenzi (1972). This study is worth picking out because it contains some features that have become pivotal parts of later research. In the first place, the content used is noteworthy. Subjects were asked to imagine they were postal workers sorting the mail. They had to look for letters — real envelopes were used as the 'cards' — which violated the following postal regulation: 'If a letter is sealed then it has a 5d stamp on it'. Just under 90% of people selected the correct envelopes: the sealed one and the one without a 5d stamp. Two other important results were that the effect was the same when Italian units of currency were used (the subjects were British), and that this high level of logical performance failed completely to transfer to a subsequent abstract task, where subjects reverted to the typical incorrect pattern.

These and other consistent results were interpreted in terms of insight into the logic of the selection task being facilitated by realistic content (Johnson-Laird and Wason, 1977). This interpretation is of the kind referred to earlier, where an obstruction to reason is cleared and logical competence exerts itself. We shall argue that while logically correct decisions did rise in frequency, this was not due to logical insight: that logically correct behaviour on the realistic selection task, as well as erroneous performance on the abstract task, can be explained without recourse to logic as a process. Evidence for such an account began to accrue after a period of five years or so, from the time of a spate of results confirming the facilitation effect with the realistic task, during which the insight view was generally accepted. Since this new evidence began to appear, virtually every published paper on the selection task, and other deductive problems, has been concerned with content effects.

Reports posing problems for the insight-facilitation view of content effects appear to have begun with a study by Manktelow and Evans (1979). In a series of experiments using a variety of presentation formats and two kinds of thematic content, performance did not differ from that observed on the abstract task. The two contents were the Wason and Shapiro journey materials and one involving rules about combinations of foods and drinks in meals. Many other similar failures of the facilitation effect have since been reported; Griggs (1983) reviews them. In a re-examination of the previous literature, Manktelow and Evans (1979) found only one result, the original one by Wason and Shapiro, which seemed to show an effect uncontaminated by procedural confounds or over rich interpretation. They proposed two mechanisms by which the other results could be explained: interaction of thematic materials with other procedural elements such as special wordings or presentation formats, and retrieval of the correct solution directly from memory, circumventing reasoning.

This second explanation, which has come to be known as the memory-cueing hypothesis (Griggs and Cox, 1982), was applied to findings such as that of Johnson-Laird, Legrenzi and Legrenzi (1972) cited above, in which realistic formats such as the one involving postal sorting were used. The argument is that such formats are *too* realistic: people know, or knew at the time, that under-stamped sealed letters were illicit, hence relevant, because a postal regulation of just that kind had been in operation until shortly before the experiment was conducted. The memory-cueing hypothesis has been tested principally in an elegant series of experiments by Griggs and his colleagues (see Griggs, 1983). For example, it follows that if memory for a relevant postal rule in real life was responsible for the effect observed by Johnson-Laird, Legrenzi and Legrenzi (1972) the effect shoud not be apparent when a subject population lacking such experience is used. Two results confirm this: Golding (1981) found that British subjects over the age of 45, who could presumably remember the regulation, did produce the facilitation effect in the postal sorting task, whereas subjects under 45, who presumably could not, did not. Griggs and Cox (1982) failed to find the effect in the United States where there has never been such a regulation. These authors went further and demonstrated a facilitation effect using materials which were known to be a part of subjects' general knowledge because an independent sample from the same population had been surveyed. Chrostowski and Griggs (1985) have since shown that memory-cueing is both necessary and sufficient for the facilitation effect: other possible factors do, indeed, only work when interacting with realistic content.

However, an important modification to the original memory-cueing hypothesis has been made necessary: the facilitation effect has been found with contents where it is implausible to suggest that subjects had direct experience. The Johnson-Laird, Legrenzi and Legrenzi experiment using British subjects and Italian currency is one such, as is the cashier problem described earlier. We should not have to propose that all subjects who get these problems right must have direct memories of posting letters in Italy or signing receipts in shops. The memories which are cued must therefore be more general than simple direct memories of actual relevant situations and contingencies. In the next section, we propose an explanation in terms of schematic memory to account for this. At the conclusion of this section, it only remains to point out that we have now arrived at the second element of a non-logical explanation of reasoning: logically correct decisions with realistic problems appear to be a function of the cueing of relevant memories, not insight into the logic of the problem.

Thinking and memory

The content *dependency* of thinking, acknowledgement of which is the heart of the upheaval in reasoning research mentioned earlier, is not confined to a single deductive problem. To counter the possibility that these findings from Wason's selection task may be unrepresentative of thinking in general, let us look at a largely independent area of research which has also shown performance to be largely a product of people's knowledge of the world rather than of abstract inference rules: that of intuitive judgement.

As in the case of reasoning research, the area is dominated by one tradition of enquiry which has built up in recent times. In this case, it is the 'heuristics and biases' approach of Tversky and Kahneman and their colleagues (see, for example, 1974; an extensive collection of related papers is contained in Kahneman, Slovic and Tversky, 1982; see also Chapter 7). A similar general proposal is made in the area of intuitive judgement as is made here: performance on decision tasks which have a formal expression is not naturally done formally, but by recourse to general, non-formal memorial constructs. These constructs are the *heuristics*; concomitant deviation from normative prescriptions are the *biases*.

We cannot go into this work in detail here, but some examples will give a flavour of this approach. The two most well-known heuristics are representativeness and availability. Representativeness is used to judge the likelihood that an item is an instance of a class, for instance. People characteristically ignore normatively relevant information such as base-rate probabilities in favour of a global judgement of how *representative* the item is supposed to be of the class. For example, if people are told that in the room next door there are 20 people, 15 engineers and five sociologists; that person X has a beard and wears blue jeans; and are asked to judge how likely it is that X is an engineer or a sociologist; they will ignore the base-rate probability in favour of engineers and rely on the prevailing social stereotype.

The availability heuristic is used to make judgement about the likelihood of events. People do this not by a judgement of statistical proportions, but by the ease with which concrete examples can be 'brought to mind'. Thus people are likely, for example, to overestimate their chances of being killed by murder and accident relative to heart disease or stroke.

Two recent theoretical formulations of thinking have drawn a parallel between the intuitive judgement literature and the Wason tradition in reasoning research. Pollard (1982) uses Tversky and Kahneman's availability heuristic to explain a range of findings from studies of reasoning, including the selection task. The gist of the argument is that responses are cued by salient features of the task. Salience can be a function of past experience, as in the realistic versions of the problem, or, when this is not evoked, of features of the task set. In the abstract selection task, naming of items in the rule makes them more available and hence likely to be selected. However, this account does not address some important aspects of thinking, for instance the relation between decision and interpretation which we discuss later in this chapter, and seems more of an empirical generalization than an explanation, in that it does not deal with the sources of differential cueing effects.

Evans (1984) takes the argument a stage further in describing thinking as a two-stage process. These two stages are termed *heuristic* and *analytic* (we should note that Evans' use of the term 'heuristic' differs from that of Tversky and Kahneman). This proposed duality is an essential part of the general view of thinking presented here, and we shall come back to it in later sections. For now, let us consider Evans' explanation as far as it bears on the performance described so far. Heuristic processes are those which lead to the selection of items as relevant to a problem, analytic processes are those involved in judgements or inferences about that information once it has been selected. The heuristic stage is the one of interest here since, as Evans points out, the demand characteristics of the selection task are *only* for relevance judgements.

We have seen that these judgements are made on different bases in the abstract and realistic versions of the task. In the abstract task, the prime determinant of performance is matching bias. The source of matching bias is stated by Evans to be linguistic: regardles of whether of not the rule is negated, it expresses its *topic* in the items named. A rule reading 'If there is not an A on one side then there is not a 6 on the other' is still about A and 6. Selection of the P card and the non-selection of the not-P card, which are scarcely affected by any task manipulation, acquire this stability by an additional linguistic bias: supposition. According to Rips and Marcus (1977), the natural function of an 'If' sentence is to express a presupposition in the P component: P is thus the major topical component of a conditional sentence. In the thematic task, relevance is cued by experiential elements of the problem as well as the linguistic composition of the rule.

Evans' theory of reasoning performance is persuasive in that it successfully addresses a wide range of empirical findings and is consistent with other approaches in similar areas. In distinguishing between the processes used to set up a model of a problem and those used to operate on it, Evans uses similar constructs to those in Newell and Simon's (1972) theory of problem-solving (see Evans, 1982, where this connection is stated explicitly) and Johnson-Laird's mental models theory, which we shall deal with in the second major part of this discussion in the next section.

However, there is a gap left by all the explanations of reasoning we have outlined. While all recognize the dependency of thinking on problem content and introduce notions such as memory-cueing to express it, none goes so far as to specify why some apparently thematic contents and not others lead to logically improved performance. A complete account of human thinking must address not only its global tendencies and memory-dependent nature, as in Evans' scheme, and its mode of operation, as in Johnson-Laird's, it must also say something about the way content influences model building.

The essential elements of the content-dependency hypothesis are (a) that content affects thinking, (b) that this reflects the cueing of relevant existing knowledge, (c) that the effect is inconsistent. The questions we need to address now concern the last point and the matter of what kind of knowledge is cued. Recall that we have some kinds of thematic contents which almost always produce facilitation of logical performance (the cashier problem), some which hardly ever do (the meals problem), and some which do sometimes but not others (the journeys problem). We also know that if the relation between the problem content and subjects' experience is established, the facilitation effect can be safely predicted, but that successful (logical) performance on a realistic problem does not transfer to a subsequent abstract task. What kind of knowledge could account for these findings?

The answer we propose is schematic knowledge. Schemata are high-order cognitive structures in which knowledge is arranged in domains or units (Rumelhart, 1980). Their most significant property is that knowledge is *abstracted*, or averaged: a schema contains information about what is typical of a concept, not a direct record of experience. There are several schema theories (see Chapter 5), and 'schema theory' in general has recently been attacked: the abstraction property and its consequences underestimate actual memory performance (Alba and Hasher, 1983). There is a danger of throwing the baby out with the bathwater here though: most of the studies Alba and Hasher cite concern episodic memory, usually for short passages of text. If we wonder when a memory based on averages would be useful, text memory would be an unlikely candidate; it seems more plausible that memory for actions or procedures, which have to be performed under infinitely variable conditions, would benefit from being represented in this way. Procedural memory brings us back to thinking.

A schematic approach which has clear applicability to the area of thinking is the script theory of Schank and Abelson (1977; see also Abelson, 1981; Schank, 1980, 1982). Scripts were originally formulated as action schemata representing knowledge about, usually, social situations, though the scope of the theory has now been considerably extended (Schank, 1982). The standard example is that of eating out at a restaurant. The restaurant script contains information about what typically happens and the order in which events occur: entering, ordering, eating, paying, and so on. Some consequences of this idea are, for example, that routine repetitions of typical scriptal events will tend not to be stored in episodic memory, whereas violations of the typical pattern will be; and that the script will generate inferences which can be used to interpret occurrences and answer questions. An example of the latter is provided by Abelson (1981). If, during an account of a person's restaurant visit, we encounter the following sentence:

Suddenly, however, he realized that he'd forgotten his reading glasses.

we understand its significance by inferring the diner's consequent difficulty in reading the menu — even if a menu is not explicitly mentioned — because 'reading the menu' is a typical part of the ordering component of the script. Lack of the relevant scriptal knowledge will lead to a failure of this process. If we read:

Suddenly, however, he realized that he'd forgotten to take off his shoes.

we will be confused, unless in possession of a Japanese-restaurant script. Scripts are thus prototypical representations which tell us, once cued, what should happen next, that is, what to infer. They are not response programs but abstract knowledge structures, and as such can be accessed symbolically, without actual performance. A further property of scripts which is significant in the current context is that they form larger hierarchical knowledge structures — it is this which accounts for the phenomenon of reminding, where one event is recognized as similar to another even though the two may not share any common surface features. For example, a dentist-visting script may be a mid-level component of a more general structure such as this:

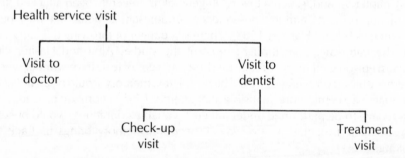

Health service visit

Visit to doctor

Visit to dentist

Check-up visit

Treatment visit

Here, the top level (health service visit) contains the information particular to that level of abstraction and common to the various instances of the lower level: finding a seat in the waiting room, browsing through last year's *Reader's Digest*, and so on. Lower levels of the hierarchy similarly represent knowledge particular to them and general between instances of the next lower level.

Let us apply these concepts to the findings of reasoning research. First, schematic knowledge will be of little use unless the schema is cued or *entered*. This requires, of course, both the possession of relevant schemata and the necessary *evoking context* (Abelson, 1981). We can expect reasoning performance to vary as these conditions are met. If we look at research on thematic tasks, where performance is indeed highly variable, we can see how this interpretation works.

Applying the script idea to performance on the postal sorting problem is fairly straightforward; being a highly routinized activity, a task which evoked the letter-posting script would enable its contents to be directly cued. At the time of the Johnson-Laird, Legrenzi and Legrenzi (1972) experiment in London this would have included information about sealed and unsealed letter rates; this information would not be part of the script for Golding's younger subjects or those from a different culture such as Griggs and Cox's. Of course, if people simply 'read off' schematic values in this way they can hardly be said to be thinking or reasoning, and the possibility exists that a schema once evoked might supply *inappropriate* information for the problem set. Some practical implications of these possibilities will be returned to later.

So far there is no difference between this argument and Manktelow and Evans' original direct memory hypothesis. However, we know that similar performance is reliably produced by contents which are unlikely to cue direct memories, as in the case of the cashier problem. It seems possible that the cashier problem contains elements — perhaps simply 'imagine you are a store cashier' is enough — which evoke, by a Schankian reminding process, a 'regulation' schema structure such as this:

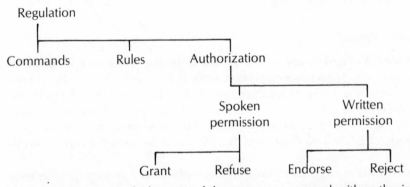

The task features match the part of the system concerned with authorization sufficiently to evoke the relevant information associated with the endorsement lower-level script; having to get an 'OK' after performing some action before proceeding further is a familiar experience.

Turning now to those formats in which the facilitation effect appears elusive, such as the journeys and meals content, we can propose that these contents fail to evoke a schema system consistently: they do not remind one of familiar aspects of knowledge beyond the meanings of the constituent words. This is certainly true of the meals problem, where subjects have been heard to protest along the lines of 'you don't go around saying things like that'. However, if such a content were presented as part of a *given* script, thus doing the reminding for the subject, perhaps the facilitation effect would emerge, rather as the meaning of an otherwise obscure passage of text emerges when a plausible title is given (see

Bransford and Johnson, 1972). Pollard and Gubbins (1982) did just that, presenting the meals content in the context of a medically prescribed diet in which only certain food and drink combinations were allowed. Sure enough, a significant facilitation effect was observed, and the same materials presented without the diet context produced 'abstract' performance.

Thus we can propose the conditions under which people will succeed in constructing a useful mental model of a problem: when they are reminded of a relevant aspect of general procedural knowledge. Failure to set up a model may result either from a lack of evocation of a relevant schema (as with the context-free meals problem); where no relevant schema exists (with abstract problems); or when highly routinized schema content is directly cued (as in the original postal sorting experiment of Johnson-Laird, Legrenzi and Legrenzi, 1972). An explanation of performance as due to direct memories is therefore limited to this last case. Of itself, this argument does not exclude the possibility of a calculus being used as a thinking procedure once the model has been set up. However, Johnson-Laird (1983) mounts a convincing case against this idea in his exposition of the theory of mental models, to which we now proceed. From this point, we shall be increasingly explicit about the practical consequences of this area of theory for user-interface design.

MENTAL MODELS

While Johnson-Laird is one of the principal figures in the recent history of reasoning research, his theory was not designed to account solely for the findings of, for instance, selection task judgements. In fact, in *Mental Models* (1983) the examples given to demonstrate the operation of mental models are largely to do with classical syllogisms. However, it is also made clear that the theory is designed as a general explanation of thought and in this section we treat it in this way.

The theory of mental models predicts that sophisticated performance depends on having a highly developed mental model of the world and accessing the right model at the right time. Information which is integrated and elaborated with material held in memory makes it possible for a user to access a model of a system and, assuming it is more or less correct, to draw inferences and predictions accordingly about the actual system. This is true even if the user has never encountered before all the relevant functions of the system first hand.

The building blocks of information on which a mental model is constructed are termed 'propositional representations' in the theory. The connections made between different items of information and the consistencies isolated between propositional representations, the complexity of the network of links made, and the compatibility between propositional representations and information held in memory, are determined by several general procedures on the basis of the *meanings* of the propositional representations. This process the theory terms 'procedural semantics'. Hence propositional representations may be seen to form the infrastructure and procedural semantics the organizing principles of a person's interaction with the environment. The next section describes these concepts in more detail.

Propositional representations and procedural semantics

The theory holds that information is encoded initially in terms of propositional representations, that is, mental representations of verbally expressible propositions. It is assumed that these representations are expressed in a 'mental language'. The syntactic structure of this mental language need not concern us here since, according to the theory, it reflects an essentially arbitrary choice provided it is linked to the appropriate semantics. The vocabulary of this mental language is presumed to relate to the vocabulary of natural language. Propositional representations do not themselves introduce any new information into the processing system — they are merely mental representations of verbally expressible propositions — but they do make the stored information easier to manipulate.

So one might see propositional representations as a mental 'echo' of the information available in the real world, expressed in a verbal format. Propositional representations enable verbatim recall of information, allow users to comment on the truth or falsity of particular events, or to respond to directives, for example. But they do not allow users to go beyond the data, as it were, because propositional representations are neither integrated nor elaborated with information held in memory. A user who works only with propositional representations can 'scan' only in those directions that have been encoded in that representation. So, for instance, using only propositional representations of information an understanding of how to use a mouse-driven word-processing system would not generalize beyond the system to other systems that are not mouse-driven. An important corollary is that information coded solely in terms of propositional representations will be difficult to remember, for not only is there little if any elaborative processing, presumably the processing done will be at a shallow level, where the probability of remembering information is relatively low (the levels-of-processing approach to memory is reviewed in Chapter 5).

Now obviously people do go beyond the data; they do make inferences and predictions, they can understand events and decide what action to take as well as control its execution, and they experience events by proxy. This suggests that propositional representations are somehow integrated into some unified mental model. The theory of mental models argues that propositional representations are mapped into mental models by way of the *semantics* of the mental language. For Johnson-Laird this mapping must be described at the level of procedures, which specify uniquely how to carry out any given mapping in a form that can be followed by a simple machine (such as a Turing machine), hence the term *procedural* semantics. The following general procedures describe the actions, conscious or unconscious, that are required to initiate a mental model:

P1   If a proposition makes no reference to any information represented in the current model of the world then a new mental model is constructed on the basis of that proposition.

P2   If a proposition refers to at least one 'bit' of information (in the information theory meaning of the term) represented in the current model of the world, then any additional information conveyed by that proposition is added to the current model.

P3   If a proposition interrelates information in two or more hitherto separate models then the models are integrated accordingly.

P4   If all the bits of information referred to in the proposition are represented in the current model of the world, then the person verifies whether that information holds true in the current model of the world.

P5   If the verification procedure P4 is unable to establish a truth value of a proposition, there may be no evidence either way about the relevant bits of incoming information, and that information is added to the model in an appropriate way.

In addition to these general procedures, which are used to build a person's mental model of the world, two additional procedures are required to ensure that the particular model constructed is the most appropriate to deal with the information available at any particular point in time. These are recursive procedures, since they are used to sort back through the mental model, making the necessary adjustments to it if incoming information has shown it to be flawed in some way, or if a better model is now available:

P6   If a proposition is *false* in the current model of the world, then *either* the model of the previous propositions is modified to bring it into line with the current proposition, *or* the current proposition is interpreted as being inconsistent with what has gone before.

P7   If a proposition is *true* in the current model of the world then checks are made to see whether there is an alternative model of the previous propositions that is inconsistent with the current propositions. *If there is such a model* then it is assumed that the current proposition is only possibly true. *If there is not such a model* then it is assumed that the proposition is necessarily true given what has gone before.

In terms of the theory then, the meaning of a proposition is functionally important, because on it depend the procedures for constructing, extending, and evaluating any mental model.

The meaning of a proposition is also important at the theoretical level. It enables the theory of mental models to incorporate the effects of the structure and content of knowledge, or its context, in any analysis of performance. The point is worth elaborating, for if it is correct then it implies that mental models are unique, if only in a pedantic sense, to the individual and setting, and there can never be the perfect interface design, just as there can never be the perfect office chair. In fact, the individual variations in users' mental models may be more extreme than individual variations in users' bodily dimensions.

The meaning of a proposition is its truth conditions: if a proposition is true, then it corresponds to a state of affairs in the world. However, to know the meaning of a proposition is not just to know its truth conditions, it also means to know what would count as its proof or verification. To know what is meant by a word-processing system, for example, is not just to point to or describe a particular machine. It also entails some notion of the fundamental need for print-formatting commands, and text input and editing modes in any system that is to be called a word-processor, and a notion that a system does not have to have a spelling-check option or a dedicated terminal for it to be called a word-processor. In other words, it requires knowledge of what *defines* a concept as well as what is merely characteristic of that concept (this topic is treated in more detail in Chapter 5). Such criteria are fixed neither by experience nor by logical necessity, but by convention.

A natural way in which to construe criteria is as default values which can be assumed unless there is evidence to the contrary, whose boundaries are set by the nature of the particular taxonomy in which they occur. This is one of the consequences of the averaging property of schemata: typical constitutents of a schema are assumed when it is evoked unless contrary information is given. Thus the default values the user would probably take for granted when approaching a word-processor would be of a system that is menu-driven, with a directory of files and a help facility, with commands for inputting text, revising text, and searching for text, and with commands for specifying the appearance of the final output. However, each of these values in turn would have a set of default values associated with it. Thus the default values the user would probably take for granted when revising text would include the ability to move, insert, delete, copy and replace text. The range and appropriateness of default values depends on the content of knowledge; yet, whether something were to count as a word-processor would depend also on its similarity to typical word-processors, microcomputers, office systems, and so on: in other words, on the structure of knowledge. So, for example, the Apple Lisa — which offers a lot more than simple word-processing — would count as an office system, not as a word-processor, despite having its word-processor software tools.

The construction, extension, and evaluation of mental models may occur despite literal failures of reference. The use of natural language to communicate, for example, depends on an intentional correspondence between a linguistic expression and a state of affairs; people use linguistic expressions with the intention of picking out certain states of affairs (see Chapter 7). This means that it is not necessary to comprehend each referent to understand what is being said, nor is it necessarily the case that what is being referenced is what is intended to be meant. The effects of failures of reference are possibly circumscribed because speakers do not coventionally intend to mislead; they are likely to order the information in their descriptions so as to prevent the hearer from going astray. In doing so, they may enable the referential intention to be recovered or messages to be disambiguated.

The human element in procedural semantics

The theory of mental models suggests that for each new item of incoming information, a search is made to ensure that this new proposition is consistent with any earlier information encountered. If the check back through the mental model (carried out by the recursive procedures P6 and P7 discussed earlier) has been systematic and exhaustive, then the model constructed or accessed will be the one most appropriate to the information available at that particular time. This is the essence of a non-deterministic device. With such a model it would be possible to make explicit inferences regarding the state of the world. But if the search has not been systematic and exhaustive, and only a simple model has been constructed, then the inferences drawn are more likely to be implicit. Moreover, the simple model is likely to be the basis for future errors of understanding. The theory of mental models predicts that an important class of errors, leaving aside for the moment those that arise simply from the incorrect integration of propositional representations into the model, includes those errors arising from the default values set up in the model. The theory predicts that these errors are systematic, not random, and are in the direction of the more usual interpretation, expectation, action, and so on, given by the schema, as in the case of over-familiar problem formats.

For instance, in one current word-processor all the editing commands and most other commands are terminated with the pressing of the RETURN key, except the 'insert' command. This command needs to be treated as an exception in this way because 'return' is a legitimate character in the insert mode, so 'insert' is terminated by pressing the ESCAPE key. A consequence of this particular design feature is, however, that the 'escape' terminator is poorly learned and there are occasions when users incorrectly press the RETURN key to terminate the 'insert' command, remain in the insert mode, and when attempting to access the HELP system or the file directory start entering gibberish into the text.

To take another instance, where the error is more one of expectation than of action, a user familiar with mainframe computers will come to expect generations of files to be kept, so that a file is never deleted by the computer unless it is explicitly told to do so. When using a dedicated terminal, however, that expectation can be a source of many errors, and unless adequate backup procedures are followed (by giving each file a unique name, for instance) vital files may be lost.

Hammond *et al.*'s (1983c) data on user performance with three interactive systems provide some examples of another kind of error: errors of interpretation. In one of the systems, a menu-driven business graphics system, a single key labelled 'end' allowed users to return to the previous menu panel. Yet instead of pressing this key, several of the users pressed a 'home' key, which returned them to the top-level menu, from where they re-entered all the choices needed to route down to the desired menu panel. From the data, the experimenters concluded that these users misinterpreted the intended meaning of 'end' — where its use was restricted to 'ending' the current menu panel — presuming instead that if this key were pressed they would have to start the session all over again. The prediction that errors are systematic and not random, and are in the direction of the more usual interpretation, expectation, action, and so on, is also very much in accord with the findings of the 'slips of action' literature (see, for example, Norman, 1981; Reason, 1984a).

This ability to search systematically and exhaustively is obviously dependent on the capacity of working memory. If only for the reason that this capacity is limited (see Chapter 5), people are not non-deterministic devices. Research on reasoning, for instance, shows that the ability to construct a model from propositional representations is very much dependent on the number of possible alternative models to be considered, and on the ability to use the information in the order in which it is encountered (see, for example, Johnson-Laird and Bara, 1982; Johnson-Laird and Steedman, 1978). At a more basic level, it has been shown that the ability to manipulate propositional representations and therefore, presumably, the ability to integrate them into a mental model, is influenced by the need to articulate negatives and semantic 'markings' (Clark and Clark, 1977). In fact, the difficulty inherent in the use of 'marked' terms and syntactic complications such as negation has been observed for a long time, for example in Wason's work on official documents in the 1950s (see Wason and Johnson-Laird, 1972). The major problem produced by these linguistic impediments seems to be their cost in terms of working memory load. A recent example will convey the kind of difficulty involved. From 1985 intending entrants to British polytechnics will be faced with the following instruction on their application forms:

> DO NOT use this form if you are applying ONLY for
> courses other than first degree or DipHE.

A roomful of admissions tutors took quite a time to determine what the applicant *should* do. In short, if verbal commands are to be used, they should be kept simple: if users have to infer what they should do from an instruction concerning what they should *not* do, working memory space will be taken up which could be used for constructing mental models.

One essential point of information still needs to be determined, however, and that is the temporal relation between propositional representations and mental models. It might be the case that individuals retain either a superficial propositional representation or else just a mental model, or that the superficial form of a sentence cannot be discarded after it has been interpreted and both forms of representation coexist. Depending on how long propositional representations remain, they may allow a 'hard copy' of the data to be held, against which any inferences and so on could be independently checked.

The content captured in a mental model is a function of the schema evoked and the procedural semantics of the mental language. So, whereas propositional representations allow scanning only in the directions that have been encoded in the representation, mental models allow scanning in a multiple of directions, the number of which depends on the sophistication of the initial schema. Likewise, whereas propositional representations have an arbitrarily chosen syntactic structure, mental models have an analogical structure corresponding to the state of affairs in the world as the individual perceives or conceives it. By breaking away from a perceptual reality and postulating the existence of a mental language, the theory of mental models and the concept of recursive embedding allow models of models, and give the individual freedom to articulate the propositional attitudes of beliefs and hopes, for instance. What counts is the model's functional role in representing the world, not the exactness of the model's physical correspondence with that world.

Thus, the construction of a single, coherent, and plausible mental model eases the integration and memorability of information. Coherence is also a desirable property of user–system dialogues and depends on the principal factors of co-reference and consistency. For co-reference, each proposition in the dialogue must refer, explicitly or implicitly, to an entity referred to or introduced elsewhere in the dialogue. For consistency, the properties and relations ascribed to the referents must be compatible with one another and free from contradiction. Plausibility, however, concerns more than interface dialogue in this instance and is the possibility of interpreting the dialogue in an appropriate 'temporal, spatial, causal, and intentional framework' (Johnson-Laird, 1983). It depends on extraneous knowledge about other systems and procedures, about natural language, and about the problem domain itself. We will come back to this supposition later, when considering the link between the theory and the ideas and methods of cognitive ergonomics.

Finally in this section, an example of the distinction between propositional representations and mental models and its empirical consequences, is provided by Mani and Johnson-Laird (1982) in an experiment on relational reasoning. Subjects heard a series of spatial descriptions. After each description, they were shown a diagram. They then had to decide whether the diagram was consistent or inconsistent with the description. Half of the descriptions were *determinate*, for example:

> The spoon is to the left of the knife
> The plate is to the right of the knife
> The fork is in front of the spoon
> The cup is in front of the knife

and were thus consistent with only one diagram:

> SPOON KNIFE PLATE
> FORK CUP

Half of the descriptions were *indeterminate*, so that not all the possible spatial relations were accessible, for example:

> The spoon is to the left of the knife
> The plate is to the right of the spoon
> The fork is in front of the spoon
> The cup is in front of the knife

and were consistent with more than one diagram:

> SPOON KNIFE PLATE SPOON PLATE KNIFE
> FORK CUP FORK CUP

The subjects were then given an unexpected test of their memory for the descriptions. They were required to rank four alternatives in terms of their resemblance to the original description: the original description, an inferrable description, and two 'foil' descriptions which served as distractor items. The results showed that the subjects remembered the gist of the determinate descriptions much better than that of the indeterminate descriptions. There was no effect of whether or not on a particular trial a diagram had been consistent with a description. Conversely, the subjects remembered the verbatim detail of the indeterminate descriptions better than that of the determinate descriptions. Johnson-Laird (1983, p.162) concludes:

> This 'cross-over' effect is impossible to explain without postulating at least two sorts of mental representation. A plausible account of the pattern of results is indeed that subjects construct a mental model of determinate descriptions, but abandon such a representation in favour of a superficial propositional one as soon as they encounter an indeterminacy in a description. Models are easier to remember than propositions, perhaps

because they are more structured and elaborate . . . and require a greater amount of processing to construct. . . . But models encode little or nothing of the linguistic form of the sentences on which they are based, and subjects accordingly confuse inferrable descriptions with the originals. Propositional representations are relatively hard to remember, but they do encode the linguistic form of the sentences. Hence, when they are remembered, the subjects are likely to make a better than chance recognition of verbatim content.

As we shall see later, this account poses problems for several analytical tools for the design of office information systems.

Mental models and cognitive ergonomics: some theoretical links

In the previous section it was noted that the construction of a single, coherent, and plausible mental model eases the intepretation and memorability of information. Now, one of the fundamental tenets of cognitive ergonomics is that good design should lead to a single, coherent, and plausible mental model. One of the most powerful theories of cognitive ergonomics, Moran's (1981) Command Language Grammar, provides a formal technique for actualizing coherence and plausibility. It seems reasonable to propose, therefore, that somewhere along the line the ideas and methods of cognitive ergonomics should link in with the theory. This section suggests where this linkage takes place.

Beginning with the idea that information is coded initially in terms of propositional representations, Hammond and Barnard (1984) refer to information acquired in the early stages of learning as being in the form of 'relatively independent knowledge fragments or packages'. They say that 'often, such knowledge fragments will be correct, resulting in appropriate user action. However, when fragments are incorrect, they can inter-relate to cause errors which are difficult for the user to interpret.' In terms of the theory, this is not surprising; in the early stages of learning there is no unified mental model in which to integrate the relatively independent knowledge fragements: they will remain in the form of propositional representations. If the user need scan these propositional representations only in those directions that have been encoded in the representation to meet the demands of the task, then the theory predicts appropriate user action. But if the task demands scanning in several, as yet unencoded directions (as in recovering from an error state), then the theory predicts inappropriate user action given an incorrect schema.

The theory states that propositional representations are integrated into a unified mental model by way of procedural semantics. Rumelhart and Norman (1978) have provided a comparable theory of integration. It comprises three modes of learning: knowledge is first acquired element by element in an additive fashion; then once a basic knowledge of the system is acquired, performance is improved by 'tuning' that knowledge; then finally, for the expert user, there is cognitive restructuring. The first process, accretion, and the second, tuning, may be thought of as the general procedures P1 to P5 outlined earlier, while the third, restructuring, may be thought of as the two additional recursive procedures, P6 and P7, postulated to cope with the simulation of the non-deterministic device.

The theory also stresses that the content captured in a mental model is a function of both the initial schema and the processes that construct, extend, and evaluate it. For support of this notion, one need only look at the range of research done on human–machine interaction. For instance, Morton *et al.* (1979) pointed to the incompatibility between the user's concept of the system structure and the real structure, between the way the database is organized in the machine and the way it is organized in the user's head, and between the way in which system details are usually encountered by users and their preferred mode of learning. The users, it seemed, were unable to set up an adequate initial model. In fact, Carroll (1984a) is more damning: users' models, he suggests, are 'incomplete, inconsistent, unstable in time, oversimple, and often rife with superstition'. Using the work of Morton *et al.*, Hammond and Barnard (1984) itemized the blocks of knowledge that might be brought to bear in the construction of a model, including a knowledge of: natural language, other machines and procedures, the physical interface and the interface dialogue, the problem, the computer version of the domain, and the consequences of system operations. From another direction, Norman (1982) focused on the errors people made. Not surprisingly, he found that individuals formed conclusions from the relationships of one system to another. As the theory of mental models predicted earlier, these errors were systematic, not random, and were in the direction of the more usual interpretation, expectation, and action. Norman's explanation was that these 'description' errors occur because 'when people lack knowledge about the proper operation of some aspect of a machine, they are apt to derive the operations by analogy with other, similar aspects of the device' (Norman, 1982), and this ties in with the notion of schema in this discussion.

Norman (1983) goes on to state that mental models 'need not be technically accurate (and usually are not), but they must be functional'. Going beyond the ideas deliberated earlier, he submits that people often feel uncertain of this model — even when it is in fact complete and correct — and their mental models include statements about the degree of certainty they feel for different aspects of their knowledge. These doubts are said to govern behaviour and force extra caution when performing operations. 'This is especially apt to be the case when a person has experience with a number of different systems, all very similar, but each with some slightly different set of operating principles' (Norman, 1983).

Many of the notions of the theory of mental models, therefore, have been taken up in one guise or another in the ideas and method of cognitive ergonomics. However, the theory provides a unified framework on which to pin the otherwise isolated findings of research on thinking and cognitive ergonomics and interrelate the various bodies of knowledge. Yet this is not all it does, as we shall see when we look at how these ideas can be applied in practice in designing the human–machine interface.

THINKING, MENTAL MODELS, LEARNING, AND DESIGN

In this final section we shall draw on and extend the theoretical and experimental review set out in this chapter to draw out some principles which can be applied in the design process. In some cases we shall refer to research already carried out in this direction, in others our proposals will be relatively novel, and will suggest what form the questions, rather than their answers, should take.

Designing mental models

Let us begin by way of a summary: the material reviewed here compels us to urge the disposal of a powerful misconception which can be termed the *formal equivalence fallacy*. There often appears to be an assumption embodied in a variety of areas of instruction that if one wishes to ensure that a difficult concept be grasped, one does it by presenting an 'easy' example of the same formal — in other words logical — structure as that concept. If the easy problem can be solved, then because they are formally equivalent, understanding of the difficult problem will surely follow, so it seems. We reject this idea because it depends on the assumption that solving logical problems is due to logical insight. The use of a calculus to solve general logical problems has not been demonstrated empirically, as we have seen in reasoning research, neither is it theoretically necessary for inference, as Johnson-Laird (1983) has shown.

Rational thinking depends on the construction and operation of coherent and plausible mental models. That good design should lead to the construction of such models is, as we mentioned before, also one of the fundamental tenets of cognitive ergonomics. Norman (1983) distinguishes between conceptual models and mental models: 'Conceptual models are devised as tools for the understanding or teaching of physical systems. Mental models are what people really have in their heads and what guides their use of things.' The prevalent philosophy in cognitive ergonomics at present is that if the designer gets the conceptual model right, the correct mental model will follow. This is clearly a more sophisticated approach than the formal equivalence assumption, and the psychology of thinking gives us some guidelines which might aid our progress along this path.

Where do mental models come from? We can say more than that they 'follow': the broad alternatives are that they can be supplied either by the evocation of an existing schema, or by construction *de novo* from given elements of a problem. We have seen some of the pitfalls entailed in evoking an existing schema in reasoning research. On the one hand, the problem content may not, as in the case of non-realistic thematic selection tasks, succeed in establishing what Abelson (1981) terms an evoking context, and one will be left with the low-level heuristic responses typically cued by abstract representations. On the other hand, there is the problem of over-familiar problem content and the evocation of routinized procedural knowledge which, in the end, also results in performance without thinking; the schema contains default values inappropriate to the problem in hand and is being operated because of its comforting familiarity. A recent example of this comes from a study by Ormerod *et al.* (1986) on thinking with some of the constructs in the logic programming language Prolog, and the instructional materials typically used in Prolog manuals. In one case, performance on the example materials (family trees) was rapid and almost error-free, but this failed to generalize to other logically isomorphic materials with less familiar content and representational structure. The 'understanding' revealed by the instructional materials was therefore quite spurious. This recalls the lack of transfer found in the Johnson-Laird, Legrenzi and Legrenzi (1972) postal sorting version of the selection task.

As we saw in the application of script theory to explain performance on the cashier version of the task, the ideal is to evoke a schema by reminding the person of a general class of procedural knowledge into which the current situation will fit. The 'conceptual model' approach of Norman (1983) is one way of going about this: a useful way of looking at conceptual models is as *advance organizers* of information (Anderson, 1980; Carroll, 1984a). This usually means an attempt to set up the most appropriate schema by the provision of metaphors. For example, Rumelhart and Norman (1981) used a composition of three metaphors to convey the more fundamental features of a system. A secretary metaphor was used to explain that commands could be interspersed with text input, a card file metaphor was used to describe the deletion of a single numbered line from a file, and a tape recorder metaphor was used to convey the need for explicit terminators in files. Halasz and Moran (1982) emphasize that the metaphor should not simply convey the defaut values of a schema of the system, but also an appropriate structural representation. Overt metaphors are a feature of iconic displays on sophisticated microcomputers such as Apple's Lisa and Macintosh.

The second main source of material for the construction of mental models is the task presentation itself, when there is no plausible existing schema to be evoked. As Evans (1984) has argued, what is important here is that appropriate information is *selected* for a role in the model, and this selection is determined by what he terms heuristic processes. An example of heuristic processing which we have already encountered is linguistic bias: in general, people will retrieve and respond to the natural usage of a linguistic expression. You will recall how this revealed itself in even the most artificial situation, such as the abstract selection task: people respond to the topical and suppositional elements of an 'If' sentence in a deductive task and hence never get as far as constructing an inference-bearing model at all. There are plenty of user interfaces in which this is an important consideration, as anyone who has stood behind a line of people waiting to operate an automatic bank till will confirm. People seem to have difficulty with even the most (apparently) elementary command language. In such situations people are proceeding, if they proceed at all, on the basis of propositional representations which, as we saw, lack the adaptability of mental models and are hard to remember. This is why the people in front of you in the queue for the bank till always take so much longer than you to operate the thing: chances are they will have to learn it all over again each time. It is important that designers do not leave it to their own intuitions to decide what a command word or phrase 'naturally' means, since their intuitions are partly supplied by their specialist experience.

The heuristic use of linguistic cues is more subtle than this as well, and can be made to work in the user's favour. In the discussion of procedural semantics it was argued that individuals can attempt to recover the supposed *intention* of a message, thus overcoming literal failures of reference. Johnson-Laird (1983) puts it thus:

> As Grice (1975) has emphasized, there is a convention that speakers tend to abide by: they do not deliberately mislead their listeners. In other words, if you construct a mental model on the basis of my discourse, then I am likely to order the information in my description so as to prevent you from going astray. I owe you an account that you can represent in a simple model without running into a conflict with information that I only subsequently divulge.

Similar 'Gricean' principles have been pursued in the design of the human–machine interface. For du Boulay, O'Shea and Monk (1981) this was achieved by designing a conceptual model (a 'notational machine') that was both 'conceptually simple', that is, it consisted of a small number of parts that interacted in ways that could be easily understood, by having a small language with few constructs and by restricting the machine's possible actions; and 'visible', that is, methods were provided for viewing selected events as they occurred in the program and the particular circumstances which led the program to be in a given state. For Carroll (1984b) this was achieved in a 'Training Wheels Word-Processor' by specifically disabling the more advanced functions or pathways 'that can distract and confuse novices' and providing a message like 'X is not available in the Training Wheels system'.

The role of working memory is also a crucial determinant of the ability to set up a mental model. This is partly why the use of existing schemata seems to make problems easier; schematic default assignments are not entered in working memory since they are explicitly constructed only when confronted, for example, by violations. Again, linguistic factors requiring inference can cause an overload here and disrupt the coherence of a model; the example of negation was given in an earlier section of this chapter.

Thinking and learning

One of the consequences of a view of thinking as content-dependent is the blurring of the distinction which might otherwise exist between thinking and memory. As inference has become indispensable to contemporary accounts of memory such as Schank's (1982), so memory has become equally essential to explanations of thought. This brings us to the question of learning: the change in memory, hence thinking skills, with experience. There was a time, in the behaviourist epoch, when psychology concerned itself with little else but learning, but with the onrush of the cognitive revolution, the focus shifted to the relatively static concept of knowledge. Psychology at present has much more to say about knowledge than it has about learning, but learning, we would venture, is due for a comeback. Learning as the construction and retention of mental models is plainly a welcome advance in this direction and in this, the final part of our review, we shall continue this theme of learning from the standpoint of the theories of thinking.

By learning, we refer to the acquisition of new knowledge, as in the retention of a mental model. It is a moot point whether the adaptive use of existing knowledge, as in response to highly familiar problem content, or heuristic decision by propositional representation when a situation precludes such action, can usefully be described as learning. In the present context, we can ask the general question: how do people learn to take logical decisions? Studies of reasoning have shown how this skill can emerge and, equally importantly from a practical point of view, the kinds of treatments that will *not* be successful in this end.

There are several major issues we wish to confront in this final part of the discussion: practice, instruction, introspective access to thought processes, and the difference between decision and interpretation. All are important both theoretically and practically, all can be addressed by looking at reasoning research, and in many cases counterintuitive conclusions emerge which designers should be aware of.

Practice

The sudden-death nature of the Wason selection task might seem to rule it out when it comes to studying practice, but it has been modified to form a useful methodological tool in this area. This modification usually involves reduced arrays and unfamiliar content. The most interesting technique of this kind was devised by Johnson-Laird and Wason (1970b) and, as Wason (1983) has justly complained, ignored thereafter. There are several features of this task, now known as the RAST (reduced array selection task), which distinguish it from the standard task and make it interesting: it involves practice, it involves unfamiliar material, and almost everyone gets it right.

Instead of thinking about the hidden sides of cards, people have to consider the properties of shapes presented in boxes before them. For example, they might be asked to prove true or false (logically the same thing) in the most economical manner a rule such as 'If they are triangles then they are black' by examining the contents of two boxes, one containing black shapes and one containing white. The optimal solution is to ignore the black shapes, which are all Q values, and examine only the white ones, since only a white triangle (a P/not-Q item) could falsify the rule. A good proportion of subjects (about 30%) get the problem right straight away, as they never touch the black shapes, and almost all succeed at some stage, because they do not look at all the black shapes but do exhaust the white ones (Wason, 1983). Two critical variables have been found, in recent studies, to be the extent to which subjects are able to form a unified — that is, schematic — representation of the problem, either by using realistic materials or simple rather than complex description rules (Wason and Green, 1984); and the syntactic complexity of the rule (Oakhill and Johnson-Laird, 1985). Coupled with the concrete nature of the task compared with the standard selection task, the mediating cognitive factors appear to be, firstly, reduction of working memory load and, secondly, the ease of selecting relevant information for modelling the problem. Independent studies have shown that the latter can also be enhanced in the standard task by removing distracting information such as the P and not-P cards themselves (Lunzer, Harrison and Davey, 1972; Roth, 1979) or by adding information about critical task features (Hoch and Tschirgi, 1983). It is apparent that once these conditions are satisfied, people readily construct a logically appropriate model; if they fail to do so initially, repeated exposure to the problem *without external feedback* will result in eventual success.

Decision and interpretation

In this section we shall consider the other factors mentioned at the end of the section on thinking and learning: decision, interpretation, conscious access, and their implications for instruction. This is because they are not separate concerns, but interlocking. This will entail, incidentally, another look at the role of language. When faced with someone who does not know how to do something, the natural inclination is to tell them. However, we are probably all familiar with the experience of feeling as if we have given perfectly clear instructions, only to be met by continued incompetence on the part of the person we are addressing. This common experience is matched in reasoning research to the extent that we can reach the startling conclusion that direct verbal instruction is of very little use in the acquisition of effective thinking skills.

The apparent split between decisions and people's verbal evaluations of them emerged right at the beginning of the modern phase of reasoning research. In the first experimental report on the selection task, Wason (1968) found that, while people could appreciate straight away the significance of the P/not-Q case for an 'If P then Q' rule when presented with it, they were quite unable to apply this appreciation to the task itself. They have to discover it for themselves (Legrenzi, 1971). Wason and Johnson-Laird (1970) confronted people with the incompatibility between their selections (typically of P or P and Q) and their evaluations of the P/not-Q case. People in this situation indulged in astonishing verbal gyrations in attempting to explain themselves, though characteristically adhering to their initial choices. The processes of selection and evaluation seemed, as the authors put it, to 'pass one another by'.

This conflict was further explored in work by Wason and Evans (1975; Evans and Wason, 1976). People were given abstract selection tasks in which the Q part of the rule was in one condition expressed in the affirmative (If P then Q') and in another negated ('If P then not Q'). Recall that people will typically choose the same items, P and Q, in both cases, thus getting the problem wrong with the affirmative rule but right with the negative rule. In the Wason and Evans experiments, people also had to explain their selections. Most explanations in the affirmative condition tended to be in terms of verification, hence illogical, while in the negative condition they tended to be in terms of falsification, hence logical. The same thing happened when people were given 'solutions' to the task and asked to explain them. Wason and Evans argue that this is not a case of logical insight mysteriously appearing and disappearing, but rather that people were constructing *post hoc* justifications of their own and others' behaviour.

·Thus people's introspections, they propose, should not be interpreted as true reflections of decision *processes*, but as evaluations of decision *outcomes*. This leads to the rejection of another attractive misconception: the *fallacy of conscious access*. It would appear that we are not aware of the processes we use in making decisions, only of their products. Indeed, this divergence may even have a physiological basis: Evans (1982) cites studies by Golding which demonstrate that impairment of right-hemisphere brain function, either due to accidental damage or unilateral electroconvulsive therapy, is correlated with a significantly higher than normal rate of logically correct solutions to the selection task. Evans also reports results from his own laboratory in which not-Q selection rates were facilitated by a forced-choice response procedure using only the right hand, which is controlled by the left cerebral hemisphere. It is tempting to conclude from these findings that initial decisions are controlled by the non-verbal, intuitive right hemisphere, while interpretations are controlled by the verbal, left hemisphere. There is a convergence here with similar ideas in other areas of cognitive theory (see Paivio, 1971, and Seymour, 1979).

Intriguingly, it would appear from all these studies that while our decisions are arrived at non-logically, our interpretations are logical. People select P and Q because they match the named items; they do not appear to be aware of this because they do not explain their actions in these terms but in terms of the logical relation of the item with respect to the rule. A splendid example of these 'dual processes' as they operate in real life is provided by Hunt (1981). Quoting a US Supreme Court judge, Hunt reports him as advising a new member of the bench: 'You must remember one thing. At the constitutional level where we work, ninety per cent of any decision is emotional. The rational part of us supplies the reasons for supporting our predilections.'

These conclusions are consistent with other psychological approaches such as Anderson's (1983b) ACT* theory. According to Anderson, Farrell and Sauers (1984), ACT* states that 'instructions are stored initially in a declarative form while behaviour requires procedures'. In a study of the teaching and learning of the programming language LISP, novices typically appear to understand verbal instructions but then blunder on regardless, as if they had not. Anderson, Farrell and Sauers recommend, as we do, the strategy of 'learning by doing'. This is an alternative to the 'advance organizer' approach described previously, or possibly a complement to it. Its justification rests on the justification for there being an interpretive stage to thinking in the first place: there must be some feedback between decision, interpretation, and subsequent decision. It is for future research to give an exact account of this process.

There are some important practical corollaries of this view of split thinking. Firstly, a broad rule of thumb seems to be that in a situation where prior general knowledge can plausibly be invoked, use the 'advance organizer' or thinking-by-analogy approach. In very novel situations such as learning LISP, which Anderson, Farrell and Sauers consider to be about as novel a situation as is possible for an adult human to face, use 'learning by doing'.

This is not as straightforward as it sounds; a mental model of a novel situation, once constructed, is highly resistant to change, even when confronted with clear evidence of its inappropriateness. Wason and Johnson-Laird (1970) showed this in a purely experimental setting, but Hammond *et al.* (1983c) have produced similar results in a study of human–computer interaction. However, people do interpret the outcomes of their decisions and will change their models with continued experience, at least during the very early stages of learning when, perhaps, alternative candidate models are competing for the ascendancy. Externally provided error feedback may be quite irrelevant to this process, and may even interfere with it (Carroll and Kay, 1985; Clark and Hillen, 1985). The essence of a user's early experience with an unfamiliar system should be salient features which are relevant to the construction of an appropriate model, and repeated practice.

What of verbal instruction? Its role would seem to be limited to cueing low-level heuristic responses which accord with natural usage and to cueing analogical schemata. 'Instructions' assert Anderson, Farrell and Sauers (1984) 'cannot set up procedures to perform the skill'. And what of logic? Logical thinking, we have argued, is fundamentally unnatural as a decision process; technological systems are unnatural with respect to human cognition because of their logicality. The theory of mental models provides a framework for integrating otherwise isolated research results arising from this incompatibility; it provides a generative description of how users understand systems; and it suggests how the designer might use our knowledge to facilitate that understanding.

SUMMARY PRINCIPLES

1. Thinking is not based on general inference rules, so competence on one task will not necessarily generalize to others of the same logical structure.
2. Performance required can be low (that is, routine, response-based) or high (that is, flexible, decision-based).
   2.1 If the performance required is low, then performance will depend on (a) heuristic processes, or (b) direct memories.
   2.2 If the performance required is high, then performance will depend on (a) existing schemata, or (b) new schemata.
3. Heuristic processes are automatic response biases generated by attention to salient task features (STFs). STFs are principally perceptual or linguistic and involve the natural meanings of these cues.
   3.1 If the STFs provide a clear task structure, performance will be facilitated.
   3.2 If the STFs are non-functional, performance will be impaired.
   3.3 If the natural and the required uses of the STFs are different, performance will be impaired.
4. Direct memories are automatic routines retrieved from the user's memory. Direct memories, existing schemata, and new schemata can be with respect to (a) the system, or (b) the task. Use of direct memories, existing or new schemata is a function of the user's familiarity with (a) the system, or (b) the task. Familiarity is a function of (a) assessment of the user's background, (b) the user's self-assessment, and (c) level of use.
   4.1 Highly familiar material cues direct memories.
   4.2 Highly unfamiliar material cues heuristic processes.
5. Existing schemata are automatic transferable thinking procedures from the user's general knowledge.
   5.1 Material at a level of general familiarity will evoke existing schemata.
   5.2 Existing schemata can be evoked by verbal examples (analogies).
   5.3 If no familiar examples are available, new schemata are required.
   5.4 Induction of new schemata requires practice.
6. Verbal instructions do not in themselves inculcate thinking skills.
   6.1 If new schemata are required, verbal feedback can be used for their evaluation.

6.2 Verbal material can be used to evoke existing schemata or direct memories.

7. If when an analogy or metaphor is first introduced in a dialogue no information is present to identify.
   (a) those task domains in which its use is appropriate, and
   (b) those tasks domains in which use is inappropriate
   then the power of the analogy or metaphor will be reduced.

8. If when an analogy or metaphor is first introduced in a dialogue no information is present to identify.
   (a) those structures and functional relations that are essential, and
   (b) those structures and functional relations that are incidental to the analogy or metaphor
   then the power of the analogy or metaphor will be reduced.

9. If no information is present in a dialogue when a structure or functional relation in the system or subsystem departs from what is conventionally the case [in the analogy or metaphor], then the power of the analogy or metaphor will become a negative power for each occurrence of that case.

10. If the sentences used in a dialogue contain 'marked' words, then they are read slower and less accurately than any root equivalents.

11. If the order of recall, or the order of user actions is important, and the order of presentation of words in a dialogue is antagonistic to that order, then the probability of comprehending the dialogue will be reduced.

12. If the sentences used in a dialogue contain negatives, then they are read slower and less accurately than comparable sentences phrased in terms of affirmatives.

13. If the sentences used in a dialogue are open to more than one interpretation, then they are read slower and less accurately than sentences that are open to just one interpretation.

14. If the sentences used in a dialogue contain referents that are *not* referred to, or introduced elsewhere in the dialogue, then the probability of constructing a single, coherent and plausible mental model will be reduced.

15. If the properties and relations ascribed to the referents of a sentence used in a dialogue are incompatible with, and contradict those that are ascribed elsewhere in the dialogue, then the probability of constructing a single, coherent and plausible mental model will be reduced.

16. If the user is a novice user, and if (s)he has not completed an online tutorial programme, then the probability of constructing a single, coherent and plausible mental model will be reduced.

17. If the item of information to be conveyed by the dialogue is left implicit, or embedded within a sentence that is verbose, then the probability of identifying that information as a separate item will be reduced.

18. If the referent common to two separate items of information is designated in the two items by two different names, then the probability of identifying the referent as common to both will be reduced.

19. If the number of referents, or the number of properties and relations ascribed to the referents used in a dialogue exceed the capacity available in working memory, then the probability of considering all the relevant referents, or relevant properties and relations, will be reduced.

20. If sentences 1, 2 or 3 of a new screen of information do not explicitly relate that screen to the previous screen of information then the probability of comprehending the dialogue will be reduced.

21. If the consequences of the possible user responses to any screen of information are not given explicitly, in terms of the information to be encountered in the next screen, then the probability of comprehending the dialogue will be reduced.

22. If the items of any screen of information are independent of one another then the probability of comprehending the dialogue will be reduced.

23. If the scoring between a system's dominant functional characteristics and those of other systems is low, then the probability of the user making the correct assumptions about the dominant functional characteristics of each of the major features and operations of the system is reduced.

24. If the probability of the user making the correct assumptions about the dominant functional characteristics of each of a system's major features and operations is low, then the probability of 'capture' will be increased.

THE NEXT CHAPTER

In this chapter we have presented the user as a cognitive system that is capable of non-rational as well as rational reasoning, supported by a mental model of particular situations which the user brings to bear in interactions with the environment. We saw how the mental model the user has of an electronic system affects the way the user approaches first encounters with the electronic system, and how the user refines that mental model on the basis of knowledge gained through the learning process. This view points to the importance of the user's memory of past events and objects in shaping present behaviour. In the next chapter, we look at the role of the user's memory in human–machine interaction in more detail, and ways in which electronic systems can be designed to be compatible with human memory processes.

Principles from the psychology of memory

PART I: WORKING MEMORY

Graham J. Hitch

This chapter begins by presenting a short analysis of the demands that are placed upon the human memory system when people use computers for such activities as writing a program, word-processing a letter, analysing data or interrogating a database. Following this, we give a brief overview of the background to current research on the psychology of human memory. An important feature of this research is a general distinction between *working* and *long-term* memory processes, the former being concerned with temporary information storage and information processing. The remainder of Part I of this chapter is devoted to a consideration of aspects of short-term or working memory that are paticularly relevant to evaluating the temporary memory demands of human–computer interaction. We conclude with some comments on the problems of trying to extract applicable 'principles' from theoretically driven psychological research. Part II discusses the longer-term aspects of human memory that relate to human–computer interaction.

MEMORY DEMANDS OF HUMAN–COMPUTER INTERACTION

In order to relate research on the psychology of human memory to the memory demands of human–computer interaction, it is useful to distinguish between remembering over short-term and long-term intervals. Information that the user has to retain for intervals of up to about a minute will be classified here as placing *temporary* demands on the human memory system. Information that has to be remembered over longer intervals will be classified as making *long-lasting* demands on memory. Since not much is known about the role of memory in human–computer interaction, the following description is based on an informal analysis of some common user tasks. It is intended to illustrate the various types of demand placed on memory but is not intended to say anything about their relative importance in practical situations, which is of course an empirical question.

Temporary demands

It may be difficult to appreciate just how much temporary information may have to be held in mind during human–computer interaction. The following examples illustrate some of the more important types of information that fall within this category.

(i)   *Temporary labels and parameters.* The user must remember the identity of any temporary labels or parameters that are relevant to his or her current activities. In word-processing, examples of such labels are the name of an unfamiliar or novel command that has just been looked up in an instruction manual, or the version number of the current file. Temporary parameters might include local alterations of line spacing, print margins and the like. Failing to remember simple items of information of this sort may lead to considerable delay and inefficiency in task execution.

(ii)   *User's current subgoal.* In many circumstances, the user's task can be thought of as involving a hierarchically arranged set of goals. For example, a user whose main goal is writing a letter may pursue subgoals of loading the appropriate software, entering the text via the keyboard, and finally printing it. These subgoals can themselves be decomposed into various subsidiary goals, and so on. From this analysis it is evident that the user must remember the hierarchy and keep track of his or her location within it in order to perform the task optimally. For routine tasks, the goal structure will be well-learned and the chief temporary memory demand will be keeping track. For less familiar tasks, remembering the goal structure itself will be a temporary memory demand.

The computer system will often supply visible reminders, such as different contexts for the different phases of a task, in which case keeping track may present few problems. When no such reminders are available, errors may be more likely. Perhaps the most familiar and incovenient errors of keeping track occur during 'housekeeping' operations upon files. In some computer systems it is remarkably easy to lose one's place in a complex sequence of file handling operations and to delete instead of saving a crucial file.

(iii)   *User's current response.* The user must keep track of current position in any sequence of responses. During typing text, for example, output might have to be monitored at a number of levels, including individual keystrokes, words and phrases. During entry of data for statistical analysis, the different levels might include the various dimensions along which the data is organized in addition to individual keystrokes. Errors of keeping track of this sort tend to result in the omission or repetition of response units.

(iv) *Current state of the computer.* The user must also keep track of changes in the state of the computer. Its state at any instant will determine what sorts of responses and operations are permissible, and may also determine the effects of individual commands. The most familiar example on small computer systems is periods of 'blank' time when the machine is busy and can only accept a restricted range of inputs. Another familiar instance is provided by systems which allow the user to switch between different modes. For example, a word-processor may have a mode for screen cursor control and a separate mode for making changes to the text. Commands entered when the system is in the inappropriate mode will not have their desired effects. In all these cases, errors will occur if the user does not monitor that current system state.

As we have noted, the machine itself often provides some 'external' memory back-up via the screen to try to minimize problems arising from forgetting temporary information. Split-screen visual displays are one of the standard arrangements whereby 'current' information is made visible at locations adjacent to, but separate from, the 'work-space' portion of the screen. However, it is seldom the case that *all* the current temporary information is made externally available in this way. For example, records of the depression of control keys, and the values of local variables during the writing of a program, are usually not available for immediate inspection. (This is especially true of electronic office systems. In other domains, such as for example digital switching systems, users are sometimes given an 'audit trail' facility, as a visible reminder of the interaction so far.) It may of course not be feasible to show certain sorts of information, such as the user's goals and intentions. An important choice confronting the system designer, therefore, is how much back-up information to make available and in what format. These decisions will have profound implications for the ease of system operation.

Long-lasting

The relatively stable memory requirements of human–computer interaction include the following, most of which are reasonably familiar and therefore do not need a great deal of elaboration.

(i) *The state of the machine the last time it was operated.* For example, it is necessary to remember the names and general contents of files or programs created during the previous user session. It is also necessary to be able to remember any configuration or hardware modifications made to the system during the previous session.

(ii)   *Files*. The user must also be able to remember the fixed set of system files and programs, so that (s)he knows what special facilities are available and how to make use of them. (S)he must also keep track of the names and contents of files created over successive user sessions. Examples of the latter are address lists, data files and correspondence.

(iii)   *Procedures*. It is of course also necessary for the user to be able to learn and remember a number of routine procedures such as switching on, logging in and initializing devices.

(iv)   *Rules*. The user must be able to learn and remember system rules, including their syntax, their conditions of use and their consequences. Standard examples are the commands for loading, copying and deleting files.

In the case of these long-lasting memory requirements the user's task is one of learning the necessary facts, rules and procedures sufficiently well that they are readily accessible when required. Crucial factors regarding the usability of a system are evidently going to be the ease of learning, the rate of forgetting, and the possibility of mutual interference from having to learn to operate similar but different computer systems.

OVERVIEW OF RESEARCH ON HUMAN MEMORY

While there is no universally accepted theoretical framework for understanding human memory, most researchers adopt a distinction between the processes responsible for short-term and longer-term retention. Such a distinction was first suggested by William James (1890) although it was largely ignored during the first half of this century, a period in which the study of memory was dominated by the behaviourist tradition (see Chapter 3). According to 'interference theory', which had its origins in theories of animal learning, human learning consisted of the formation and strengthening of associations between stimuli and responses. Conversely, forgetting was due to the weakening of such associations. This approach involved a concentration of interest in the learning and forgetting of verbal materials over relatively long periods such as hours, days and even months. It was not until the late 1950s, when novel experiments revealed circumstances in which there was rapid forgetting over intervals of only a few seconds, that an interest in short-term memory was reawakened (Brown, 1958; Peterson and Peterson, 1959).

The consequent upsurge of research on forgetting over brief intervals culminated in a number of attempts to model human memory as an information-processing system containing separate short-term and long-term memory 'stores' (Atkinson and Shiffrin, 1971; Murdock, 1967; Waugh and Norman,

1965). These models differed in various matters of detail but were agreed with regard to their major assumptions. They assumed that the short-term store had a severely limited holding capacity and that information in this store was rapidly forgotten unless maintained by active control processes. Chief among the latter was 'rehearsal', a process of recirculating material around the short-term store. The models also assumed that the short-term store acted as a gateway to the more durable long-term store, which was thought to have a virtually unlimited capacity. They assumed that the longer material remained in the short-term store, the greater the probability that it would be stored in long-term memory. Hence rehearsal was seen as serving a dual role in both maintaining material in short-term memory and causing the material to be transferred to long-term memory.

Although this 'modal' model of memory was widely accepted for a few years, problems of interpretation gradually began to accumulate (see Baddeley, 1983, for a brief summary). Some of the more important difficulties were (a) results challenging the idea that material must necessarily pass through short-term memory in order to gain access to long-term memory; (b) evidence that rehearsal did not inevitably result in increased learning; and (c) a growing lack of consensus about the coding, capacity and forgetting characteristics of the short-term store. The modal model was eventually discarded, even though none of the evidence ruled strongly against its basic proposition of separate stores.

The most influential alternative was Craik and Lockhart's (1972) proposal, which saw memory as a byproduct of perceptual processing and replaced the idea of separate stores with that of a continuum of 'levels of processing'. According to this theory, the deeper the level to which a stimulus was processed during encoding, the more durable the memory trace. (See Part II for a more detailed description of the Levels approach.) However, despite making a forthright rejection of the modal model, Craik and Lockhart nevertheless retained the idea of a separate limited capacity 'primary memory', acting as an attentional system similar to that originally discusssed by William James. Other workers have also found that the concept of some sort of short-term store remains useful, despite the inadequacy of the modal model.

It has been suggested that the modal model was rather too simplistic in its assumption of a unitary short-term memory system (see, for example, Crowder, 1982), and that instead a number of separate limited capacity systems contribute to short-term retention. These subsystems have been thought to act as a temporary 'working memory' in several aspects of human cognition (see, for example, Baddeley and Hitch, 1974; Broadbent, 1984; Monsell, 1984). The term working memory is intended to emphasize the functional characteristics of an active system for combining information processing and information storage. According to Baddeley and Hitch (1974), the working memory system comprises a general-purpose 'central executive' linked to special-purpose stores, a 'visuo-spatial scratchpad' and a speech-based 'articulatory loop'. The central executive is an attentional system responsible for a wide range of control processes which include accessing and manipulating the contents of the special-purpose stores.

The remainder of Part I of this chapter is devoted to a brief review of some of the research findings about working memory and related topics that are most relevant to understanding how the temporary memory demands of human–computer interaction load the user. Research on longer-term memory, which is more relevant to the longer-lasting memory demands of human–computer interaction, is reviewed in Part II.

We begin with sections devoted to remembering verbal and visual materials over short intervals, the first of these being an area of extensive psychological investigation. We then turn to two important topics that have been rather less well researched, the role of working memory in complex tasks, and individual differences in working memory capacity.

WORKING MEMORY

Verbal materials

Experimental studies of short-term memory processes have typically focused upon the retention of randomly ordered sequences of verbal material such as digits, letters and words over periods of up to about 30 seconds. The materials themselves are already familiar to the experimental subjects, so their task is to remember which particular items were presented. The characteristics of memory of this sort appear to depend critically upon whether or not the temporal order of presentation of the items has to be remembered: situations that are referred to as 'serial' and 'free' recall respectively (see Hitch, 1980).

Accurate *serial* recall is typically only possible for fairly short sequences of items, even when it is required immediately following presentation. The 'span' of immediate memory is a measure of the maximum length of list that can be accurately recalled. In a classic review, Miller (1956) proposed that span is more or less the same for a wide range of materials, and suggested that it corresponds to about 7 ('plus or minus 2') 'chunks'. A chunk can be defined as a unit of information forming a familiar pattern or organized according to a rule (see Zechmeister and Nyberg, 1982). Thus a verbal chunk could comprise a familiar group of letters such as 'USA' or 'BBC', or a common group of words, such as 'Secretary of State'. However, Miller was certainly making an oversimplification in his emphasis upon chunking, and subsequent research has shown that span is also limited by the rate at which material can be rehearsed.

The clearest evidence comes from studies of the effect of word length, usually manipulated by varying number of syllables. Numerous studies (see, for example, Baddeley, Thomson and Buchanan, 1975) have shown that words that take longer to articulate are remembered less well than shorter ones. Furthermore, it has been shown that there is a quantitative relationship between the time taken to articulate the words and how many can be recalled: people appear to be able to recall, in the correct serial order, about as many words as they can articulate in 1 to 1.5 seconds. Baddeley and Hitch (1974) suggested that a limited capacity, time-based *articulatory loop* subsystem of working memory was responsible for the word length effect. This subsystem was also thought to be the basis for the phonemic similarity effect, the finding that words or letters which sound alike are typically much more poorly recalled (see, for example, Conrad, 1964; Baddeley, 1968). A key piece of evidence here was the finding that when people are prevented from rehearsal by repeating an irrelevant word during the memory task, recall is made not only poorer but also insensitive to phonemic similarity and word length (see overview by Baddeley, 1983). The word length and phonemic similarity effects are found independently of whether material is presented visually or auditorily.

The chunking and articulatory loop hypotheses obviously represent two contrasting views of the limitation on memory span. Some interesting light is shed on them by Simon (1974) who found that span is equal to a fixed number of chunks only when the chunks are rather small (specifically, one- or two-syllable words). For larger-sized chunks, such as three-syllable words or phrases, span measured as number of chunks was rather lower. Similar results have been found in experiments on Chinese-speaking people using Chinese characters as stimuli, showing that the phenomenon has considerable generality (Yu *et al.*, 1985). It seems therefore that both chunking and articulation contribute to the limit on span. Zhang and Simon (1985) have suggested that retrieving chunks and articulating them are processes which each occupy the same time-based memory system of limited duration. An alternative hypothesis is that the two processes reflect separate limited capacity systems in working memory. On this view, chunking is attributed to the 'central executive' attentional component of working memory (Baddeley and Hitch, 1974; see also the 'abstract working memory' in Broadbent's 1984 Maltese Cross model), while word length effects are attributed to the more peripheral articulatory loop. Support for this second interpretation comes from studies showing that disrupting the loop by requiring irrelevant articulation does not interfere with chunking (Broadbent and Broadbent, 1981a; Chase and Ericsson, 1982).

To sum up, we have only a very limited capacity for remembering the order of a sequence of verbal materials. The nature of the materials exerts important effects such that recall will benefit if they can be organized into meaningful or familiar 'chunks' or if they can be rapidly rehearsed.

The foregoing limitations describe *immediate* serial recall only. A delay before recall of even just a few seconds may worsen performance by permitting rapid forgetting to take place. The standard laboratory technique for investigating this is the Brown–Peterson paradigm where the experimental subject is presented with a subspan sequence and then attempts recall after a variable retention interval spent performing an attention-demanding task such as counting backwards by threes from a given number. The basic findings from such studies are as follows:

(i)   there is rapid forgetting over intervals of up to about 20 seconds, after which retention is at a poor but stable asymptotic level (Brown, J., 1958; Peterson and Peterson, 1959);

(ii) 'proactive interference' (PI) from having recently remembered similar materials is an important contributor to such forgetting (Keppel and Underwood, 1962). However, switching between different categories of materials can give 'release' from proactive interference (Wickens, 1970);

(iii) the more material there is to be remembered, in terms of number of chunks, the more rapidly it is forgotten (see Melton, 1963);

(iv) the more demanding the interpolated task the more rapid the forgetting (Posner and Rossman, 1965); with no task there is very little or no forgetting.

(v)   there is no fixed 'decay rate' at which material is forgotten, indeed there is controversy as to whether a temporal decay process can be implicated in Brown–Peterson forgetting (see Baddeley, 1976).

To sum up, it appears that rapid forgetting can be alleviated if a person is either (a) relatively free to continue to rehearse subvocally the memory materials, or (b) free from effects of proactive interference from recent exposure to the same materials.

When recall of serial order is not required and subjects have to remember only what items have been presented, results follow a slightly different pattern. The laboratory task that has been most thoroughly investigated is that of free recall, where typically a fairly long list of words is presented. The usual finding is that in immediate free recall there is a well-defined recency effect such that the final two to three items are recalled much better than earlier items (see, for example, Glanzer, 1972). As in immediate serial recall, the memory system appears to store 'chunks' rather than single words (see Glanzer and Razel, 1974) and displays rapid forgetting. Delaying recall by only a few seconds of attention-demanding activity leads to a selective loss of the recency effect. However, in contrast to immediate serial recall, recency does not appear to be dependent upon active rehearsal processes. The phonological characteristics of the materials are not important and neither articulatory suppression nor more attention-demanding concurrent activities appear to have much influence on the size of the recency effect (see, for example, Hitch, 1980, for a summary). This conclusion is confirmed by the finding that the recency effect occurs in incidental learning (Baddeley and Hitch, 1977). It appears that memory for the identity of recently presented items depends on a passive aspect of working memory which is independent of active control processes.

To sum up, when order is not important, there appears to be good memory for the most recent two to three verbal items provided that recall is fairly immediate. This recall ability does not depend upon the subject engaging in active rehearsal processes and presumably reflects the operation of some sort of passive store.

Visual materials

Research within the working memory framework has tended to concentrate on visual imagery and its sensitivity to interference from various sorts of concurrent task as a method for investigating the characteristics of the visuo-spatial scratchpad subsystem (see Baddeley, 1983). The usual method has involved having people construct mental images to represent the content of oral messages. Although theoretically interesting, this work may be of less direct relevance to human–computer interaction than studies of short-term memory for visual materials. Accordingly, the present discussion will focus on the latter, even though the links with the concept of working memory are not well developed.

The simplest case to consider is memory for meaningless visual stimuli such as random checkerboard patterns (see, for example, Phillips, 1974) or abstract designs (Broadbent and Broadbent, 1981b). Here, it is argued, memory is unlikely to be contaminated by effects of verbal labelling or recoding of the patterns. Experiments by Phillips and his co-workers (reviewed by Phillips, 1983) have led to the following conclusions:

(i) subjects can maintain the detailed appearance of a single pattern for several seconds without loss of information;

(ii) such maintenance appears to involve an active rehearsal process, termed 'visualization' by Phillips;

(iii) there is an upper limit on the complexity of patterns that can be visualized in this way. For matrix patterns this limit is of the order of 30 cells (L. Wilson, unpublished data);

(iv) visualization is disrupted by the presence of an interfering task during the retention interval. In order to interfere, such tasks need to involve a high attentional load: they need not involve the processing of visual information. Indeed, merely looking at a further visual pattern or making a predictable sequence of eye movements does not disrupt visualization.

Broadbent and Broadbent's (1981b) data differ slightly from those obtained with checkerboard patterns. In the case of abstract designs it appears that visualization, as indexed by the size of the recency effect in memory for a series of patterns, is not restricted to a single design. However, despite this discrepancy the overall balance of evidence appears to weigh in favour of a very limited ability to remember meaningless, purely visual information over short intervals.

When realistic pictures are used as materials, recency may not be observed (Shaffer and Shiffrin, 1972), suggesting that they behave rather differently from abstract patterns. A particularly interesting comparison has been made between short-term memory for pictures of familiar objects and for the written names of the objects (Schiano and Watkins, 1981). It was found that phonological characteristics of the object names, such as their phonemic similarity to one another and their length, had comparable effects on recall whether the material was presented as pictures or words. This suggests that verbal labels for the pictures are stored in the articulatory rehearsal loop subsystem described earlier. However, pictures were also consistently better recalled than words, in agreement with a general finding obtained across a broad range of long-term memory tasks.

This general advantage to picture presentation has been interpreted by Paivio (1971) in terms of his highly influential 'dual-coding hypothesis'. According to this view, memory comprises two functionally independent symbolic systems, one specializing in imaginal coding and dealing primarily with perceptual information, the other specializing in verbal coding and dealing with linguistic information. It is assumed that readily nameable pictures and their written names each activate both types of code, but that there is an asymmetry such that verbal codes for the pictures are more available than imaginal codes for their names. Superior memory for pictures is explained by assuming either that they are encoded with greater redundancy in the two systems or that imaginal codes are intrinsically more memorable than their verbal counterparts. Paivio's hypothesis can be readily extended to working memory tasks, where the two coding systems would presumably correspond to the verbal articulatory loop and the visuo-spatial scratchpad.

It seems then that our ability to remember the appearance of novel, unorganized visual patterns over the short-term is extremely limited. On the other hand, our ability to remember the identity of a concrete item is better when it is presented as a picture than as a printed word.

Working memory and information processing

The term working memory is intendend to emphasize the role of short-term storage systems in complex information-processing tasks. The following brief overview will focus on principal empirical findings with a minimum of theoretical interpretation.

It is assumed that in complex tasks, the working memory system stores knowledge states activated from long-term memory and the results of intermediate computations, in addition to recent inputs from the environment (cf. Chase and Ericsson, 1982). Working memory is also thought to act as an attentional system responsible for the execution of general-purpose control processes (see, for example, Hitch, 1980). The range of tasks in which the use of working memory has been studied experimentally is broad, and includes reading (Baddeley and Lewis, 1982), performing arithmetic (Hitch, 1978) and solving verbal reasoning problems (Hitch and Baddeley, 1976).

A major conclusion from the study of such tasks is the importance of capacity limitations in working memory. In the standard way of exploring this, subjects are asked to perform a short-term storage task such as digit span whilst attempting to carry out a separate, complex task. The general conclusion from such studies is that there is very little interference with performance of the complex task when the additional storage load is well below span, but that there is clear and measurable disruption when the additional load approaches span (see, for example, Baddeley and Hitch, 1974). Where it has been possible to vary the level of difficulty of the complex task, it has been found that the interfering effect of an additional memory load is greater the more difficult the task (see, for example, Hitch and Baddeley, 1976). Similar interactions between concurrent storage load and processing speed have been reported in complex tasks where the temporary storage load is intrinsic to the task rather than extrinsic. Such tasks have included mental artithmetic (White, unpublished data) and an alphabet transformation task (Hamilton, Hockey and Rejman, 1977). In the latter, subjects were asked to 'transform' a letter by counting a specific number of steps through the alphabet (for example, 'J + 4' gives the result 'N'). Storage load was manipulated by giving subjects a series of such transformations to carry out and asking them to report the results only when they had finished all of them. In this way the number of results that had to be held in mind whilst carrying out any given transformation could be varied. It was found that the greater the storage load, the slower the rate at which transformations could be performed.

It appears that the source of interference in these situations is at a fairly high level within the working memory system, such as the central executive, and that subspan storage loads can be delegated to special-purpose subsystems such as the articulatory loop. Consistent with this interpretation, concurrent articulation gives rise to little or no interference with complex tasks such as reading (Baddeley, Eldridge and Lewis, 1981) and verbal reasoning (Hitch and Baddeley, 1976).

Research on the involvement of working memory in the retrieval of information from long-term memory has yielded some interesting and surprising results. In a series of studies, Baddeley *et al.* (1984) found that a demanding concurrent task had very little effect on the probability of recalling an item stored in long-term memory, although the latency of retrieval was increased. The same tasks had a large disruptive effect on learning, however. Baddeley *et al.* interpreted the effect on latencies in terms of response factors and make the interesting suggestion that memory search is an automatic process. If so, it would seem that although the working memory system is thought to store information retrieved from long-term memory, its capacity is nevertheless untaxed by searching for that information.

Interesting further clues about the functioning of the central executive have come from studies of errors in the performance of routine tasks. In one set of studies (see Rabbitt, 1981), experimental subjects were first given extensive practice at typing various letter sequences until they reached a criterion of a few hundred flawless reproductions. In some of the sequences the letters were all different while in others there were occasional repeated items. The latter can be thought of as involving 'loops' in an otherwise linear chain of actions. In the next phase of the experiment subjects attempted to type these highly practised sequences under the distraction of simultaneously counting backwards by sevens. Distraction was effective in inducing typing errors, and was particularly disruptive in the case of sequences containing repeated items. Furthermore the nature of the repeat structure turned out to be important. Sequences containing nested loops were more vulnerable to distraction effects than those containing only single loops. Rabbitt suggested that performing routine sequential tasks involves active control processes which continually cross-check between a temporary memory record of the most recent actions and a permanent memory record of the whole sequence. The latter may be regarded as the 'program' or 'plan' for the action sequence. The role of cross-checking is to keep track of progress in relation to the plan. Such checking is evidently more elaborate for plans with a complex structure and is presumably more susceptible to effects of distraction because of the limited capacity of the central executive.

A similar analysis has been proposed by Nairne and Healy (1983) to account for omission errors in the routine task of counting backwards from the number 100 in ones. Though rare, omissions are non-randomly distributed and tend to occur on numbers containing repeats (99, 88, etc.) and on multiples of ten (90, 80, etc.). Nairne and Healy argued that people keep track of their progress by paying special attention to a representation of the second digit in working memory. This representation is checked immediately prior to emitting a response to verify that the response has not yet been made. Nairne and Healy go on to suggest that numbers with repeated digits cause problems because 'activation' from the first digit may give a false signal that the response has already been emitted. A similar argument is advanced to account for the tendency to omit multiples of ten. Within the Baddeley and Hitch (1974) theory of working memory one might suppose that a subsystem such as the articulatory loop could keep the temporary record of recently executed responses that is checked by the executive. However, in a written version of the counting task Healy and Nairne (1985) showed that omissions were unaffected by irrelevant articulation, suggesting that the monitoring process is located entirely within the central executive.

Another way of studying the control of routine behaviour is to ask people to report on slips of action in their everyday lives (Reason, 1984a). An interesting finding here is that slips tend to occur when the subject reports being distracted, either by some external event or by a persistent train of thought. This would be consistent with the suggestion that the central executive performs a critical monitoring function in such activities.

Some years previously, Miller, Galanter and Pribram (1960) wrote of the importance of a working memory system for the execution of plans. They suggested that plans have a hierarchical structure, with the lowest levels corresponding to the smallest units of behaviour, such as muscle twitches, and the highest corresponding to much larger units, such as goals (for example, 'perform task X'). Working memory was seen as holding the parts of any plan or plans currently being executed. By this means, if one plan was interrupted by the requirements of another, there would be a record enabling its execution to be resumed when the interruption was over. Such an idea is highly relevant to our discussion of the experimental work of Rabbitt (1981) and Nairne and Healy (1983), though there are of course numerous questions that remain to be answered.

To sum up, it seems that the limited capacity central executive may play an important role in a very wide range of complex tasks. Overloading this system in any of a variety of ways is likely to cause errors of task execution, even when the task itself is familiar and routine.

Individual differences in working memory

Given the modularity of the working memory system, it follows that individual differences in the capacities of the various subsystems may be independent of one another. In contrast, measures of individual differences thought to be related to the same subsystem ought to be strongly correlated. Testing expectations of this kind is therefore a potentially valuable way of assessing ideas about the structure of working memory. Although this approach has yet to be fully explored, the existing evidence is consistent with the general viewpoint expressed by Baddeley and Hitch (1974). For example, Baddeley, Thomson and Buchanan (1975) reported a correlation between individuals' immediate serial recall of verbal materials and their speech rate, as one might expect given the involvement of a time-based articulatory loop. On the other hand, there appears to be a lack of correlation between individual differences in memory span and the size of the recency effect in free recall (Byrne and Arnold, 1981; Martin, 1978), suggesting a dissociation between the underlying memory processes. This is inconsistent with the concept of a unitary short-term store as in the modal model, but fully in agreement with the distinction between the articulatory loop and the system responsible for recency (Hitch, 1980).

The study of individual differences may also draw attention to important variables that might otherwise be missed. One particularly interesting example is given by Chase and Ericsson's (1982) studies of the effects of practice on digit span. It will be recalled that the average span for the normal population is about seven items. Chase and Ericsson found that after giving extended practice for some 200–300 hours, one of their subjects attained the enormous span of 82 digits and the other recorded a no less impressive span of 68 digits. The subjects were found to make use of complex recoding schemes in order to achieve these phenomenally high scores, for example 3492 = '3m. 49.2s, a near world-record mile time', 1943 = 'near the end of World War II'. They each had a rich store of knowledge about running since they were experienced athletes, and it appeared to be their ability to translate numbers into a variety of running times that played an important role. Chase and Ericsson concluded that an extensive knowledge base is an important component of skill in memory span. Their study also points to the importance of developing a 'retrieval structure' for indexing material in long-term memory. In the case of their two experts, these structures were hierarchies comprising digits, groups of digits, 'supergroups' of groups and clusters of supergroups. Interestingly, the size of each of these types of set was just three or four elements. The usefulness of grouping by threes as a general strategy for improving short-term recall has been known for some time (see, for example, Ryan, 1969). Chase and Ericsson's results suggest that this surprisingly low limit on optimal group size continues to apply even in highly practised subjects exhibiting very high spans, suggesting that it reflects a fundamental capacity limitation. Furthermore, despite their very high digit spans, the *letter* spans of both Chase and Ericsson's subjects were well within the normal range. There was no transfer across materials. This finding confirms the fundamental nature of the capacity limitation underlying span and it draws attention to the possible 'domain-specificity' of individual difference measures.

A related point emerges from Daneman and Carpenter's (1980) investigation of individual differences in working memory capacity and reading ability. They developed a reading span test in which subjects read aloud a series of sentences and then at the end of the series attempted to recall the final word from each sentence. Reading span was a measure of how many words could be recalled in this task. Daneman and Carpenter found that reading span was a much better predictor of performance on various tests of reading comprehension than the standard digit or word span. They argue that reading span combines the information-processing demands of comprehension with information storage and is a much better measure of working memory capacity than storage-only tasks like traditional memory span. It may also be, however, that reading span taps knowledge and procedures specific to the domain of reading that are not captured by traditional span measures.

A final point of some interest here concerns individual differences in state anxiety and working memory. Eysenck (1983) reports studies of the effect of anxiety on performance on the verbal reasoning task used by Hitch and Baddeley (1976). Anxiety interacted with difficulty of the reasoning task, such that it was most detrimental for the most difficult problems. Eysenck reports a similar pattern of results for the alphabet transformation task used by Hamilton,

Hockey and Rejman (1977; see also earlier). Here, there was no effect of anxiety on the speed of simple transformations, but a tendency for highly anxious subjects to do worse on more complex transformations. Thus it seems that anxiety may be associated with a reduction is some aspect of working memory capacity.

In summary, we have emphasized three major points about individual differences and working memory. Firstly, such differences can occur in the separate components of the working memory system. Secondly, although the capacities of the various subsystems appear to reflect fundamental limitations, domain-specific factors associated with skill and knowledge can exert an important influence on an individual's performance in any particular context. Finally, there is some evidence for a link betwen anxiety and the functioning of working memory.

CONCLUDING COMMENTS

Though it is possible to collate together summary 'principles' of the key findings reported here — and indeed such principles are listed at the end of the chapter — it is important to note that this does not mean that the researchers have answered all the important questions and that no serious problems are presented in applying them to practical examples of human–computer interaction. Therefore, in addition to listing specific points, we shall look back in a general way at what is known about the human working memory system in relation to the temporary memory demands of human–computer interaction. A number of interesting points emerge from attempting to do this which may be used to qualify the summary principles presented.

First, it is clear that there is not very good agreement between the questions addressed by psychologists interested in short-term memory and information processing and those posed by human–computer interaction. Thus the early days of research interest in short-term memory were dominated by the study of recalling random sequences of verbal materials. Consequently we know a good deal about human performance in these situations. Although this knowledge is applicable to the temporary memory demands of remembering labels, command sequences and parameter values in human–computer interaction, we have seen that these constitute only a part of the user's total load. Indeed, if our analysis is correct, then a key problem for the user during human–computer interaction is keeping track of the multiple streams of information that must be constantly updated, such as the user's goals, the user's actions and the states of the computer system.

Ideas about working memory as a system for combining general control processes with special-purpose subsystems are evidently highly relevant to multiple monitoring and updating. However, it is not an easy matter to see when and how to apply these ideas to a specific user–system interface. This difficulty is in part a problem of complexity, since theoretically driven research tends to seek out simple paradigms which appear to focus successfully on a single psychological process. Thus laboratory investigations of the allocation of working memory capacity tend to make use of dual-task performance rather than examining multi-task situations. Generalizing from the former to the latter is not necessarily a straightforward matter. Laboratory studies on monitoring in the execution of skilled behaviour have also emphasized relatively simple skills, again making generalization difficult. Another problem of applicability is connected with the question of 'domain-specificity' (cf. earlier). We have seen that it is unsafe to base predictions of a person's performance on a task involving working memory on a measure of working memory capacity in a different domain. It appears that factors such as individual skill and knowledge can make enormous differences to performance, even though the basic capacities of the working memory system appear to remain unaltered. For any computer system, therefore, the effective demands on working memory will be a joint function of the system itself and the skill and knowledge of the individual user, not a function of the system alone. (An interesting practical point here is that the relative demands of two systems could conceivably reverse as a function of practice. See also Chapter 6 for a more comprehensive discussion of the effects of practice on performance.) A final point about applicability concerns the difficulty of identifying the key variables in a multifactor practical situation. It is always a non-trivial matter to make an appropriate task analysis and to map from this to the demands on the user.

Taken together these problems are considerable, and they underline the danger inherent in looking into *any* aspect of psychology in the search for instant solutions to practical problems. What seems crucial is that empirical research should be carried out on the practical problems themselves to assess the relevance and applicability of ideas and investigative techniques drawn from the psychological research literature. Such a strategy should not only minimize the dangers of overgeneralizing from laboratory paradigms but should also act as a force for the development of research that is directly relevant to practical questions. The present chapter has drawn attention to aspects of research on working memory which could benefit in just this way.

PART II: EPISODIC AND SEMANTIC MEMORY

Margaret M. Gardiner

In this second half of the chapter, we address longer-term memory phenomena, and discuss their potential relevance to the problems of user-interface design. The focus is on outlining the capabilities and limitations of the human memory system which are to do with the way users remember events that happened in their experience, and organize their stores of 'knowledge'. In a way, this section provides a more 'static' view of memory than the preceding discussion. If working memory draws on information stored in long-term memory, and utilizes this information to satisfy the requirements of the task at hand, then this section can be seen to provide the theoretical background to the way such information is stored and organized after acquisition. The constraints of domain-dependence and context-sensitivity apply here as much as they do in research on working memory. The intention is to provide possible suggestions which the human–computer interaction research fraternity may wish to take further, in the context of the complex and real-life problems of interface design.

INTRODUCTION

The distinction between 'episodic' and 'semantic' memory was coined by Endel Tulving (see, for example, 1972, 1983). It is based on the fact that in most traditional memory experiments and, by generalization, most memory phenomena, people are not really learning and then remembering words, sentences, stories or pictures, but rather remembering that in a certain situation a word, sentence, story or picture which they knew, and had encountered many times before, was presented for their attention. They are thus remembering the 'episode' associated with that item's presentation. Hence episodic memory is 'autobiographical' since it contains information about different *episodes* in a person's life. Semantic memory, on the other hand, contains what is commonly known as 'knowledge': information about the meanings of words, their interrelation, etc. Obviously, at some time the information stored in semantic memory will have been contained in episodic memory. How the latter comes to contribute to the former is not, however, dealt with explicitly in Tulving's work. (Chapter 4 provides some insights into some of the theories that have emerged to explain how knowledge is acquired, but to date no really systematic effort appears to have been expended on linking together these two specialty areas of cognitive psychology.)

Proposing these two types of memory does not necessarily mean that more than one memory 'system' is involved in a person's normal interaction with his or her environment. The question of whether memory can be conceptualized as a single system or as several different systems, with different characteristics and 'responsibilities' is currently attracting a considerable amount of interest in the field (see, for example, Tulving, 1985, for a comprehensive discussion). Until a clearer, more stable view of the area emerges out of the current debate, however, it may be counterproductive to try to find direct application for these very recent research findings. The rest of the chapter will concentrate on mapping out other, more established, though none the less important findings which may in the future come to be subsumed under or modified by further developments in the single/multiple memory system debate.

SOME GENERAL THEORIES OF EPISODIC MEMORY

Broadly speaking, general theories of episodic memory have concentrated either on the features of the *encoding* (learning or 'storage') of information into memory, or its *retrieval* from memory. There are also theories which consider both encoding and retrieval.

Encoding theories

Possibly the best known and best documented encoding theory of memory is Craik and Lockhart's (1972) levels-of-processing approach. This states that one of the most important determinants of the probability of remembering an item one has stored in memory is the 'work' or 'processing' one performs on that stimulus at the time of entering it into memory. Items can be processed at a 'shallow' level, or at progressively deeper levels of processing, and recall probability is assumed to increase as a direct function of depth of processing. So, for instance, checking whether there are two 'e's in 'sweet' would be a shallow level of processing, if that is all one does in order to learn that 'sweet' is a word one needs to remember. Learning that same word after deciding that it refers to something nice and tasty, and applies to things like chocolate, sugar, etc., would be processing it at a deeper level. The theory would predict that the second set of learning activities ('encoding operations') would lead to better recall of 'sweet' at a later stage. Like most theories in most fields of science, the levels-of-processing approach has not met with unqualified approval from all concerned. Later versions of the approach have added to its original formulation the notion that depth of processing as a determinant of recall needs to be complemented by 'elaboration' of processing as well. Elaborative processing refers more to the *amount* of processing done at encoding than to the level associated with it. Hence for a given level of processing there may be more than one level of elaboration. Consider for instance an experiment by Craik and Tulving (1975), which was used by these authors to propose the notion of elaborative processing. Craik and Tulving asked their subjects whether a particular word — 'watch' — made sense when it was embedded in a variety of sentences such as

He dropped the ——

and

The old man hobbled across the room and picked up the valuable —— from the mahogany table.

After a series of such sentences, using a variety of stimulus words, the subjects were given an unexpected recall test for the words they had had to consider. On average, words that had been embedded in longer, more elaborate sentences were better recalled, even though the task ('does this word make sense in this context?') always required semantic, deep processing from the subjects. The experiment thus shows that at the same depth of processing recall for words for which elaborative encoding was required exceeded recall for words encoded in less elaborative contexts.

The findings of experiments within the framework of the levels-of-processing approach suggest that in order to maximize the probability that the user will retain a reasonably good memory of a particular event, for example, the action of filing a particular item in an electronic system, the encoding context should force the user to process deeply and elaboratively the actions or the keywords involved in the storage process. This needs, of course, to take into account the fact that people normally try to 'get away' with the minimum of work for a particular task. Hence dialogue design needs to ensure that deep and elaborative processing does not impose on the user such an additional load that the user bypasses features of the system that are meant to increase his or her productivity. Form-filling, direct manipulation of objects on screen, and avoidance of complex command sequences all help with reducing the load imposed on the user.

Retrieval theories

While the levels-of-processing approach concentrates on the factors associated with the *storage* of an item and, in that respect, puts the blame for forgetting on factors pertaining to the particular representation or *trace* stored, there are other theories that argue that remembering depends critically on the operations that go on at the retrieval stage and which are to do with search prompts, or cues, people use to help them remember. Formally, because these latter theories attribute forgetting to the failure of retrieval prompts or cues, they are lumped together under the generic name of 'cue-dependent forgetting' theories, to contrast them with theories similar to the Levels approach, often known as trace-dependent forgetting theories. We shall consider two different versions of cue-dependent forgetting. For convenience, these will be referred to as the 'inaccessibility hypothesis' and the 'cue-overload hypothesis'.

The inaccessibility hypothesis

This version of the cue-dependent forgetting notion was initially proposed by Tulving (see, for example, Tulving and Madigan, 1970; Tulving and Psotka, 1971; Tulving, 1974) who, indeed, also coined the phrase 'cue-dependent forgetting'. Briefly, the inaccessibility hypothesis states that what is commonly known as 'forgetting' does not, in fact, mean that information is lost from memory, but simply that the retrieval environment, that is, the prompts involved in the recall process, or present at the time the information needs to be retrieved, are not good enough to gain *access* to it.

Tulving and colleagues demonstrated that even in well-researched memory paradigms traditionally used to support theories which attribute forgetting to a loss of stored information, recall could be dramatically improved when the subjects were given at the time of recall fresh prompts, or cues, which were strongly associated with the items they had previously been unable to recall. A typical experiment of this kind (for, example, Tulving and Pearlstone, 1966) involved presenting the subjects with rather long lists of words, representing several categories (for example, names of vegetables, of fruit, of animals). After learning the list, the subjects tried to write down as many words from it as they could, and typically remembered only a very small proportion of the words presented. That is, their recall was poor unless they had been given a list of the category names present in the list, before they started recall. If they had been prompted with these category labels, they were able to recall a considerable proportion of the words in the list. It was also found that the increase in recall with prompting was due to the fact that the prompted subjects recalled at least some words from *every* category, whereas the subjects who received no prompts left out some categories altogether. The difference in the number of words recalled, per category, between the two groups was very small. Tulving and Pearlstone's experiment thus demonstrated that information is not *lost* from memory, rather, it needs to have the right kind of environment or context in order to be retrieved.

Since Tulving and Pearlstone's study, many more studies have supported their conclusions and elaborated on them, until in the 1970s Tulving and Thomson (1973) proposed what came to be known as the Encoding Specificity Principle. This states that in order to be useful for recall (that is, in order to help a person remember a past event) a recall cue (or prompt, such as a category name) must have been linked to the information that person is trying to retrieve *at the time that information was stored*. In simpler terms, if a person 'stored away' in memory the word JAM, in connection with the fact that (s)he needed to buy some JAM before going home (so that presumably that word was stored in association with the prompts 'shopping', or 'strawberry' or 'raspberry', etc.) then sitting in a traffic JAM, or knowing that someone is in a JAM, is not going to help him or her remember to pop into the local supermarket and buy JAM. Only those words, or ideas, that were in that person's mind at the time (s)he made a mental note to buy JAM before going home will help in remembering to do so. This has, in fact, been verified experimentally under somewhat less arbitrary circumstances.

Note, too that even though in the Tulving and Pearlstone study providing the category names at recall increased the number of *categories* from which items could be remembered, it had no significant effect on the *numbers* of items from each category the subjects were able to recall. In other words, in the presence *or* absence of the category names, subjects still could only recall a certain, fixed number of category members. This led Tulving to suggest that what prompting recall does is to facilitate access not so much to the words themselves as to the higher-order units (category names, etc.) in which these words belong. Again, this conclusion has been substantiated by the available evidence, most of which is based on experiments which used categorized lists, or organized materials.

To summarize, then, it has been shown that information retrieval is facilitated (a) if at the time information is being retrieved at least part of the context in which it was stored is reinstated; (b) if there are known 'prompts' or cues for recall that refer to and organize the information stored, which can be presented to the information seeker at the time of retrieval. These features of the human memory system suggest that interface design could benefit from capitalizing on the ease with which people can use regularities and categorizations. This can be reflected in a number of different features of interfaces, such as, for example, the appropriate selection of the constituents of given menus (the 'categories' which are used in the dialogue), the naming of such menus at all times (the 'category labels'), the formatting of screens of information to facilitate chunking together of items of information which should be considered as related, the definition of which items should be on which screens, so as to adequately focus the user's attention and ensure that relationships that exist amongst items are perceived as such, and so on. Observance of these design features can then aid in the important task of allowing the user to build, gradually, a 'picture' of what the system can do and how it does it which, in turn, will facilitate using the system to maximum advantage.

The cue-overload hypothesis

The cue-overload hypothesis is also an example of cue-dependent forgetting, and it specifies in more detail the relationship between the prompts used for recall and the probability of retrieving an item. It will be remembered that in the Tulving and Pearlstone (1966) experiment reported earlier, there seemed to be a set number of items per category that the subjects could recall, and that prompting only improved recall by enabling the subjects to recall more *categories* rather than more words per category. Cue-overload theory attempts to specify why this is so.

The original version of the cue-overload hypothesis was proposed by M.J. Watkins and O.C. Watkins, in a series of papers spanning the six years between 1975 and 1981 (see, for example, Watkins, 1979; Watkins and Watkins, 1975, 1976; Todres and Watkins, 1981). Like Tulving, Watkins and Watkins argue that all recall, or information retrieval, is mediated by cues or prompts, but they add that these prompts have a limited capacity and tend to become 'overloaded' as they come to refer to more and more items. When they are overloaded, they become less effective for retrieval. Hence the probability of recalling a set of items associated with the same prompt is said to be an inverse and monotonic function of the number of items in the set. This view of retrieval has received a fair amount of support in the literature. It can, for instance, fully explain the Tulving and Pearlstone (1966) results. These showed that number of items recalled per category was constant, but that some categories were not recalled at all unless they were prompted with their names at recall. Consider first the constancy of category exemplars recalled. The lists presented to the subjects for study were made up of *equal numbers* of items per category, and items were presented blocked by category, preceded by the appropriate category name. It is therefore more than likely that the appropriate category name was associated with each block of items, and that at recall, irrespective of whether the name was re-presented or not, subjects used those category names to retrieve list items (for example, they thought to themselves 'there were some names of vegetables, which were they?', etc.). For each separate category, however, the number of items presented was constant, and so, therefore, was the load on the category prompt, or cue, used to retrieve them. So recall level was very similar across categories.

We then have to consider the 'loss' of recall for some categories, for the subjects who did not receive any prompts at recall. It is reasonable to assume that the subjects knew that in the *list* there were several categories. 'List' then becomes the prompt for the names of the categories presented at study. Since it is a prompt, or cue, 'list' can also be overloaded — so that if there are many category names in the list, the 'list' prompt is not going to be able to retrieve them all. Obviously, presenting the category names at recall to the 'prompted' subjects, will eliminate any overload problems on the 'list' cue; subjects do not have to use the 'list' cue to retrieve any of the category names, so it does not matter whether it is overloaded or not.

The cue-overload hypothesis has not been specified beyond this level. In other words, not much is known about exactly how many items need to be subsumed under a cue before recall probability falls by a certain amount, or, indeed, whether all cues suffer similar degrees of overload from any given number of items. There are suggestions (for example, Gardiner, 1983) that the more similar the items being retrieved by a given cue, the higher the probability is of retrieving those items, even by an overloaded cue; but at very high degrees of similarity (where the differences among items subsumed by a given prompt are minimal) other factors come into play which may affect recall. For instance, if a group of items has a very high degree of inter-item similarity, it becomes very hard to *differentiate* between items, and recall will suffer. Similarity in this case was defined in terms of the 'family resemblance' among the items the subjects had to remember, and was quantified using appropriate norms of 'family resemblance'. (The notion of family resemblance is dicussed further later on in this chapter, as a possible organizing principle of semantic memory, and is also addressed in Chapter 7 in the context of language.)

The notion of differences in item 'distinctiveness' due to similarity has been well researched by Craik and Jacoby (1979; see also Cermak and Craik, 1978; and Lockhart, Craik and Jacoby, 1976). The basic assumption is that the more distinctive an item is, in memory, the greater the probability of recall (it stands out among other contents of memory). Distinctiveness is a *relational* measure; that is, it applies to the perceived similarity between an item and all the other items stored together with it in memory. While the original formulation of the distinctiveness idea was put forward in the context of the levels-of-processing approach (where distinctiveness was seen as a consequence of depth and elaboration of encoding), there are no strong reasons why it cannot apply pretty much across the board, irrespective of theoretical orientation. Also, as will be seen in the next section, the distinction between encoding (for example, levels-of-processing) and retrieval (for example, cue-dependent forgetting) views of memory has now been eroded and both processes are now believed to be largely interdependent.

To summarize, then, the main message this section conveys is that though people are highly efficient at organizing information for storage in memory, and at using knowledge about that organization (for example, cues or prompts referring to category names, etc.) for *retrieving* that information, there are relatively rigid limits to the number of items, of any kind, that can be successfully retrieved at any one time. Similarity among the items to be retrieved, though it can improve recall by reducing the effects of 'overload', also brings with it other factors which may have the antagonistic effect of *impairing* accurate recall. This suggests, amongst other things, that care should be taken when assigning names to specific tasks, functions or procedures within a system, so that they are sufficiently similar (in the sense of having a 'family resemblance', rather than similar names) for it to be possible to chunk together items relating to the same task, but not so similar that it becomes very hard to tell the different items apart, and causing them to compete with each other for retrieval.

The interdependence of encoding and retrieval

That encoding and retrieval are closely linked has already been hinted at both in the section about the inaccessibility hypothesis and in the latter part of the discussion about the cue-overload hypothesis. Current thinking does favour a view of memory that emphasizes the interdependence of the two stages of information processing. It is possible, for instance, to conceive of the three approaches outlined so far — levels of processing, inaccessibility hypothesis and cue-overloaded hypothesis — as component elements of one single global theory to do with the encoding, storage and retrieval of information. This section will now consider this global approach in more detail.

The changing face of the levels-of-processing approach

Lockhart, Craik and Jacoby (1976) proposed a different version of the levels-of-processing approach, intended to broaden its scope in terms of the types of experimental data to which it could apply, and to bring it more into line with the then emerging (now prevailing) view that encoding or retrieval theories alone cannot fully account for the wide variety of memory data accumulated over the years.

This new version also draws heavily on the distinction proposed by Tulving (1972, 1983) about two kinds of memory which was discussed at the beginning of this section: episodic and semantic memory. The 'new look' levels-of-processing approach argues that there are differences in the way people retrieve information, depending on the *length of time* that is allowed to elapse between putting information in memory and trying to retrieve it.

According to the theory, if the information one is trying to retrieve is very recent, for instance was encountered within the last 20–30 seconds or so, then retrieval is done by quickly scanning through recent events stored in episodic memory, using any known information about what is being searched for as a means of discriminating, or selecting, among recent traces. An example will help clarify this process. Consider the situation where a subject has been told to try to retrieve a particular word, recently presented. (S)he is further told that the word (s)he is looking for rhymes with TRAIN. The expanded version of the Levels aproach suggests that what the subject does is to simply scan backwards through recently stored information until (s)he hits upon an item that rhymes with TRAIN. (S)he will then produce that item. The theory also proposes that for this kind of retrieval, where information is very recent, the level, or depth at which the information was originally processed does not really matter, so long as there is some information at the time of retrieval which the subject can use as a selection device while scanning.

Retrieval of information which has been stored for a longer time proceeds along different pathways. According to the new version of the Levels approach, this type of retrieval is a fully interactive process of *reconstructing* the environment in which an item was encountered. In order to achieve this, stored information and retrieval information go through successive stages of comparison and checking, until eventually the memory system is sure a match has been achieved. The theory uses the metaphor of 'resonance' to explain the process of retrieval of information stored in the recent past. It is assumed that whatever information a person possesses about a stimulus, at the time of attempted retrieval, will have an effect on the memory system, akin to the application of a specific frequency to the system, which tends to elicit, as feedback, sympathetic vibrations in all the episodes ('tuning forks') set to that frequency in the memory system. It is argued that the fewer the 'forks' with that specific frequency, the stronger the stimulation will be, and the stronger the feedback to the person. Positive feedback of this kind will include information about the stimulus which was not initially present when resonance was initiated, but which can now be used to try to retrieve the item required, producing more feedback, etc., until the test (retrieval) context closely matches the context in which the stimulus was first encountered. At this point, the stimulus is recognized and/or produced. The depth or elaboration of processing associated with the original stimulus *do* matter for this kind of retrieval, since both depth and elaboration contribute to making the particular 'trace' of an item stored in memory more distinctive or unusual, thereby increasing the 'reasonance' of that particular 'tuning fork' and increasing the speed and accuracy with which the memory system can reinstate the original learning context, and retrieve the item needed.

Interestingly, some recent approaches to the design of query interfaces for information-seeking also rely on the notion that the process of retrieving information from memory is, in certain circumstances, a process of reconstruction and reformulation. The query interface RABBIT, for example, is based on Williams and Hollan's (1981; see also Williams, 1981; Norman and Bobrow, 1979) 'retrieval by reformulation' approach, which allows users to refine successive descriptions of the items they are looking for, on the basis of the examples that can be retrieved using the original description. So far no systematic research has been done on evaluating the interface, but on preliminary trials it appeared to be received very favourably by users (Williams, 1984).

The foregoing account of the 'new look' Levels approach argued that the *time* between learning (or storing) something and attempting to find it again in memory can critically influence the types of actions the subjects perform to gain access to the information. This new account of Levels was originally fomulated to explain mainly recognition performance, in other words, the processes subjects go through to try to match a stimulus presented at retrieval with one assumed to be in store. Though there are no strong reasons why the same mechanisms should not apply to the situation involving information recall, care should be taken in the initial stages of extrapolating from one test procedure to the other.

A recent review paper by Craik (1983) continues to support the view that the 'new look' Levels approach must relate strongly both to encoding and to retrieval. Craik's argument is that retention reflects the *qualitative* type of trace formed. Hence more elaborate, semantic representations, should in general be better retained. And, just as different encoding operations will be associated with differences in retention, so different retrieval *tasks*, or cues, will be differentially effective, as a function of the compatibility between the operations induced by the retrieval task and those carried out at encoding. Let us now turn to the retrieval end of the process of memory and see how the two cue-dependent forgetting hypotheses described earlier may interact both with each other and with the Levels view.

A possible 'global view'

The inaccessibility hypothesis proposed by Tulving claimed that information is not very often 'lost' from memory, so that most apparent failures of memory are failures to retrieve material that is *in* memory. In order to access such available material, one much use cues, or prompts, which can be stored with the information at the time of learning. The closer we can match the retrieval environment (the retrieval cues) to the encoding environment, the more likely it is that access will be gained to the information available. The cue-overload hypothesis then attempted to impose some limits on this view by arguing that even a perfect match between encoding and retrieval prompts will only produce perfect recall if the retrieval cues are not 'overloaded'. Overload was said to be dependent on the number of items subsumed under each cue, and the effectiveness of any given cue (at a certain level of overload) was said to depend too on how similar the items in memory were — too similar, and retrieval may be impaired because the items are so easily confusible and indistinct; too dissimilar, and each item may have to be retrieved independently.

Hence the inaccessibility hypothesis and the cue-overload hypothesis complement each other well. Their relation to the Levels approach is encapsulated in the Encoding Specificity Principle that was also described earlier. This states that *no cue*, however strongly associated with the items to be remembered, will aid recall *unless* it was specifically linked with those items (was present in the encoding environment) at the time the items were put in memory. It follows from this that if items were processed semantically, the cues or prompts should be semantic, if the items were processed phonemically, the prompts should be phonemic, and so on. Hence the level (depth and elaboration) at which an item was processed when stored needs to be reinstated at retrieval before recall can succeed, and all the constraints imposed by cue overload should then determine the degree of success experienced. There is some evidence for this type of global view. For example, Parkin (1980) showed that the degree to which a retrieval prompt becomes overloaded depends on all items being encoded at the *same* level of processing. If only some were processed deeply, then overload was lower (and recall for the semantically processed items was better) than when all were processed at the same level. Other evidence has also supported other separate aspects of the global view (for example, Fisher and Craik, 1977; Geiselman and Bjork, 1980).

As previously said, the above description of a global model specifying the relation between study context and retrieval context concentrated exclusively on the field of 'episodic' memory: the memory for particular events, or episodes, in which certain things happened which involved information well known to the rememberer before such events. It is easy to see how such a conception of memory could be applied to the design of interfaces aimed at helping users find information stored in their personal electronic files, or information they need to remember in order to be able to use the system. This includes, too, the ability to 'internalize' enough information that interacting with the system does not have to start from first beginnings every time the user logs on. However, there are other kinds of information that users may want to retrieve. Retrieval of information from databanks which are not personally known to the user, for example, must involve instead some interaction between the interface procedures required for the search and the users' way of searching for information in their own 'data-bases' — their memories. This will determine the types of search they are most used to, and are most likely to use. The users' store of knowledge can more easily be described as their 'semantic' memory store, in Tulving's words. The second part of this chapter describes some of the theories associated with semantic memory and how they may contribute to interface design.

Before we proceed to that section, however, let us first consider a brief series of basic phenomena of memory — still within the episodic memory domain — which also have implications for the design of the user–system interface. The list is meant to be illustrative rather than exhaustive. A complete listing would greatly exceed the total space available. Similarly, consideration of the *theoretical bases* of the phenomena described is not extensive. In many cases the theoretical interpretation of the phenomena described is still in a state of flux. Yet the effects are consistently obtained. It is likely that at some future time these different phenomena will come to be integrated into a more general model of human memory, or into the models reported earlier. Nevertheless at the moment they are offered as isolated facts to be taken into account. Not knowing why a certain phenomenon comes about does not detract from the fact that it does exist and affects user performance.

SOME BASIC MEMORY PHENOMENA

The generation effect

People are more likely to remember words from a list if they had to *produce* those words than if they just had to read them. This advantage in recall to generated words is known as the 'generation effect'. Research on the generation effect has shown that it is present at 'shallow' as well as 'deep' levels of processing, with different degrees of elaborative encoding, and occurs just as strongly for digits as it does for words (for example, McElroy and Slamecka, 1982; Slamecka and Graf, 1978). There is also as yet non-replicated evidence that the effect applies to symbolic items (traffic-sign analogues) as well (Maoutsos, unpublished data). The experimental data have shown that the generation advantage cannot be attributed to any processing characteristics inherent in the generation task *per se*, such as greater cognitive effort (having to 'work up more steam') or increased arousal, particularly since it is known that the effect does *not* occur when the items generated or read are, in fact, non-words. So long as materials are meaningful (even if they are abbreviations), however, the effect is present.

The modality effect

Recall of the last few words in a list tends to be higher if the list is presented auditorily than if it is presented visually. This recall advantage to spoken, as opposed to seen items, is labelled the 'modality effect'. Recent research has shown that in certain circumstances the effect can occur, too, for *all* items in a list (Gardiner, Gregg and Gardiner, 1984; see too Gardiner and Gregg, 1979; Routh, 1970; 1976), and that it is not affected by activity interpolated between each pair of items in the list, even when that activity involves spoken distractor items. The effect is present regardless of *who* speaks the words — the subject or the experimenter — and/or the distractor items — subject or experimenter. A similar effect has been demonstrated using sign language rather than spoken presentation. This latter finding has prompted some researchers (such as Shand and Klima, 1981) to claim that at its root is the need to *add together*, or combine a variety of features (for example, the spoken syllables of a word, the several signs that make up a word in sign language) compared with the relatively 'instantaneous' nature of the perception of a written word (for the very common words normally used in these experiments).

Though other interpretations of the modality effect are possible, it is curious to note that the 'combination' explanation bears some resemblance to another memory phenomenon as well, described — amongst other — by Bower (1970): memory and imagery.

Memory and imagery

Assume, for example, that you are given a list of items to recall, and that you know you will later be asked to recall those items in the *same order* in which you studied them. A strategy that can be used to improve recall in these circumstances is the 'pegword system', which involves learning first of all a series of number–object rhymes (ONE-bun, TWO-shoe, THREE-tree, etc.), and then mentally associating the rhyming objects with the words in the list to be remembered. For instance, imagine that the list to be learned contained these three initial items: ELEPHANT, SNAKE, PIG. The pegwood technique would link ELEPHANT to bun, so the subject might imagine an elephant daintily eating an iced bun, SNAKE and shoe would be associated, so for instance the snake might be seen as the laces for the shoe; the PIG might be imagined up a tree, etc. Bower (1970) demonstrated that if such imagery strategies are to help memory, the image of the pegwood and that of the list word must actually be *superimposed*, mentally, by the subject. Hence, imagining a bun and an elephant separately does not help recall any. Similarly, combinations of meaningful images help recall, but combinations of random patterns or shapes do not (Bower, Karlin and Dueck, 1975) and, as with the generation effect, the ability to choose which images to use as pegwords greatly improves the strategy's effects on performance (Bower and Winzenz, 1970).

Graphic versus text presentation

In a wide variety of memory tasks pictures are often remembered better than words (Paivo, 1976; see also Part I of this chapter). Pictures are also better recognized than either words or sentences (Shepard, 1967) and, indeed, the memory system's ability to recognize previously seen pictures can be surprisingly good, as an experiment by Standing, Conezio and Haber (1970) demonstrated. They found that recognition memory for pictures (when recognition was tested immediately after presentation) averaged 90% of a 2560-strong list of pictures. It took the experimenters 7 hours, over 4 days, to present all the pictures.

Recognition versus recall

By and large, all things being equal, recognizing items one has learned before tends to be better than having to recall those items without prompting (see, for example, Wolford, 1971). However, there are circumstances when people can recall items which they earlier failed to recognize (see, for example, Watkins and Tulving, 1975). As in most of Tulving's work, the finding that recognition can sometimes fail where recall succeeds is attributed to the failure to reinstate at test the conditions that were present at learning. In a typical 'recognition failure of recallable words' experiment (as the finding is generally labelled), subjects first study a list of pairs of words, consisting of a series of prompts (or cue words) and of targets (or words the subjects know they have to memorize). Then the subjects are given a second list which contains the target words paired with a different (but related) set of cue words. For instance, fat-MUTTON from the first list may become leg-MUTTON in the second list. In this second list there are, too, additional pairs of words, 'lures', which were never presented at all. The subjects have to decide which of the right-hand words in each pair were, in effect, in the first list. Finally, the left-hand (cue) words from the first list are represented and the subject is asked to produce the word that was paired with each cue in the first list. In the earlier example, in this final recall test the subject might be faced with a series of prompts of the sort 'fat——?'. The usual finding is that subjects fail to recognize words in the second list which they are perfectly happy to recall in the cued recall test. According to the Encoding Specificity Principle described earlier, this effect comes about because the prompts contained in the second list (all different from those encountered when studying target words in the context of the first list) do not provide a suitable *retrieval environment*, in other words, they do not match the prompts stored with the target words at learning. Obviously, re-presenting these latter prompts in the final recall test *does* reinstate that learning context, so retrieval is more efficient here than it can be in the recognition test with the second list. This is, however, only one of the possible explanations that have been offered for this effect. A full review of these explanations is outside the scope of this chapter.

Incidental learning

In some cases, intent to learn is not the critical variable determining what is learnt and what is later remembered. In other words, one need not have meant to learn some information to be able to retrieve it from memory.

An experiment by Hyde and Jenkins (1973) helps demonstrate this effect. Hyde and Jenkins presented their subjects with lists of 24 common words and asked them to analyse the words in a variety of ways. For instance, subjects in one group were asked to rate the words on a five-point scale according to how pleasant or unpleasant they felt them to be. Other subjects had to detect the occurrence of the letters E and G in the spelling of the stimulus words, etc. The tasks were designed in such a way that they could be roughly divided into semantic (first example) and non-semantic (second example), as defined by the levels-of-processing approach. All items were presented verbally by the experimenters at the rate of one word every 3 seconds. Half the subjects were forewarned that their recall for the list of words would be tested, the other half were not. After the last list word had been presented, however, all subjects were asked to try to recall as many of the words in the list as they could.

The results showed, among other things, that there was very little difference in level of recall between the subjects who had performed the tasks in the expectation of the memory test, and those who had not been told they would be asked to recall the words, even though for both groups the semantic task led to better recall.

CONCLUSIONS FROM THE RESEARCH ON EPISODIC MEMORY

The basic conclusions from the literature on episodic memory make some specific suggestions for the kinds of interfaces that may facilitate human–machine interaction. For instance, graphical interfaces may offer considerable benefits over text-based interfaces, particularly where complex information is being displayed that users will need to retain for later decision-making tasks, for example. Similarly, dynamic types of interface, where the user is free to manipulate and combine iconically the information displayed could — if properly implemented — offer significant benefits both in terms of speed and in terms of better memory for the different steps involved in a complex sequence of actions. As with most of the suggestions offered in this book, however, care must be taken to establish the boundary conditions for application of these theoretical findings, and the interdependencies between different findings, from different areas, which may reduce, increase or completely change the implications a given, isolated, phenomenon may have. In this respect, the technological field may be seen as a valuable naturalistic test-bed for the establishment of both the boundary conditions and the interdependencies: it provides the necessary complexity and integration that is essential to making concrete decisions concerning application.

SEMANTIC MEMORY

Theories of semantic memory organization concentrate on the possible ways the users' 'knowledge' system is organized. A common conclusion has been that memory is organized, and organized in such a way that information can be retrieved quickly from it, new information can be easily entered into the existing structures, and these can be modified by, or accommodated to, new experiences. These theories can potentially have implications for user-interface design, particularly interfaces to systems aimed at retrieval of information which users did not themselves enter into the store, such as large public databases or corporate databases. Unfortunately, knowledge about the users' semantic memory system has not yet reached such a state of unquestioned perfection that it allows simple interpretation of information about the structural units of the semantic memory system to the electronic domain. It is, nevertheless, possible to extract from the available theories of semantic memory some 'principles' which may be useful to the design of effective electronic systems for information storage and retrieval in unstructured environments, where the user is also an information seeker. The following is a brief overview of some approaches to semantic memory organization.

APPROACHES TO SEMANTIC MEMORY ORGANIZATION

Clustering approach

According to this approach concepts (that is, objects, ideas, words) are stored in memory in an organized fashion: similar items cluster together. For example, DESK is stored together with memories corresponding to other items of OFFICE

FURNITURE. Clustering models came about when it was realized that, when asked to recall long lists of words coming from different categories, people produced words in an organized form, with one 'spurt' of words from one category following a 'spurt' of words from another category, etc.

Unlike other approaches to semantic memory organization, the clustering model does not have a lot to say about how the members of a particular cluster relate to other items in the same, or related clusters. Partially for this reason, it has lost a lot of its importance as a full explanation of memory organization.

Set-theoretical approach

Like the clustering model, the set-theoretical approach also assumes that similar concepts cluster together in memory. Here the similarities end, however, because the character of these clusters (or sets) is very different. According to the set-theoretical approach, concepts are not just organized according to their category, they also cluster in terms of their attributes (for instance, DESKS 'don't move', 'are solid', etc.). Hence sets are assumed to contain not just concepts, but also the *features* that are essential if a concept is to be included in a particular cluster. This model is still the subject of much research.

Semantic feature-comparison approach

This approach is, again, similar to the previous one, but differs in one critical way: while the set-theoretical approach assumes that clusters have concepts and that concepts have features, the semantic feature-comparison approach discriminates two different kinds of features. Specifically, it says that concepts have *defining* features (which are essential aspects of the concept's meaning, without which the concept would not be a member of the category in question) and *characteristic* features (which are more descriptive of the concept, and are not essential for determining a concept's membership in a category). For example 'is solid', 'is inanimate' are defining features for concepts that belong in the category of OFFICE FURNITURE. A DESK is hence an item of office furniture. But a DESK also 'has a top', 'has drawers', etc. features which the average CHAIR does not have, even though it is as much an item of furniture as the DESK.

Network theories

Possibly the best known ways of modelling memory organization, network theories have often adopted computer analogues for the representation of semantic memory models, and have often used computer simulations to test the models' appropriateness. Prominent among such models are Collins and Quillian's Teachable Language Comprehender (TLC; see, for example, 1972), Anderson and Bower's Human Associative Memory (HAM; see, for example,

1973), and Norman and Rumelhart's ELINOR (see, for example, 1975). Anderson and Bower's HAM model has now been extensively restructured and extended by Anderson into a series of ACT theories, where ACT stands for Adaptive Control of Thought (see, for example, Anderson, 1976; 1984). ACT theories extend beyond the realm of pure memory research into attempts to theorize about cognitive processes in general.

Network models assume that concepts exist in memory as independent units which are related to each other through the links of a hierarchical network. Positioning in the network is determined by a complex set of relationships. For example, DESK and OFFICE FURNITURE are stored in terms of the relationship between them: A desk IS office furniture. Other types of relationship are also entertained, such as, a desk HAS drawers, a desk CANNOT move, all set in a hierarchical fashion, with features stored at specific levels of the hierarchy according to the principle of cognitive economy (that is, why store features like 'is solid' at the DESK level when storing them at the OFFICE FURNITURE level will mean that they apply to all items subsumed under office furniture?)

There are several key problems with the network approach, one of the major ones being that in an attempt to create truly universal and logical models, each of the systems postulated tends to assume from the human host an amount of structured knowledge which, on testing, the human does not seem to have. For example, most experimentation in this domain has been done using so-called 'natural' categories, like names of birds, names of animals, etc. Experiments are designed which test the format of the hierarchy by correlating the time it takes people to confirm or disconfirm a particular sentence, with the assumed distance in the network between the concepts whose relationship the person has to confirm or disconfirm. For example, a subject might be asked to confirm or disconfirm that 'a dog is a mammal', or 'a dog is an animal'. Typically, people tend to take longer to say that a dog is a mammal than they do to say that a dog is an animal. In terms of the theory, since the longer it takes to respond, the farther apart two concepts are, one can only assume that in this network all animals are mammals: because mammals are 'further away' from dog than animals are then, according to this definition, mammals must be higher up in the hierarchy, and hence must subsume animals — a clearly illogical conclusion.

Hence, on testing, network models have usually broken down because people appear to have no clear idea of the 'correct' stages in their postulated memory networks and, as a result, fail to produce the 'correct' patterns of results. The models are generally not flexible enough to allow for the breaking of that many rules. One exception is Collins and Loftus' (for example, 1975) 'spread of activation' theory, which rejects a strict hierarchical model and postulates instead a system whereby items are related to all other items in memory in terms of 'semantic distance' (that is, perceived relatedness). Hence it is possible to have a dog placed closer to animal than to mammal, if the person has most frequently associated dog with animal than dog with mammal (even though, zoologically speaking, that pattern of relationships is illogical). The major problem with the spreading activation model is that there are many ways of conceptualizing semantic distance, and depending on which one you choose, so the fit between theory and data is good, bad or mediocre. Most network models are also exceedingly complex and ungainly when it comes to actually predicting performance. For these reasons, most of the current research tends to concentrate on the feature-comparison and set-theoretical models. We will now consider these approaches in slightly more detail, with reference to particular theories which describe how the models are used in practice.

Two models in detail

Meyer's model for verification of propositions

This model (Meyer, 1970) belongs in the set-theoretical tradition and is based on the rules of set logic. Most of the empirical support for it has come from experiments which require subjects to verify a number of different types of relationships between the subjects and predicates of particular types of sentence. (for example, in the sentence A DESK IS FURNITURE, DESK is the subject and FURNITURE is the predicate). According to the model, when verifying the truth or falsity of sentences like 'all desks are furniture' or 'all furniture is desks', subjects go through a matching process where they check for the overlap or intersection of the sets of features for DESK and FURNITURE in set-logic style. The number of matchings done, and the degree of precision of such matches, depend on the features of the particular task the subject is undertaking.

Meyer's model is typical of set-theoretical models in general and, like these, it has come up against problems when it has been tested with materials that differ in the degree to which items relate to other items in the same category. (For example, DESK is generally considered to be a particular good member of the category of OFFICE FURNITURE; a CARPET tends to be considered a less good example: DESK belongs in the category of OFFICE FURNITURE to a greater degree than CARPET does.) This has led to feature-comparison models now having very much the upper hand in the field of semantic memory research. We will now consider one such model — Rips, Shoben and Smith's model.

Rips, Shoben and Smith's model

As said above, the major difference between set-theoretical and feature-comparison models is that the latter conceive of defining and characteristic features. In practice, this means that they can accommodate differences in the degree of relatedness among items and between these and the categories they belong in (such as the example given above concerning the relationship between DESK, CARPET and the category of OFFICE FURNITURE). According to the Rips,

Shoben and Smith theory (1973; Smith, Shoben and Rips, 1974), when performing a memory task (that is, when using their feature store to retrieve information about a concept's relation to another concept) people first of all try to check whether the set of features for one concept roughly matches that for another concept. So, for instance, when deciding whether 'a desk is furniture' is a true statement, people retrieve the set of features for DESK and the set of features for FURNITURE and check one against the other to see whether they overlap. This rough comparison is supposed to yield a 'similarity' index, which will lead to further processing if it falls above a certain criterion value. If it falls below that value, the system knows that it can simply deny that any relationship exists between the concepts being considered. That explains why it is so easy and quick to answer 'no' to nonsense sentences of the form 'a banana is a computer' or 'a rabbit is a mountain' (it will be interesting to see what effects the current fashion for giving computers 'fruity' names has on this state of affairs. . .).

The system is assumed to continue the feature comparison process at progressively more detailed levels, until it checks the list feature by feature, depending on the degree of precision demanded by the task.

Theories like Meyer's and Rips, Shoben and Smith's are processing accounts of semantic memory; that is, they deal both with the way memory is organized, and how it is used. Processing accounts are not, however, the only kinds of theory that have emerged within the field of semantic memory. Schema theory, which was described in the previous chapter, is a *structural* account of memory organization, that is, an account which describes how memory is organized and how this organization imposes constraints on information processing, but does not itself have overmuch to say about the processing side of the system. It can, however, be combined with other theories to produce accounts which deal with information processing as well as storage (Chapter 4 contains one such account). Another structural account of memory organization is Rosch's theory of typicality, which is now described.

Rosch's theory of typicality

This theory departs from the traditional view of category structure, where items are seen to belong in a category or not to belong in it, in that it conceives of differences in the *degree* to which a particular item relates to a particular category (for example, Rosch, 1973, 1974a and b, 1975a and b, 1978; Rosch and Mervis, 1975; Rosch, Simpson and Miller, 1976; Rosch *et al.*, 1976). Chapter 7 describes in more detail how typicality theory can be combined with other theories to produce an account of language behaviour, in particular word usage and meaning. Here we will discuss instead those features of the theory which are more specific to the semantic memory domain.

Rosch's contention is that there exist category 'prototypes' — words or concepts which are central to the particular aggregation of concepts and around which other items in the aggregate are arranged. Hence in natural categories (for example, names of birds, flowers, and animals) there are items which are very close to a category prototype (the idealized bird, animal, etc.) and items which are progressively more distant from that prototype. An example might be, for instance, the difference between a ROBIN and an OSTRICH, in relation to the category 'birds'. A typical bird, for most people, tends to be a smallish, feathered, flying, singing creature that eats peanuts and seed and can be rather cute at times. A ROBIN fits the bill almost perfectly. An OSTRICH breaks just about all these rules: it is a large, partly bald, non-flying, mute creature, who eats pretty much anything and does not look very appealing. Yet both ROBIN and OSTRICH are usually classified as birds by subjects who are asked that question. This difference in *representativeness* among category examplars spans most, if not all, natural categories, and can also be seen in other types of category, such as furniture, sports, etc.

Another of Rosch's findings is that people are remarkably consistent in their judgements of the typicality of specific items that belong in a category. So not only will the same person give the same, or very similar typicality value (for example a number on a scale) to specific exemplars of a category on different occasions, but across subjects a very consistent pattern emerges as well. Rosch used this consistency in typicality judgements to produce 'norms' of typicality for a number of categories across a variety of category members. These norms have been used, in turn, to conduct experiments into the relationship between rated typicality (the numerical value subjects give, on a sliding scale, to each category member according to the degree to which the item is a good or bad example of the category) and a variety of memory tasks. Hence typicality has been shown to be a good predictor of categorization time (how fast people can decide whether an item is a member of a particular category; see, for example, Smith, Shoben and Rips, 1974; Hampton, 1979; McCloskey and Glucksberg, 1979) and of associative frequency (the measure of the probability of an item being generated to its category name; see Mervis, Catlin and Rosch, 1976; Hampton, 1979). It also correlates well with measures of 'semantic distance' (perceived distance in a conceptual 'map' of the category; see, for example, Rips, Shoben and Smith, 1973) and of the overlap between the features that describe an item and either its fellow category members (Rosch and Mervis, 1975) or the category concept itself (Hampton, 1979; 1981).

Research has also shown that typical items (the good examples of the category) are easier to learn (Rosch and Mervis, 1975), and they are better recalled than atypical items (Gardiner, 1983; Keller and Kellas, 1978). People can also generate more information about the typical than the atypical category members (Ashcraft, 1978). This latter finding has led to the suggestion that what determines whether an item is a member of a category or not is 'family resemblance' between the item and other category members, rather than a simple 'all or none' criterion (Rosch and Mervis, 1975). Family resemblance is, in turn, determined by the overlap between the features that describe the different concepts being considered.

IMPLICATIONS OF SEMANTIC MEMORY THEORY FOR INTERFACE DESIGN

The above discussion has outlined some major approaches to how semantic memory is organized, and has described in some detail the basic principles of some more specific theories belonging to the set-theoretical and feature-comparison frameworks. None of the approaches and theories described here (including the structural accounts of memory which are elaborated further in chapters 4 and 7) can truthfully claim to provide a full account of how semantic memory is organized and used. However, some basic principles can be extra-polated and incorporated into the thinking behind user-interface design.

The main message of the semantic memory research done to date appears to be that though strict hierarchical conceptualizations of memory storage look neat and tidy, and may indeed be used to *mimic* memory performance (such as in artificially intelligent systems), there are almost unsurmountable problems associated with using these models to explain and describe *human* memory. Hierarchical models normally assume too much knowledge on the part of the human, and they cannot readily accommodate notions such as differences in typicality or degree of relatedness of members of the same category. They are also particularly difficult to square with the argument that a 'good' memory model is one that can be easily updated. How do you update a hierarchy without scrapping it and starting again? This suggests that an interface which allows the user to retrieve information by specifying what (s)he knows *about* the item, (that is, the item's features), may have considerable advantages over similar interfaces which require precise identification of the correct name and status of the information being looked for.

This points to interfaces which allow repeated passes at retrieval: a process which we also saw would be beneficial in terms of facilitating learning (Chapter 4), and which is also consistent with the theories of retrieval by reformulation which were discussed in the section on episodic memory (for example, the query interface RABBIT).

Turning now to the possible implications of typicality research for interface design, it will be remembered that typicality is supposed to reflect differences in the 'family resemblance' among items in a given category. Good examples of the category also tend to be more similar to one another than bad examples of a category. People also find it exceedingly easy to group items together on the basis of vague similarities, and they show surprising consistency in the ratings they give about an item's degree of membership within a given category. The concept of 'family resemblance' is also very similar to another concept — Malone's (1983) notion of 'piles' of information in professional people's offices. Basically, this relates to the fact that sometimes people find it difficult to categorize specific documents as members or non-members of particular categories (for example, for filing), and resort to putting them in piles of roughly similar items. Piles are also used to 'remind' people to do certain things, and their distance from the main work area sometimes reflects the urgency with which they have to be attended to. Piles are hence seen as adjuncts to memory, or reminding aids. The concept of typicality embodies the notion that so long as items are roughly similar to one another, and refer roughly to a specific thing, they can not only be accurately classified in terms of their 'cognitive distance' from the specific topic, item of information, etc., but can also be easily retrieved in the same way. For example, people 'know' that item X is not quite in the centre of category A, but is close, and can specify how close; when it comes to retrieving the item, they also know roughly how 'distant' it is, and can represent that distance. So, in a way, theories which postulate differences in degree of membership in a category may provide methodologies for quantifying and operationalizing the concept of 'piles', so that it can find some kind of translation in interfaces to electronic systems. Considered application of this kind of approach to organizing information could lead, for example, to the development of interfaces that allow for easy and fairly unconstrained 'browsing' through a database; a key feature lacking in most current electronic systems.

Interestingly, prototype systems are already being discussed in the systems design literature which are based on theories similar to Rosch's, though they come from other spheres of science. This is particularly true of 'fuzzy' logic, along the lines defined by Zadeh (1965; 1975). Though this is a promising direction in system design, one cannot but feel that some cross-fertilization from the cognitive psychology domain and its more 'naturalistic' approaches would enhance the potential benefits that applications of this kind can give.

At a slightly more pragmatic level, too, because typical items have been shown to be better recalled, typicality research also has implications for the choice of icons, keywords, command names, etc. which are inherently the system's (as opposed to being generated by the user). Clearly, the more typical these are of the particular class they represent, the more likely it is that users will be able to utilize them without continual prompting from the system.

ADDITIONAL COMMENTS

The major sections on episodic and semantic memory outlined psychological aspects of the user's memory and knowledge systems. This section will now briefly note one additional facet of the user's psychological make-up which has recently received a fair deal of interest in the literature. It concerns the changes that occur as the user's age increases. There are cognitive changes which go hand in hand with ageing and, considering that electronic systems are beginning to find their way into most spheres of activity, servicing a wide cross-section of the population, the question of age-related differences in interface design should be borne in mind. Work done by Craik and colleagues (1977; Craik and Byrd, 1982) has shown that ageing brings with it a reduction in 'processing power'. In other words, older people tend not to process material as richly and extensively as younger people, to the extent that in some studies younger people's performance only matched older people's performance under conditions where the younger subjects were performing the same task *in addition to* other tasks (that is, were learning under conditions of divided attention).

The implications for interface design of the above findings are that ideally interfaces should be designed to be flexible enough to allow the users to vary the amount of information they have to deal with at any time and, conversely, should not allow users to 'get away' with inadequate amounts of processing where the consequences of poor recall will be dire.

CONCLUSIONS

To summarize, in this second major part of this chapter we have looked at the factors that determine good memory performance and have considered the possible structure and organization of the human store of 'knowledge'. In general, good memory was seen to depend on the amount of 'work' involved in the learning of information, as well as the match between the context in which information is recalled and that in which it was learned. A number of other determinants of recall were also discussed which, in some cases, operate above and beyond the effects of level of processing and matching of the retrieval and learning contexts. For example, the beneficial effects of generating the information that is to be learned, and of the hearing or speaking that information were discussed, as was the common finding that recognizing information is easier and more effective than having to recall it from cold.

It was also seen that the format in which information is presented has its effects on memory: pictures tend to be better remembered than text, and imagery was seen to have very beneficial effects as well, particularly where people actively use imagery as an aid to recall. And, overlaying all of these effects, was the finding that organization facilitates recall, so long as it is suitably implemented.

We then considered how knowledge is stored and discussed some theories which concentrate on how its structure is reflected in behaviour. We saw that a person's store of 'knowledge' is an organized entity, where concepts are stored as featural descriptions which cluster together in categories. The structuring principles behind such clusters are still uncertain, though much of the empirical data amassed over the years seems to point to a number of organizing dimensions, to do for example with the 'family resemblance' of the items in the cluster. This indicates a 'fuzzier' nature to the 'rules' of category membership that had been assumed until recently, and points to eventual fruitful application of this knowledge in interfaces which satisfy some of the key requirements for successful, 'compatible' information retrieval: requirements such as easy browsing, iterative retrieval,

retrieval in the absence of complete recall, reminding functions, and so on.

An important conclusion of the research on semantic memory, and related theories to do with how information in semantic memory is utilized (for example, those discussed in Chapters 4 and 7) is that context and the type of activity being engaged in are important determinants of performance. This has direct implications for any attempts to apply the research findings described here; any empirical work involved in the interpretation and translation of these concepts to the applied domain must be done within the kinds of complex environments which are the norm in the applied domain. Simplification can produce biases which may be impossible to resolve.

Yet, those examples of application which do exist (such as, RABBIT, some of the available guidelines concerning menu structuring and screen layout) suggest that application is a fruitful exercise and it may provide valuable empirical evidence to help refine and extend the theories presented above.

SUMMARY PRINCIPLES

1. Accurate immediate recall of a random sequence of verbal 'chunks' is possible only for sequences of less than five to seven chunks. For longer sequences recall is limited to about five to seven chunks. Chunks are either familiar patterns of elements (for example, 'BBC' but not 'ZJE') or groups of elements combined according to a rule (such as recoding binary numbers into digital).

   1.1 Experts can cope with hierarchies of verbal chunks, resulting in 'super-chunks' containing large numbers of elements.

2. A further limit on the accuracy of immediate recall is set by the spoken duration of verbal materials. This factor limits recall to the number of items that can be articulated in from 1 to 1.5 seconds. Thus words that can be spoken quickly are remembered better than words which take longer to say. The relative importance of the limits set by spoken duration and number of chunks has yet to be fully explored. It appears that duration is more important than chunking for polysyllabic words.

3. Letters or words that rhyme are particularly difficult to remember in the correct sequence in the short term.

4. The presence of irrelevant speech sounds will impair immediate recall, regardless of their source.

5. Even a short sequence of verbal chunks will be forgotten within 20 seconds or so if this interval is filled with some irrelevant, distracting activity.

6. The rate of short-term forgetting increases with the number of verbal chunks to be remembered.

7. The rate of short-term forgetting for verbal chunks increases with the difficulty of the distracting activity.

8. The rate of short-term forgetting for verbal chunks is increased when similar material has recently been remembered.

9. People can usually remember the last two to three verbal chunks from a long series of verbal items immediately after presentation when accurate order of report is not essential, even when they have not been deliberately memorizing the materials.

10. People have only a very limited ability to remember the detailed appearance of novel, visual abstract patterns even over intervals of a few seconds.

11. Immediate memory is poorer the more compex the visual pattern.

12. Immediate memory for visual abstract patterns is disrupted by even small amounts of distraction.

13. Immediate memory for the names of familiar items is usually better when they are presented as pictures than when they are presented as words.

    13.1 This effect will depend on the pictures being readily nameable.

14. Principles that apply to memory for verbal materials will also apply to memory for the names of pictures.

15. In general, the speed and accuracy with which people can process information (for example, for carrying out thinking, reasoning and routine skills) will depend critically upon the load on 'working memory' at any instant.

    15.1 Working memory load is increased when more than one task must be carried out at the same time.

    15.2 Working memory load increases the greater the amount of material that must be remembered temporarily, or 'held in mind'.

    15.3 Working memory load increases with task complexity, even in familiar, well-learned skills. Task complexity increases with the number of nested control loops that need to be carried out. Linear tasks are less complex.

    15.4 An important exception to 15 is the retrieval of information from long-term memory. This appears to be a relatively automatic process and its efficiency is largely unaffected by the current load on working memory.

16. The probability of recalling an item increases as a direct function of the depth of processing at which the item was encoded when put into memory. Depth of processing increases with the requirement to consider the meaning of an item and its relation to other items.

17. The probability of recalling an item increases as a direct function of the elaborateness of processing associated with its encoding into memory. Elaborateness of processing increases with the richness of the context information present at the time of storage.

18. The greater the time that elapses between storage and retrieval (for example, >30 seconds) the greater the importance of principles 16 and 17 above.

    18.1 For very short time spans (for example <30 seconds), retrieval is done by scanning backwards through the information stored in memory and checking each item against any available information about the item sought (see also 9).

19. The probability of gaining access to an item in memory increases as a monotonic function of the match between the storage and retrieval environments (the Encoding Specificity Principle). The match between the storage and retrieval environments increases in proportion to the number of cues present at both storage and retrieval.

   19.1 Assuming that items can be categorized according to some rule, a cue presented at recall which is effective for gaining access to one particular item will also facilitate access to other items in the same category. It will *not* facilitate access to items in other categories presented at the same time (that is, it will obtain access to the category *concept*).

   19.2 Strong associates of items held in memory, but not stored in a given episode in association with those items, may prompt recall of those (strong associate) items that *were* present in the episode.

20. The effectiveness of a given cue for retrieval (expressed as the probability of recalling an item related to that cue) is an inverse function of the number of items which are subsumed under it (the cue-overload principle).

   20.1 Up to a certain level, similarity among items subsumed under a given cue will reduce the effects of overload on that cue.

   20.2 The level of overload on a cue is higher when all items subsumed under it are processed at the same depth and level of elaboration.

21. The more distinctive an item is in memory, the greater its probability of recall. Distinctiveness is an inverse function of the degree of similarity between an item (or the features defining an item) and all other items associated with it in a given episode stored in memory.

22. The greater the compatibility between the operations carried out to store an item in memory and the operations carried out to retrieve it, the greater the probability of recall. Compatibility increases when the same types of processing are used, for the same cues, at both storage and retrieval (for example, semantically processed cues at storage should be semantically processed cues at retrieval).

23. The probability of recalling an item stored in memory is greater if the item had to be generated in response to a cue or rule, at the time of storage, than if the item was simply read or seen at the time of storage.

24. The probability of recalling the last two or three items in a sequence is greater if the items were spoken or heard at the time they were presented, than if they were simply read or seen at the time of storage.

25. Recall is better for dynamically interacting items than for items stored in isolation.

26. Recall is better if items are presented pictorially, or are easily visualizable as

pictures, rather than if they are presented as words and these are not visualizable.

27. People can retain information they did not specifically try to learn. The richer the storage environment, the greater the likelihood that incidental information will be stored in association with the item being learned. This incidentally learned information can help retrieval at a later stage.

28. So long as the context in which information is retrieved approximates the context in which it was stored, recognizing an item stored in memory is easier and more efficient than having to recall that item unaided.

29. The greater the similarity among items stored in long-term memory, the greater the probability that they will be treated as a unified whole, called a category. Similarity increases with the number of features (at the semantic—meaning—and perceptual—appearance—level) shared by all items.

30. Category exemplars held in semantic memory are described in terms of *defining* and *characteristic* features.

   30.1 Decisions concerning an item's membership in a given category are taken on the basis of the match between that item's defining features and the 'rules' dictating the creation of the category.

   30.2 In making decisions about an item's membership in a given category, or about several items' membership in the same category, defining features are compared first.

31. Categories are collections of items organized around a central concept called a prototype. The greater the similarity among items in a category, the closer to the prototype they are stored in semantic memory.

32. The closer to the category prototype an item is, the more typical it is of the category in question.

   32.1 The more typical an item, the greater its probability of recall.

   32.2 The more typical an item, the greater its probability of being generated on presentation of the category name.

   32.3 The more typical an item, the more people agree that it belongs in its assigned category.

   32.4 The more typical an item, the more information (characteristic features) people can retrieve and generate about it.

   32.5 The more typical an item, the faster it is recognized as a member of its category.

   32.6 The more typical an item, the easier it is to learn.

33. The older the user (for instance, >55 years of age), the less information (s)he can hold in working memory at any given time.

34. Memory is a reconstructive process — queries to memory are iteratively processed, each iteration allowing the rememberer to get 'closer' to the information needed.

THE NEXT CHAPTER

In this chapter we discussed the role of human memory in user–system interaction, looking at human memory from a number of different angles. For example, we considered the role of working memory in keeping track of what the user is doing during user–system interaction, and then went on to review more 'static' aspects of memory, such as the features of the environment that determine efficient storage and retrieval of information, and the organization of 'knowledge' in the semantic memory system. The point was made at the beginning of the chapter that as users become more proficient at a particular task, so the demands that task places on memory are concomitantly reduced. This is, however, only one of the effects that skill acquisition has on human performance. The next chapter now reviews the nature of the skill acquisition process and the factors that facilitate or hinder it.

Principles from the psychology of skill acquisition

Nick Hammond

INTRODUCTION

There is a story of a music-lover lost in New York. He asked an old lady how to get to the Carnegie Hall. 'Practise, practise, practise,' came the reply. Certainly people have a remarkable capacity for refining their skill; practice makes perfect according to the maxim. At the very least, practice usually leads to improvement, even after extended training. According to Hayes (1985), levels of skill accorded the accolade 'genius' require at least ten years' practice, but were it that a mere ten years of diligence was all that ultimate expertise required, then geniuses would be commonplace. We all know that some people develop particular skills faster than others, that some things are easier to learn than others, and that training regimes vary in their efficacy. Unfortunately intermittent use of office systems seems to be an area where progress is all too often painfully slow (Long et al., 1983; Mack, Lewis and Carroll, 1983).

How people learn is not obvious. The process of transition from spasmodic, error-prone uncertainty to smooth, effortless accomplishment is not available to our own introspections; we are well aware of, and can talk about, our early performance inadequacies, but not of the mechanism by which performance becomes streamlined (Ericsson and Simon, 1980). Furthermore, a skill once obtained may not be articulable (Anderson, 1982). It is said that, when teaching, the pianist Artur Rubinstein made use of an observer to note how he executed difficult passages so that his methods could be passed on to the budding pupil (Scholes, 1955). There are many activities at which most people are reasonably proficient, such as reading, recognizing faces or riding a bicycle. These activities improve through practice, and with experience they seem to happen on their own; we cannot observe how we accomplish them. Indeed, attempts to improve well-practised skills by focusing on their component parts can have an effect that is precisely the opposite of that intended (Baddeley and Woodhead, 1982). Given our lack of insight into the acquisition and performance of a skill, it is little surprise that designers of computer systems do not always arrive at solutions that optimize ease of learning.

In this chapter we review some general aspects of research on skill acquisition. Following each major section, we consider how system design might capitalize upon psychological evidence and theory. Before starting the review, though, some remarks on the approach to be taken are in order. The topic of skill acquisition has a long history in psychology, and it is an enormous field—taking in much of the body of work on human learning. Our perspective has to be restricted. First, we are concerned with the application of this body of knowledge to the learning of office systems by people with no special computer expertise. So our interest is mainly focused on people with modest levels of skill rather than experts with many years of training behind them. Second, office systems support a wide range of tasks making diverse demands on users' abilities and resources, and particularly so when possible future systems are to be considered; these tasks are both more complex and less easily characterized than typical laboratory tasks. So the review will paint with a broad brush the issues in skill acquisition rather than pick out the fine details of particular studies or the *minutiae* of specific theories. In any case, many of the applicable consequences are indifferent to theoretical detail. The intent, therefore, is to cover a broad range of systems and tasks, but at the risk of trivializing the psychological underpinnings. In view of the paucity of direct empirical evidence about the transition from novice to expert use of computer systems, it would in fact be unwise to be too specific.

Many issues raised in this chapter are covered in more detail elsewhere in the book; for instance the use of problem-solving strategies and of mental models to organize knowledge (Chapter 4) or the nature of processing resources underlying memory (Chapter 5). Our focus here is on the *dynamic* nature of these issues, how they interrelate and develop with experience, not their psychological bases.

There are many kinds of skill. Some, such as playing tennis, coordinate perceptual and motor components. Others may be mainly sensory (as in wine tasting), mainly perceptual (reading, mirror-writing) or mainly motor (tracking tasks or many athletic skills). Others still are predominantly cognitive, where development of the skill does not depend on specific input or output processes. Playing chess, computer programming and solving crossword puzzles are examples. Note that the term skill is used here in a wider sense than in its common usage. Thus the industrial definition of the term tends to be a formal one in terms of level of training on certain perceptual-motor acts. Everyday usage often emphasizes motor aspects, perhaps reinforced by teaching methods relying on 'drills' such as repetitive practice of scales and *arpeggios* when learning a musical instrument. The psychological use is wider, covering any organized sequence of activities which becomes competent, rapid and accurate, not just manual performance. Note that the term 'skilled performance' is also a relative rather than an absolute one; there is no sharp divide between the skilled and the unskilled, between the novice and the expert. One might suppose that with such a wide definition there would be little common ground between explanations of the development of disparate types of skill. In fact, while there are important distinctions to be made, it does seem that many fundamental characteristics of skill acquisition are common across the range of skill types (Welford, 1968). It is mostly these common themes which we shall address.

As any skill develops, performance tends to become more efficient and rapid. Across a surprising range of skills, speed of performance improves in a regular and predictable fashion, obeying a relationship known as the power law of practice. This relationship is discussed in the next section. A number of psychological changes underlie skill development. For convenience, these can be divided into changes in knowledge, changes in processing and changes in strategy. These are each discussed in further separate sections. It is perhaps a truism that for many cognitive skills the knowledge base that the person calls upon, either directly or indirectly to interpret incoming information, increases and changes in structure. This is particularly so with skills in novel domains, such as in the use of office systems. Less self-evident are the changes in the processes that the person employs during the course of performance, for instance in the deployment of attention, in the use of working memory and long-term memory and, more generally, in the expenditure of 'processing capacity'. These changes, too, have implications for the design of systems. Concomitant with changes in representation and process are alterations in reported awareness of performance. Finally, many skills require the strategic organization of perceptual, cognitive or motor resources; several possible paths to successful performance exist and a person may learn to select the most appropriate given the resources available.

The division of skill acquisition into changes in representation, process and strategy in no way implies independence of these characteristics; for instance a process change may reduce the need for monitoring of feedback and hence alter the use of the person's knowledge base while at the same time freeing capacity for an alternative strategy to be employed. In learning any complex skill, these characteristics are intertwined. The division here is purely for ease of exposition.

QUANTITATIVE ASPECTS

The power law of practice

Whether or not practice makes perfect, the relationship of practice to performance is a law of diminishing returns. A plot of the logarithm of time to perform a task against the logarithm of the amount of practice nearly always approximates to a straight line. This relationship — the power law of practice — is found, for example, in perceptual tasks such as reading transformed text (Kolers, 1975), in perceptual-motor tasks such as mirror-tracing (Snoddy, 1926), drawing under a variety of conditions of distorting feedback (Smith and Smith, 1962), transferring pins from one hole to another (Gould, 1965) or learning to use a hand-operated cigar-rolling machine (Crossman, 1959) and in reaction-time tasks (see, for example, Fitts and Seeger, 1953; Klemmer, 1962; Siebel, 1963). The same law holds for pattern recognition (Neisser, Novick and Lazar, 1963), for problem-solving (Neves and Anderson, 1981; Newell and Rosenbloom, 1981), for mental arithmetic (Blackburn, 1936, cited in Crossman, 1959) and for retrieval from long-term memory (Anderson, 1983a). Further examples come from the area of human–computer interaction. Card, English and Burr (1978) demonstrated the power law in the learning of cursor positioning using four different input devices — joystick, mouse, stepping keys and text keys. The law also holds in more complex editing tasks (Card, Moran and Newell, 1983; Moran, 1980). These examples illustrate the ubiquity of the law as well as its relevance to components of the use of office systems.

The equation relating performance time (T) to amount of practice (P) is

$$T = aP^{-b} \qquad \text{(Equation 1)}$$

where a is the speed on the first trial and b is the slope of the function. As it stands, the law makes two assumptions which are implausible in some tasks: that the task can be performed in an arbitrarily small time after enough learning; and that the first practice trial measured is the start of learning. In many situations there is an asymptotic level below which performance speed is unable to fall. (A notable example is seen in the data of Crossman, 1959, where, after producing 20 million cigars, operators' times were close to the machine cycle time.) In other tasks, prior learning may well have occurred. Violations of these assumptions cause deviations from the linear relationship near the start of training and when performance nears asymptote. A more general form of the law is therefore.

$$T = c + a (P + d)^{-b} \qquad \text{(Equation 2)}$$

where c is the asymptotic speed as P becomes very large and d represents the notional number of learning trials that occurred prior to the first measured trial. Plotting $\log(T-c)$ against $\log(P + d)$ still yields a straight line, but the difficulty is that c and d are not known in advance. However other than early in learning and after very extended practice these constants are usually negligibly small.

The reason for this particular relationship is not clear. In some ways an exponential relationship might be expected as this underlies many naturally occurring developmental processes. An exponential would imply that on each trial a person could improve his or her time by a constant fraction of the current time taken. However, the evidence fails to support an exponential relationship: the power function fits the available data better than an exponential function, although hyperbolic functions can also model the data adequately (Mazur and Hastie, 1978; Newell and Rosenbloom, 1981).

Crossman, (1959) was the first to suggest an explanation for the power law in terms of underlying psychological processes, and since then the law has been the focus of a number of subsequent theoretical analyses, particularly by Newell and Rosenbloom (1981) and Anderson (1982). Briefly, three classes of explanation have been put forward: mixture models, stochastic selection models and exponential exhaustion models. Mixture models suppose that components of a skill tend to be learned at different exponential rates, so initial learning is dominated by the quickly learned components while later learning depends on the remaining slowly learned components. With a large number of components, they can be combined to yield a power relationship. There is indeed some evidence that skill components show exponential rates of learning (Neves and Anderson, 1981). Stochastic selection models suppose that performance improves because the likelihood of selecting an optimal method for each component of the skill increases. Performance improves at a decreasing rate because as practice continues, the pool of optimal methods reduces. Crossman's (1959) explanation is of this type. Exponential exhaustion models claim that learning is basically exponential, but that the exponent tends to decrease as practice continues. This yields a relationship more like a power function. Exhaustion — causing a decrease in the exponent — occurs because the learning process itself makes further improvement successively more difficult to obtain. For example, improved methods might become more difficult to find or improvements, once found, might tend to become less relevant or less generally applicable. Newell and Rosenbloom (1981) develop this latter possibility by means of a chunking model in which practice leads to the combination of low-level chunks (units of knowledge about the environment) into higher-level and less generally applicable chunks.

Discussion of these theoretical issues is beyond the scope of the present review, and anyway they have little application consequence. It is worth pointing out that the various models are not mutually exclusive and may all contribute to the power law. It may well be the case that the nature of the task environment and that of the learner both determine which model contributes to improvement at different stages of learning.

Design implications

Use of office systems requires the development of a variety of skills. For some of these skills a user may never progress far along the learning curve; important aspects of the skill may be forgotten from one session to the next or some other block to learning may never be overcome. In such instances (to be discussed below) the exponent of the power law effectively reduces to zero. However the power law plays an important role in understanding other aspects of skill. An obvious example is keying performance, which is a highly repetitive activity. Since the function has a steep initial slope, the law predicts a wide individual variation in the typing speed of casual or of new users based on their prior experience. In addition, frequent users of keyboards will pass from an initial state of incompetence to a reasonable level of proficiency moderately quickly (provided complex combinations of key presses are avoided). Since the latter part of the power function is fairly flat, once this modest skill has been attained keying rates will be relatively stable, improving only slowly.

This pattern is also likely to be characteristic of the learning of many dialogue components such as simple command or menu choices that are used repeatedly and consistently. Anecdotal evidence comes from systems requiring the use of single or multiple control characters to perform low-level functions such as cursor control. Initially users find the commands arbitrary, hard to remember and error-prone, but after some practice the commands seem to become 'fixed in the fingers' and performance becomes fast and efficient. In such cases the law of practice does not in itself help in deciding which of several design alternatives is the best or what the rate of learning is likely to be (aspects related to the parameters a and b in equation 2). A more analytical approach is needed to answer such questions, as discussed below.

The initial steep learning curve has another important consequence for design: early learning is very important. Novice users who experience a sticky start may be handicapped not just initially but over a considerable part of the learning curve. This effect has been noted in observational studies of system use (Hammond and Barnard, 1984; Mack, Lewis and Carroll, 1983) and has been the focus for training methods using highly restricted versions of the system (Carroll, 1984b; Carroll and Carrithers, 1984a, 1984b).

The designer may be able to capitalize on prior learning (parameter d in equation 2) by using dialogue components compatible with non-computer tasks familiar to the user. The law predicts that this will especially benefit early use, a critical stage for discretionary users (Bennett, 1979). Likewise, the designer may wish to help highly skilled users by minimizing the asymptotic component of the law (c in equation 2). This could be achieved by optimizing system performance and by designing user actions for maximum speed (such as by reducing the number of keystrokes). This may, of course, detract from early learning.

One further use of the power law is as a predictive tool. For example, human performance trials might be conducted on a number of alternative interface designs. Provided sufficient data are collected to allow reliable estimation of the power law parameters, then the likely performance of experts can be extrapolated from users who have attained only modest levels of performance. This can result in considerable savings in data collection. Some worked examples of the application of the power law can be seen in Card, Moran and Newell (1983).

QUALITATIVE ASPECTS

The power law of practice applies to virtually all skill learning, whether perceptual, motor or cognitive. However, it predicts only speed of performance; it has nothing to say about quality of performance. In itself it gives insight into neither the psychological nature of learning nor the optimal means of learning. We now consider some of the qualitative changes that occur under the impact of extended learning.

Experimental psychologists have mainly studied tasks that can be learned in the laboratory in a matter of minutes. Most significant skills, however, require many hours of learning; for instance a student learning a musical instrument for 100 hours would achieve only a modest facility. Learning to use a word-processor with competence and confidence takes many hours, despite advertisers' claims. Psychologists have, on the whole, been content to deal with changes in performance under this order of practice descriptively; psychological theory has had little to offer on the topic, although this picture is now changing (see, for example, Anderson, 1982; LaBerge and Samuels, 1974; Logan, 1985; MacKay, 1982; Newell and Rosenbloom, 1981; Rumelhart and Norman, 1982).

Stages in skill acquisition

Based on an extensive review of laboratory studies and on interviews with instructors (Fitts, 1964), Fitts and Posner (1967) describe the acquisition of complex skills in terms of three stages or phases. They term the first stage the early or *cognitive* phase: the beginner tries to understand the task and is able to perform it in a crude fashion using existing habits. Verbal mediation, rehearsal and the extensive use of feedback are characteristic of this phase. During the intermediate or *associative* phase, new patterns of skill components are tried out and inappropriate actions are gradually eliminated. The skill is gradually refined and at the same time the need for verbal mediation and for low-level feedback reduce. The final or *autonomous* phase involves further refinement during which the component processes become increasingly automatic, less subject to interference from other tasks and less available to conscious awareness. Indeed, there is some evidence that overt verbalization interferes with a highly developed skill (Baronowski, cited in Ericsson and Simon, 1980; Danserau, 1969; Eccles, 1977), although experimental support for this point is rather sparse (see Klatzky, 1984, for a discussion). Despite the individual's lack of awareness of many of the components of a developed skill, learning does not cease; as we have seen in the previous section, improvement can continue almost indefinitely. However, some skills may never reach the autonomous stage: this is discussed further below.

The extent to which these three stages reflect distinct sets of underlying psychological processes is a matter for debate, but in descriptive terms Fitts' observations hold true for the acquisition of many types of skill. The following section looks in more detail at changes in the nature of knowledge as skill develops, and in particular outlines one recent theory which provides an explanation for many of the phenomena described by Fitts (Anderson, 1982; Neves and Anderson, 1981).

Declarative and procedural knowledge

When learning a new skill, a person both acquires new knowledge and reorganizes existing knowledge. As part of this development, the nature of the person's knowledge appears to change from an explicit verbalizable form to an implicit automatically accessed form. Thus in contexts where the development of skill is monitored over a period of time, verbalizations are found to decrease gradually (Anderson, 1982; Chase and Ericsson, 1981; Dean and Martin, 1966). Chase and Ericsson, for example, observed the development of the digit span of a subject over a period of two years. After about 100 hours of practice, when he had a span of about 40 digits, the subject was unable to report details of how the digits were encoded. He was nevertheless able to continue improving both his digit span (to about 80 by the end of the study) and his speed of performance.

These and other findings support the idea that knowledge may be held in memory in at least two forms: declarative and procedural (Anderson, 1976, 1980; Winograd, 1975). Declarative knowledge represents facts which can be articulated and which are stored as propositions (for this reason it is also known as propositional knowledge). Procedural knowledge represents direct knowledge of actions, either physical or mental. This distinction is fundamental to most, if not all, of the recent theories of skill acquisition, although there is some dispute about the detailed representation of these forms of knowledge. For example, Anderson suggests that declarative knowledge is represented in terms of relationships between nodes in a propositional network, whereas procedural knowledge is represented in productions — action rules consisting of a condition that specifies when to act and an action formulation specifying how to act (Anderson, 1983b). However, the precise nature of the form of knowledge representation need not concern us here.

Anderson's approach to skill acquisition can be summarized as follows. In early stages, the person has available (or is able to obtain) a certain amount of declarative knowledge about the task in hand. External instructions seldom specify the detailed procedures to apply, and so this declarative knowledge must be interpreted by means of pre-existing general procedures for action. This process of interpretation is assumed to make heavy demands on working memory and attention. Additional difficulties occur if the knowledge or the pre-existing procedures are inadequate; in such a case, analogies or other problem-solving strategies may have to be used. The process of interpretation underlies some of the phenomena described in Fitt's cognitive phase of skill acquisition (more recently also termed the *declarative* stage). With increasing practice, task-specific procedures are developed, allowing the declarative knowledge to be bypassed (but not necessarily forgotten). The process by which specific procedures are formed is termed *knowledge compilation*, and it is divided into two distinct processes of *composition* and *proceduralization*. Composition occurs when a sequence of low-level productions is merged into a single higher-level production; proceduralization occurs when a production is made more specific in terms of the values or activities that it deals with. These processes are discussed further below. The processes of knowledge compilation account for many of the phenomena described in Fitts' associative stage. Finally, when all appropriate knowledge has been compiled, Fitts' autonomous stage is attained. Improvement in performance of the skill still continues due to a process termed *tuning*. Complex tasks have alternative routes to successful performance, and the person must choose between them. A beginner's search of the task space is likely to be an inefficient hit-and-miss affair, but with experience the search becomes more selective. This process of tuning, similar in some respects to the explanation of exponential exhaustion proposed by Newell and Rosenbloom (1981), is dicussed in a later section (p. 182).

Changes in knowledge: design implications

The declarative stage of skill acquisition is particularly crucial in the learning of office systems. Users may often experience extreme initial difficulties (Mack, Lewis and Carroll, 1983), probably due to problems in gaining and interpreting initial declarative knowledge. Compare the situation of tennis novices having their first lesson with that of word-processor users seated at the terminal for the first time. The tennis novices may be told how to grasp the racquet, how to go through the motions for a forehand stroke and so on. While these activities may seem strange and awkward, the learners will at least be able to understand the instructions without too many problems; they may even be able to interpret them and perform the actions in a crude fashion. They can call upon their general procedures for moving their limbs which are also used, amongst other things, for grasping sticks and swinging golf clubs. The novice word-processor users, on the other hand, may have few such general procedures to back up their initial instructions. There are likely to be both problems of understanding declarative instructions and problems of interpreting such instructions into action. Many of the presented concepts may be meaningless or wrongly interpreted; for example, in one study 80% of novice users thought the term *command* referred to an instruction the system gave to the user (Bott, 1979).

How can the designer tackle these problems? Difficulties arise not because there is insufficient declarative information, but quite the reverse: there is too much to deal with at once, and little of it can be interpreted in terms of procedures for action. This point has been recognized by Carroll *et al.* (1984) who recommend training methods which combine minimal presentation of declarative information with maximum exploration by the learner. This allows users to interpret and compile their knowledge into procedures as quickly as possible. Other workers have pointed to information overload in initial learning as a prime cause of user difficulties. Thus, a recognized problem with step-by-step training manuals is that users blindly follow the instructions while making little sense of what they or the system are doing (Hammond *et al.*, 1983b; Mack, Lewis and Carroll, 1983). Another common observation is that novices tend not to read documentation for more than a few minutes before trying to use a system (Carroll and Mazur, 1984). Anderson, Farrell and Sauers (1984) report that subjects learning the language LISP are not able to read instructions of even modest complexity and then perform the actions described without error.

In addition to minimizing unnecessary declarative baggage, the designer can help the user by limiting user choice during training. This approach has been taken by Carroll and Carrithers (1984a, 1984b) using a 'training wheels' system ('stabilizer wheels' might be the analogous term for UK readers). These authors liken the new user of a text editor to a person in an unfamiliar city with an inadequate map: (s)he may not even be aware of taking a wrong turn because everything looks so strange. Providing a restricted system during training serves to reduce the blind alleys down which the user will inevitably stray.

Yet people do learn even when initial comprehension is seemingly non-existent. Novices launch into the unknown, and if something can be interpreted, then it will be interpreted. The human information-processing system is fortunately highly adaptive and if declarative information fails to result in procedures for action, then knowledge in one domain can at least help in the understanding of another. Analogical reasoning is one way of doing this. For example, the first-time user of a word-processor is likely to know something about typewriters, documents, files and paper-and-pencil editing techniques as well as more general facts about computers, natural language and so on. Armed with this knowledge, a host of analogies can potentially be drawn with the word-processing environment. As islands of knowledge about the system emerge from a sea of ignorance, further analogies and extrapolations can be drawn.

Analogies are only one way of transferring knowledge between domains. More generally, abstract knowledge across domains may be organized into schemata, the complex groupings of knowledge embodying typical instances or categories, which were discussed in Chapter 4 (see also Abelson, 1981; Alba and Hasher, 1983). Schemata may help the user to make inferences about missing or uncertain knowledge (Brewer and Tryens, 1981). There are a host of theoretical issues concerning how domains might be spanned (analogically or otherwise) which need not concern us here (see, for example, Rumelhart and Norman, 1981). For further discussion of design principles arising from consideration of schema theory see Chapter 4.

Inferring missing knowledge has its risks, though. Early in learning, users seek structures on which to hang their excess of free-floating declarative knowledge.

They may draw inappropriate analogies and wild extrapolations; theories may be hastily assembled out of oddments of partially relevant and partially extraneous information. Lewis and Mack (1982) term the process by which users form general hypotheses to account for some specific fact about the system *abduction*. Abduction is adaptive in many learning situations, but for unfamiliar office systems abduction may lead the user down many false trails (Hammond and Barnard, 1984; Mack, Lewis and Carroll, 1983). The root of the problem is that initial confusions lead the user into a cascade of interrelated errors; one mistake leads to another, and things very often get worse before they get better.

There are some particular parallels between domains that ensnare users across a range of office systems. One is the analogy of the screen as a window, leading to the belief that there is always a one-to-one correspondence between displayed information and the information 'inside the system'. This might seem a plausible assumption since the screen is the main source of information about what the system knows; but many systems do not stick to this analogy consistently. Examples of ensuing user problems can be seen in Hammond and Barnard (1984) and Rumelhart and Norman (1981). A second commonly occurring problem results from the natures of characters such as space and new line in typing and in word-processing. On a typewriter, the result of the action of typing a space (and new line) is to move the typing position, analogous to moving the cursor. There is no concept of a space as a specific character. A number of authors have documented difficulties arising when the two domains fail to match (Carroll and Mazur, 1984; Douglas and Moran, 1983; Hammond *et al.*, 1984).

These examples illustrate that, during the early stages of learning, users call on a range of problem-solving strategies for understanding and interpreting their task. This has important implications for training, for example in the provision of analogical frameworks for helping users to cope with initial understanding and interpretation (Halasz and Moran, 1982; Carroll and Thomas, 1982; Rumelhart and Norman, 1981). A common recommendation is to provide many simple conceptual or analogical models, each one of limited scope and making one or two key points. This may be preferable to providing only a unitary conceptual model, an approach sometimes advocated by designers (Hammond *et al.*, 1983a).

Intermittent users of particularly hostile systems may proceed little further than this along the road of skill development. In most cases, one hopes, users will be able to start compiling their knowledge into procedural form. To consider the implications of knowledge compilation we will have to look at some of the underlying processes in more detail.

Changes in processing

Problem-solving and, more generally, the interpretation of declarative knowledge requires much use of working memory, a processing resource discussed in more detail in Chapter 5. Heavy use of working memory has a number of important processing implications. First, manipulation of knowledge will be under attentional control rather than occurring automatically (Schneider, Dumais and Shiffrin, 1984). Second, since the capacity of working memory is small and the declarative knowledge often unfamiliar, processing will be serial, effortful and rather slow. This is certainly a characteristic of much novice performance. Third, again due to the limited capacity of working memory, only small steps can be interpreted at a time. Each step is thought to reflect one or more chunks of information held in working memory. Between each step, the person is likely to require feedback about the success or failure of the step. In other words, the person is operating as a closed loop system rather than as an open loop system (Schmidt, 1975). Finally, since information in working memory is normally available to awareness (Klatzky, 1984), people are easily able to articulate the actions they are taking and the feedback received. Thus this interpretative mode of processing declarative knowledge can be characterized as effortful, slow, requiring the close monitoring of feedback and involving awareness of both relevant states of the environment and of the actions controlling performance.

Controlled and automatic processing

This pattern of processing changes systematically as learning progresses. As we have already described, skilled performance tends to be fast, have minimal requirements for feedback and can be largely automatic. This last characteristic, automaticity, has been the focus of much recent research, and we will discuss some aspects of this before considering the nature of compilation of declarative knowledge. A strong experimental case has been made for distinguishing two qualitatively different forms of processing: controlled and automatic (Schneider and Shiffrin, 1977; Shiffrin and Dumais, 1981; Shiffrin, Dumais and Schneider, 1981; Shiffrin and Schneider, 1977). The underlying reality of this distinction is not without its critics however (Hirst *et al.*, 1980; Ryan, 1983), and there are good reasons for considering it as a continuum rather than a strict dichotomy (Logan, 1985). At one end of the continuum, automatic processing is seen as fast, parallel and fairly effortless; it is not limited by working memory capacity and is not under the direct control of the subject. Automatic processing can coexist with other activities provided there is no competition for specific resources. In contrast, controlled processes are slow, serial, effortful, capacity-limited and subject-regulated. Two simultaneous tasks requiring controlled processes will interfere with each other.

Clearly this dimension embodies many characteristics of the novice-expert dimension. It is therefore no surprise that automatic processing is thought to underlie much of skilled performance (Shiffrin and Dumais, 1981). However a number of *caveats* should be borne in mind. First, automaticity is not the same as skill, but a component process of skilled performance; skilled performance is more than the sum of its automated components (see Logan, 1985, for a discussion). For instance, experts may be able to control their performance very closely despite the fact that components of the skill are automatic (Logan, 1982). Second, most of the experimental work investigating automaticity had used quite simple tasks, particularly visual search and visual detection. It has yet to be demonstrated how automatic processing is involved across the range of cognitive skills. Third, any complex task is likely to involve a mixture of controlled and automatic processes. In general, people remain aware of certain activities during performance, and some actions never seem to become automated at all. One can think of automaticity as one of several processes influencing skilled performance, increasing with practice, but also dependent on other skill components.

Under what conditions does a skill component become automated? The answer seems to be when its triggering conditions and associated actions can be fully compiled into a procedural form. The major precondition is that the stimulus ensemble and the action should be consistently associated; automation will not develop if a stimulus ensemble requires one action on some occasions and another action on other occasions. Interestingly, consistency does not seem to have to be absolute. Schneider and Fisk (1982) have demonstrated the development of automaticity in a detection task under conditions of less than perfect consistency, albeit more slowly than with perfect consistency. A related finding, according with everyday experience, is that automatic processing can generalize from a specific stimulus to others in the same category (Schneider and Fisk, 1984). For example, we can use automatic processes to help us catch flying objects generally rather than just one ball thrown in a particular way.

Automation is also helped by high discriminability between stimulus ensembles, and is influenced by context. Thus under some circumstances it seems that different automatic sequences can be initiated by the same stimuli in different contexts (Schneider and Fisk, 1980). However, this requires special pretraining and especially discriminable stimuli, and there are large differences between individual subjects. This finding has consequences for the use of moded systems, where the same user action is associated with different system functions in different modes.

These findings are all consistent with the notion that knowledge and actions which can be compiled into a single procedure will be performed automatically. Take as an example dialling a telephone number. For unfamiliar numbers, the sequence must be found and held in working memory. General-purpose procedures can be used to peel off each digit and dial it. Many phone numbers, although not committed to memory, fall into a familiar structure. I know that, from York, London numbers are of the form $01 + <3$ digits$> + <4$ digits$>$. A structured set of production rules (a hypothesized form of procedural knowledge) would be able to capitalize on this knowledge. For example, specific 'macroproductions' could develop for dialling 3-digit sequences and 4-digit sequences. Such macroproductions are produced by 'composition' of several lower-level but more general-purpose productions. Note that they still need to access information in working memory — the digits themselves. The whole activity cannot therefore be automated, although within one of the macroproductions, automaticity is achieved once the production variables (the digit values) are instantiated. Finally, imagine dialling a familiar number. Now the second process of compilation can occur, proceduralization. A specific production is generated in which the digits themselves are represented. In this case, working memory is not called upon; the action sequence flows directly from long-term memory. Clearly proceduralization can only usefully occur when the specific information represented in the production recurs consistently. Otherwise a general-purpose production must be used. Note that proceduralization has associated risks of inflexibility. If circumstances change, the production may become inappropriate, and meanwhile the declarative form of the knowledge may have been forgotten. Even after a friend has moved house, one may tend to dial the old number. The production may fail to operate when confronted with a push-button phone instead of a dial phone. Such errors — expert slips — are discussed in the next section.

This formulation also accounts for two other related phenomena associated with increasing skill: the diminishing role of feedback and the shift in attentional control from low-level processes to more conceptual high-level processes. Once the triggering conditions of a fully proceduralized production are met, it will fire without further reference to the contents of working memory. The only form of feedback that might be called upon is information gathered by automatic processes; in dialing, for example, a check that the finger is correctly positioned, that the dial has been rotated the requisite distance and so on. As more elaborate productions are developed, there will be a reduction in the feedback which passes through working memory. Note, however, that feedback may be required by the automated production itself, and the timing of this feedback may be crucial. Also implicit in the theory is the notion of a hierarchy of actions, where low-order actions are represented by specific productions, controlled by higher-order productions. This is very similar in concept to the hierarchical goal structures posited in problem-solving (see, for example, Newell and Simon, 1972). A high-level production cannot be automated until all its embedded low-level productions have been automated too, so conscious control is likely to move up the hierarchy as skill develops. Thus a skilled pianist may reel off complex sequences of actions without awareness of each finger movement, but these movements will be modulated by higher-order processes. These will determine, for example, the expression or musicality of the performance, and it is at this level that the performer's attention is likely to be focused. In contrast, the beginner will attend only to mastering low-level procedures. A fascinating description of the acquisition of a skill (Zen archery) where automation reaches an unusually high level can be seen in Herrigel (1953).

It should be noted that the idea that skilled performance relies on preformed automated productions or action sequences is not a new one, dating back at least to James (1890) and Bryan and Harter (1899). The concepts of motor programme (Keele, 1973), action system, (Shallice, 1979) and action schema (Norman, 1981) also convey much the same notion as Anderson's compiled productions.

Expert slips

The transition from the use of declarative to procedural knowledge and of controlled to automatic processing has a further important consequence. This is that novices and experts are prone to different sorts of errors. As we have seen, novices misunderstand, fail to interpret available information, jump to erroneous conclusions and so on. Expert performance is not necessarily error-free performance: experts show characteristic slips of actions and memory. These errors have been studied most extensively by Reason (1984a); a descriptive account of his work can be seen in Reason and Mycielska (1982).

Slips of action — actions not as planned — are particularly interesting to psychologists because they shed light on the extent to which attentional mechanisms are needed to guide even highly practised activities. For ease of exposition, we have characterized automatic and controlled processing as a dichotomy, whereas introspective evidence, at least, suggests that some sorts of control can operate on the fringes of consciousness, at one moment taking the limelight, at another slipping into the background. Reason (1984b) neatly encapsulates these shades of attentional control by the metaphor of an 'attentional blob' which moves over a 'cognitive board', the blob assuming many different shapes though with usually only a single peak. Although the theoretical underpinnings of this interplay between control, conscious awareness and open-loop *versus* closed-loop activity are largely unexplored, expert slips show strong regularities which have direct implications for the design of information systems to be used by experienced operators.

Many slips of action appear to be due to inappropriate control over sequences of automated behaviour. Thus the great majority occur within highly practised routines, and errors which are intrusions are almost invariably intact segments of automated behaviours themselves. The automaticity framework suggests two basic causes of control failure: failures occurring when the person is in automatic mode but should have been exercising controlled processing; and the obverse, where controlled processing interferes with an automatic process best left to its own devices. This division seems to reflect quite well natural categorizations of slips (Reason, 1984a). In particular, many intrusion errors, where a highly practised activity as it were snatches the reins of behaviour from the intended but less familiar activity, seem to be due to lapses of attention. Typical examples are taking off both shoes and socks when intending to remove shoes only, or intending to stop at the shops on the way home from work but driving straight past. Such errors, termed 'double-capture slips' by Reason, occur when attention is occupied elsewhere at a point when it is needed to divert activity from a well-trodden (or recently trodden) path to a less familiar one. (The particular term stems from the extraneous capture of attention together with the capture of behaviour by the more practised production or action schema.)

Another class of intrusions, and one likely to be relevant to system use, stems from recognition errors due to perceptual similarity. Here an external object (or any stimulus configuration) may trigger an inappropriate recognition schema because the object looks like or has a similar function to some other object (spooning salt rather than sugar onto breakfast cereal; turning off a light when leaving a room with other people still in it). In such cases rather meagre attention may have been allocated to the recognition process due to the habitual nature of the particular behaviour. Some disastrous consequences of recognition failure are explored by Reason and Mycielska (1982).

A related group of errors, probably due to recognition failure on some occasions, are 'wrong object' errors where the intended action is performed but in relation to the wrong object. A typical example is throwing away a sweet while putting the wrapper in one's mouth. Finally, failure to apply controlled processing can give rise not only to slips of action, but also to apparent slips of memory, such as lost intentions ('what did I come in here for?') or local unawareness (looking for a key already held in one's hand). The extent to which these distinctions represent different underlying mechanisms is still a matter of debate.

The second possible cause of slips is the overzealous control of an automated sequence. Errors of omission and of repetition often seem to result from attention being directed at an ongoing and routine activity. Activities such as making tea or coffee are particularly prone to these errors probably partly because they involve delays. Errors occur when inadequate checks by the attentional system conclude either that the activity has progressed less far than it has in effect — in which case a repetition occurs — or alternatively that it has progressed further than it really has — in which case an omission results. These types of errors are particularly to be expected at intermediate levels of practice, where the sequence is sometimes achieved automatically and sometimes under attentional control. As control drifts away from and back to the activity, possibilities for failing to keep track may blossom.

Many of these errors can be seen either as slips of memory or as failure of attention. While at the extremes this distinction appears to have validity, more often the distinction merely reflects two sides of the same coin. For example, 'forgetting' to stop at the shops on the way home results from a failure to attend to the habitual activity of driving along a familiar route; this activity normally proceeds with little reference to working memory and without leaving a memory trace in its wake. The error can be categorized as a memory failure only because the attention system failed to monitor ongoing driving activity; categorization as an action failure is only possible because of a failure to maintain in working memory the intention to stop.

There is little reason to doubt that computer users fall foul of these kinds of errors; in fact preliminary surveys confirm this (Green *et al.*, 1984; Norman, 1982). While designers cannot control the stranger vagaries of the human information processor, they can at least minimize the possibility of some types of error occurring. Increased discriminability will minimize perceptual confusions which could lead to inappropriate triggering of productions. Errors of omission and repetition can be reduced by eliminating delays and by avoiding command sequences with potential for cyclical confusion. Forms of dialogue which encourage either controlled or automatic processing can be selected where appropriate.

Under certain circumstances, it may even be the case that experts actually perform worse than novices as a consequence of the different forms of representation or of the processing used. For example, Adelson (1984) demonstrated that novices were able to answer concrete questions about computer programs better than experts when the program had been originally studied with the help of an abstract description. She hypothesized that novices, in contrast to experts, were likely to represent the program in concrete terms despite the presence of the abstract description. A particularly interesting suggestion is that individuals with an intermediate level of skill perform worse than those with either less or more experience (Lesgold, 1984). He provides preliminary evidence for a non-monotomic relationship between experience and performance in a study of radiological diagnosis. The kink in the learning curve might happen as a consequence of a major shift in processing or knowledge representation; immediately after a shift, intermediate practitioners are more likely to make errors than they were before. An alternative possibility is not that a major shift occurs, but that at intermediate skill levels processing is partly but not completely automated, with a fluctuating level of control. Certain aspects of the task may be especially prone to error at this point.

Changes in processing: design implications

The more components of a skill can be automated, the faster it will be performed. The risk is that it will also become rigid and insensitive to unusual circumstance. How, then, should systems be designed which can be quickly learned and which support error-free user performance? An initial step for the designer is to identify those components of the user's task which would benefit from automation and those components which should remain controlled. Routine action sequences used often and which are amenable to a consistent mapping between user command and system function are prime candidates for automation. Examples for a word-processor might by cursor control, common commands for deletion, saving documents and so on. Other task components are non-routine and may never be automated. These may require active problem-solving and will call upon the user's working memory. An example is the specification of a complex Boolean expression for searching a database. A further special class is those commands for which automatic processing would be possible but unwise. An example is a command which irrevocably deletes many files from a disc. In such circumstances controlled processing could be encouraged by showing a message such as:

Press <x> to confirm the command

where <x> is a character selected at random on each occasion.

Since extent of practice is a prime determinant of level of automation of a skill component, it is important for the designer to be clear about the expected mean usage of the system (and its subcomponents) and possibly too about the range of usage. For one system it may be more important to optimize learnability over the first few hours, for another ease of use after many months of training may be the prime objective. Principles derived from the literature reviewed above would clearly play different roles in the design of these two contrasting systems.

A number of such principles are listed at the end of this chapter, and so will not be repeated here in detail. Some general points on changes in processing are worth raising though. First, much of the dialogue conducted by novices will be governed by controlled processes. This will make heavy demands on working memory, so system dialogue should be designed to minimize such memory load. Feedback following any user action which terminates a transaction 'chunk' (see Chapter 5) should also be provided. Second, the probability of a given dialogue transaction becoming automated depends on a range of systems and user factors. These include the discriminability amongst the user actions for performing the full range of functions, and the compatability between attributes of the user action and of the system function, such as the schematic, physical or spatial attributes. An example of a compatible spatial code is the use of spatially-positioned control keys to move a cursor. Also important is the consistency of action to unique function. A menu system in which the letter D means delete in one context, display in another and edit data in a third will not be easily automated if there is any contextual ambiguity (and if it is automated, it will be error-prone). The more modes or contexts a system has, the harder it is for the user to discriminate between modes and consequently the more resistant ambiguous dialogue sequences will be to automation. Mode issues are discussed further by Monk (1986), Poller and Garter (1984) and Thimbleby (1982). Automation is also dependent on rapid and clear feedback of information upon which subsequent user action is contingent. In general, research on skill learning suggests that system function and dialogue should be as simple as possible, compatible with the required task support. For example, provision of syntactic variants to cater for individual preference (such as alternative means of menu item selection) may inhibit automation and slow down learning (Barnard and Hammond, 1982). It is relevant that even relative experts tend to use only a subset of commands in a system when use of a larger set of commands would be more effective (Draper, 1984; Rosson, 1984).

STRATEGIC FACTORS IN SKILL ACQUISITION

People do things in different ways. If you ask a group of people to add 732 to 641, some will add the units first, others the hundreds or tens. Some will rely on subvocal rehearsal to hold intermediate results, others will rely on visualization. In many tasks a variety of processes can be mobilized, and in varying orders. Strategy refers to the particular means chosen for achieving the task. The choice of strategy may or may not be deliberate; sometimes optional strategies may be called upon without any conscious control at all.

Choice of strategy appears to be an important determinant of certain types of problem-solving and in the construction of mental models, both important components of initial comprehension of office systems (Chapter 4). Strategies also play their part in the different stages of skill acquisition. During the declarative stage, a number of important heuristics appear to influence the strategies employed. As we have already noted, the novice user can be faced with an imposing barrage of new information. One strategy for coping with this burden is to find means of selectively ignoring information, such as taking on board only those aspects which are directly relevant to immediate task goals. Thus Young and Hull (1982), in noting how Viewdata users 'fail' to read important information on display frames, hypothesized that people's current goals govern their immediate expectations and hence their strategies for searching for information. Further examples of goal-directed learning by novice users are given by Hammond and Barnard (1984).

Another important heuristic, relevant throughout learning, is Zipf's principle: people attempt to minimize mental effort (Zipf, 1949). This often results in roundabout strategies using familiar routes, but which avoid unnecessary thinking, mental computation or learning. Sometimes the familiar route may mirror the non-computer means of achieving the same task, in which case an existing memory schema may be called upon to organize the sequence of actions. In other situations, users may just stick with the subset of tools which do the job adequately, tools perhaps acquired early in learning. The finding that even expert editor users fail to use optimal commands probably stems from such strategies (Draper, 1984; Rosson, 1984). Of course the user may not know that more efficient routes exist if the system fails to make evident alternative options and their consequences.

Strategies can influence the rate of learning more directly. Barnard *et al.* (1982) studied novices learning different versions of a simple editor. When the required command was unknown, some users adopted a *passive* strategy of looking up the information in help displays, while other users were more likely to have a guess, or at least to spend time considering what to do before consulting the help information. Generally speaking, users who adopted this more *active* strategy learned the meanings of the commands more rapidly. The choice of strategy was influenced both by the nature of the command terms (very general terms tended to induce a passive strategy; see also Chapter 7 for a discussion of the optimal levels of generality for command names) and by the predisposition of the user. Choice of strategy may have been directed by the 'minimum mental effort' heuristic: if the command terms give little clue as to their possible meaning, there is little gain in rousing the mental effort to make an informed guess. Hence it is quite plausible that systems with sufficiently hostile interfaces will induce strategies in the user which effectively terminate any further learning.

Strategies can also play an important role in the later stages of skill acquisition, although the task itself may limit the scope for strategic improvement. For example, a skilled touch typist may have such a well-structured set of motor schemata that little scope for further strategic improvement remains. Residual gain may accrue merely from streamlining existing productions. However in other tasks, and a good example is the digit-span task used by Chase and Ericsson (1981), major strategic reorganizations may still occur after many hours' training. The learning curve of Chase and Ericsson's subject (who, it will be recalled, increased his span to over 80 digits) shows evidence of plateaus where performance is static, followed by improvements where some new organizational strategy is hit upon. The question of whether such rises preceded by plateaus are a general feature of skilled learning has been a contentious one (for example, see Keller, 1958). It does seem that cognitive skills calling heavily upon problem-solving are more prone to plateaus, presumably because of the possibility of large and significant shifts in strategy. In contrast, perceptual-motor skills more typically improve smoothly.

This difference may lie in the grain of the productions being modified rather than in any more fundamental differences in learning. As Anderson (1982) points out, all tasks can be characterized as having a search associated with them, although in some cases the search is trivial. According to his theory, the efficient route taken through the task space by the expert is a result of procedural learning, or *tuning*. Tuning calls upon the basic learning mechanisms of *generalization* (where productions become broader in their scope), *discrimination* (where productions become more specific) and *strengthening* (where successful productions take precedence over less successful ones). The first two of these can be used to generate a search by successively expanding and narrowing the scope of productions to try new pathways. The mechanism of strengthening serves to evaluate the productions. Whether or not changes brought about by these processes are termed strategies may be a function of the scope of the productions, their level in the production hierarchy, and the availability of their inputs and outputs to conscious scrutiny.

CONCLUDING REMARKS

The reader may feel that (s)he is little wiser about the theoretical basis of how people acquire complex skills. Psychology can perhaps claim to improve slightly on the contention that cognitive skills are learned by magic, but only slightly. Nevertheless, the review has outlined the much greater success of psychology in pointing to the conditions that facilitate or inhibit skill learning, to the errors and difficulties that people encounter and to the typical course that learning takes. All these areas have implications for learners of information systems, and so for the designers of such systems too. A final note of caution should be sounded, though. As mentioned before, computer use typically involves much more diverse activitives than laboratory tasks. Extrapolation of laboratory findings becomes increasingly risky both as the distance between the laboratory task and the application task increases and as the level of precision required rises. So while general qualitative principles may apply to the design of information systems quite validly (though perhaps not very usefully), attempts to quantify complex learning precisely have to move well beyond the present knowledge of psychology and will be founded as much on fortune as on science.

SUMMARY PRINCIPLES

Specification of a set of summary principles inevitably results in a tension between the need to provide interpretable information widely relevant to design and the need to keep within shouting distance of empirical findings. Within the spirit of this book, we have probably strayed more towards applicability than strict academic respectability would warrant, and without doubt some of the principles will be wrong in some, even many, situations. Some may also be uninterpretable. Much of the psychological evidence underlying the principles has been reviewed above, and readers can make their own judgements. Our plea is the one expounded elsewhere in this book (Chapter 2), that the provision of psychologically based principles maybe is a flawed form of communication between psychologist and designer but it is less flawed than many others.

The principles are organized into sets or bundles, each bundle consisting of a general statement about user cognition together with a number of more specific statements intended to provide links into the domain of design. The first three bundles concern the acquisition of declarative knowledge, an area dealt with in more detail in Chapter 4. Hence they are specified only generally, and as such they are unlikely to be directly interpretable into design decisions.

1. Since much of the interaction with office systems requires no verbal mediation, information which can be interpreted procedurally (that is, using existing memory schemata) will be easier to learn and to use.
    1.1 Users attempt to interpret unfamiliar concepts in terms of existing procedures or schemata; the system should support compatibility with and access to such knowledge. (Note that such knowledge might concern task or system.)

1.2 Where no appropriate knowledge for procedural interpretation exists then users attempt to understand unfamiliar concepts by means of analogy with other more general knowledge; the system should support access to and reasoning with such knowledge.

2. User learning and knowledge retrieval are context-dependent.

2.1 Users interpret, process and retrieve unfamiliar concepts in terms of current task and system contexts (see Chapters 5 and 7).

2.2 Users interpret unfamiliar concepts in terms of the immediate task goal. (This is a particular instance of 2.1.)

3. Interpretation of declarative knowledge is verbally mediated and requires controlled processing.

3.1 Interpretation of unfamiliar information makes heavy demand on working memory (see also Chapter 5).

3.2 Interpretation of unfamiliar information is subject to the limitations of memory for verbal material and of language processing (see Chapters 5 and 7).

The next four bundles of principles are all concerned with conditions influencing the extent to which a sequence of dialogue transactions will become automated. Further bundles deal with the consequences of extent of automation. It will be clear that, in the hope of deriving applicable principles, we have made some naïve psychological assumptions. In particular, we treat the learning of a transaction as a single dimension whose extremes are the controlled and automatic modes of processing. At any particular time a given transaction sequence can be located at a position along this dimension.

4. Level of practice is a major influence on learning, and time to complete a sequence is determined by the power law. Degree of automation is a linear function of sequence completion time and so is also related to level of practice according to the power law (this working assumption is, as far as we know, unsupported by empirical evidence).

4.1 Level of user experience can be defined (a) by the intended usage of the system averaged over the population of users, and (b) by the total time spent on the system by the particular subset of users at which the interface design is targeted.

4.2 Since forgetting occurs between user sessions, users of 'occasional use' systems will learn less quickly than users of 'frequent use' systems matched for total time of use.

4.3 The level of practice of a given dialogue sequence is the product of (a) the frequency of use per unit time of the sequence within the same task and system contexts (or in different contexts provided the meaning and consequences of the sequence are the same) and (b) the level of user experience. Level of practice predicts completion time and extent of automation according to the power law of practice.

Note that bundle 4 makes no claims about the parameters of the power relationship; these are determined (in part) by the factors outlined in bundles 5 to 8.

5. The nature of system feedback influences the extent of automation. Feedback can be divided into *required feedback*, upon which a subsequent user action is contingent, and *redundant feedback*, which may be informative but is not formally necessary for further user action.

    5.1 A sequence involving required feedback is less likely to be automated than one not involving feedback.

    5.2 If the required feedback within a sequence demands 'attention' then that sequence will not be automated: 'attention' is needed for (a) waiting for an event, (b) mental computation or calculation, (c) thinking or reasoning, (d) very precise perceptual analysis or motor control; 'attention' is not needed for accessing and operating with familiar information stored in long-term memory.

    5.3 A crude operational measure of the attention-demanding characteristics of a system action is the estimated difficulty and slowness of the subsequent user action.

    5.4 A consequence of 5.2 is that presenting the user with redundant alternatives (for example, different means of achieving the same goal) will reduce the probabily of automation.

6. The nature of the user's goals, either self-generated or required by the system, will influence the extent of automation.

    6.1 A sequence is unlikely to be automated if it crosses a major boundary in the user's goal structure.

7. Organization of user actions and system functions will influence the extent of automatization.

    7.1 Automatization is more likely if each possible user action is assigned to a single system action (the consistency principle).

    7.2 Where the consistency principle cannot be maintained, automatization will be maximized if user actions are grouped into different system or task modes (contexts or environments) which are maximally discriminable in terms of (a) conceptual system and task features, and (b) perceptual display features.

    7.3 If the consistency principle cannot be maintained despite 7.2 (that is, within contexts), then, for maximum probability of automatization, those occasions on which consistency is violated should (a) be kept to a minimum, and (b) be clearly signalled.

7.4 The more discriminable the user actions, the greater the probability of automation.

7.5 Given maximum discriminability, automatization will be maximized if semantic, spatial or other physical relationships between user actions map onto equivalent (such as isomorphic) relationships between the associated system actions.

7.6 Where alternative contexts are used, automatization will be maximized if the relationship between a given user action and its resultant system action in one mode is the same as (or conceptually related to) the relationship between the same user action and its resultant system action in another mode.

8. The length of dialogue transactions will influence the extent of automation. (This principle is an acknowledgement — in impoverished form — of the hierarchical nature of knowledge compilation.)

8.1 The less transactions in a dialogue component, the greater the probability of its automation.

8.2 The shorter the user action within a transaction, the greater the probability of its automation.

The remaining principles take as input the extent of automation of a given dialogue sequence and relate this to user performance. For clarity of exposition, we treat controlled and automatic modes as a dichotomy rather than as a continuum.

9. Desirability of controlled versus automatic processing.

9.1 Controlled sequences are sensitive to stimulus context and exception conditions: automated sequences are fixed (or at most are subject to only minor modification once invoked). Hence sequences with possible risky consequences (especially when the most frequent user action is the 'safe' option — due to principles 12.1 and 12.2) should be controlled sequences.

9.2 Controlled processing is verbally mediated: automatic processing is not. Therefore when the task requires modification to the action sequence as a consequence of processing other declarative knowledge, then controlled processing is desirable. More colloquially, controlled processing is desirable when users should stop and think about what to do, otherwise they might jump the gun.

9.3 Controlled sequences are performed slowly: automated sequences are performed quickly. Hence, other than for conditions described in 9.1 and 9.2, automatic processing is desirable (but refer to bundle 12).

10. Feedback and controlled versus automatic processing.

10.1 For controlled sequences, confirmatory feedback is needed at the end of every dialogue component which might form a chunk in working memory (that is, a meaningful unit of dialogue; see Chapter 5).

10.2 During the course of an automated sequence, only required feedback need be provided, and this should occur as rapidly and as clearly as possible.

10.3 Feedback following a controlled transaction should (a) differentiate the user action just completed from other potentially confusable actions and actions which would have had different system or task consequences; and (b) provide any relevant information on the system and task states to help the user determine future actions.

10.4 At the termination of an automated sequence, confirmatory feedback (both required and redundant) may be needed. (This is a specific instance of 10.1, since at this point processing would be controlled.)

11. Memorial consequences of controlled and automatic processing.

11.1 Controlled sequences require use of working memory to hold at least alternative possible actions and outcomes: automatic processing does not load working memory. (This principle may not be applicable in itself, but has implications for principles concerning working memory, Chapter 5.)

11.2 Only one controlled process can proceed at one time: automatic processes can coexist with other automatic or controlled processes provided they do not overlap in their demands for perceptual or motor mechanisms.

12. Controlled versus automatic processing and errors.

12.1 The probability of an inappropriate automated sequence being triggered (activation via an inaccurate recognition schema) is a monotonic function of the similarity between the triggering configurations of the appropriate and the inappropriate components. Critical aspects of the triggering configurations include task features (a similar sequence of goals) as well as system features.

12.2 The probability of a capture error — an automated component 'capturing' a similar sequence of transactions (usually a sequence which starts with or includes the same sub-sequence of transactions) — is a monotonic function of the similarity between the two system states at the point that the two sequences should have deviated.

THE NEXT CHAPTER

This chapter has outlined the conditions that facilitate or inhibit skill acquisition, the errors people make and the difficulties people experience when confronted with new situations, and the typical course that learning can take. All these areas have implications for learners of information systems, and for the designers of such systems.

A major difference between skilled performance at a human–machine interface to an electronic office system and skilled performance in other areas (for example, at a typewriter) is that the machine more obviously 'answers back' in a quasi-intelligent way. This is why one talks of human–machine 'dialogue'. Such dialogues have, at least at a superficial level and increasingly at a more fundamental level, the characteristics of a true language. In the next chapter, we consider aspects of the psychology of language that can usefully be applied to the design of human–machine dialogue.

Principles from the psychology of language

James A. Hampton

INTRODUCTION

Our concern in this chapter will be to describe the psychology of language from two very different and contrasting perspectives. On the one hand, we can conceive of language as the most evolved and sophisticated natural system of symbolic representation known to us. Using natural language we are able to define, manipulate and operate on symbolic representations of the world. We use word meanings to provide a set of readily available categories for indentifying our experience to ourselves and others, and we understand and interpret our experience, and even our actions by composing verbal descriptions of it. There is a common sense view in which 'putting something into words' is equivalent to making it more precise, more understandable, and more amenable to analysis. Informal evidence suggests that the actual process of formulating thoughts in a linear verbal form can have marked effects on the clarity and development of those thoughts. Language does not give us a direct window onto someone else's thoughts. Rather those thoughts are changed by the very process of putting them into words. Word meanings also form a large and important part of the shared culture within a linguistic community. As a child learns to talk, so (s)he is gradually and subtly socialized into the community, through learning the appropriate use of the words in his or her language.

From the other perspective, language can be seen as a great deal more than a means for the symbolic expression of concepts and propositions. Language is also a form of behaviour in the pursuit of which we spend a great deal of our time. Taken in this broad sense of communicative social interaction, language need not be confined to mere words and spoken utterances. Deprived of oral language, the deaf are able to develop alternative sign languages capable of equivalent levels of sophistication and subtlety. Indeed there is considerable evidence (Lenneberg,

1967) that there is a biological instinctive faculty for language development in humans, which ensures that almost all of us develop the full range of syntactical complexity embodied in the local dialect to which we are exposed. Our spoken utterances are also accompanied by a wide range of additional channels for communication. These include intonation and stress, pauses and rhythm, facial expression and bodily posture. Most important of all, for understanding language as a means of communication, is the fact that language is a form of *social* behaviour, requiring the cooperation and coordination of activities on the part of all the people (or other parties) involved in any interchange (this may include the speaker, the addressee, and others who may be merely listening to the conversation at that point, but may contribute at a later stage).

Clearly not all of these many aspects of the social activity of talking are going to prove relevant to the designer of user–system interfaces. Since the early days, when the user was required to learn lengthy and tediously fussy amounts of computer language in order to communicate with the system, the modern revolution in design continues to stress *friendliness* to the user as a prime object of a system. Friendliness is, however, not so easy to define *a priori*, and often depends on a trial and error approach to the problem. By understanding the nature of language as it is used between people in their conversations, it should become easier to see what an electronic system should embody in order to appear more friendly. Being a speaker of a language gives the user a strong set of expectations about how conversations should run.

Our argument is, therefore, that both the study of word meaning, and the study of conversation will provide rich sources of insights for the design of friendlier user–system interfaces. Consequently this chapter will be divided into two main sections. In the first section, issues of meaning will be discussed: how we understand what words refer to, the flexibility and the vagueness of natural concepts and word meanings. User–system interfaces that intend to use natural language terms in their dealings with the user must take account of the context-dependent and slippery nature of meaning in everyday speech. In the second section, we will discuss the psychology of language as a type of social behaviour. To the extent that electronic systems fail to obey the conventions and practices of language interaction, they will continue to be seen as unfriendly, intolerant, rude and uncooperative. Efficient communication, successful training of users, and a happy customer require that the interface be capable of following the rules and conventions of conversation. Alternatively, it must be designed in a way that minimizes the need for open and free conversation — as for example with menu selection, where the user's possible contribution to the conversation is severely limited to one of a small number of options.

Finally, by way of setting the scene, we should point out that this essay is in no way a general review of the psychology of language. We will have nothing to say about work on speech perception and production, on reading and writing, sentence comprehension, parsing, or language development in children. For the purposes in this book, it seems to us that these topic areas, although posing fascinating and important questions for psychologists and linguists, may be less central for providing design guidelines for user-interface design. What the designer needs to be aware of, we will argue, is the way in which language maps onto the thoughts of the user, and the expectations that the user has about other users of his or her language, which in this case include information systems.

WORD MEANINGS AND CONCEPTS

One of the chief difficulties facing designers who wish to improve the language-like appearance of a user–system interface concerns word meaning. When a program talks of files, documents, records, discs and the like, or of operations such as editing, copying, cutting, erasing and so forth, the concepts underlying the meanings of such terms *as understood by the computer system* are fixed (that is they remain constant across different contexts and different content domains), and they are well-defined (that is their meaning can be given by pointing to the particular role they play in the interface as a whole, the effects they have, the other concepts with which they can interact, and so forth). Unfortunately, natural language terms simply do not abide by these two constraints. In an office environment, we may use the words 'file' and 'record', at times interchangeably, sometimes as naming disjoint sets of things, and at other times as naming nested sets. Similarly, different operations may sometimes have the same name, and sometimes different names. The reference of a term (the class of objects, events or processes for which we can use the term as a name) is neither fixed across contexts and domains, nor is it well-defined. When system users have to learn the use or meaning of a term within the system, they are therefore faced with the problem of relating the technical use of the term to the cluster of common everyday uses and meanings that it may have.

This is not a new problem. In the development of science, there has frequently been a deal of confusion caused by the lack of conceptual clarity in our everyday concepts of processes in the physical world. Wiser and Carey (1982) describe the case of the physics of heat, where for a long time progress in understanding was impeded by failing to distinguish between heat, as in the degree of heat contained within a body, and hotness, as in the measured temperature of the body. Similar conceptual confusion arose with the concept of speed in pre-Gallilean physics (Kuhn, 1977). One way to try to evade the problem is to invent a new terminology specific to the field, in which terms receive clear, well-constructed definitions. Thus one might replace 'heat' with a notion of 'calorific content', in a prescientific attempt to free oneself of the confusion caused by lay language concepts. The problem with devising new terms is of course the proliferation of non-standard jargon, which is difficult to learn and more likely to lead to greater confusion still. As Piaget pointed out, learning necessarily involves assimilation of new learnt material to existing schemata, so the best hope is to elucidate those schemata and their structure, and to develop software that is compatible with them, and easily assimilated to them (see also Chapter 4).

In this section we will review the psychological evidence concerning the nature of concepts. In particular we will stress their flexibility and indeterminacy. No distinction will be made between word meanings and concepts, although these are not the same class of thing. We shall make the assumption that most of the words that an interface is likely to want to use correspond to (can be mapped onto) concepts whose structure is very similar to those that have been the subject of much close scrutiny in the psychological literature.

Linguistic relativity

As a way into the subject, let us start with the problem of how thought depends on language. Following the work of Whorf (1956), a great deal of interest was generated by the notion that our thinking is placed in a straightjacket of language. Depending upon which of the world's languages we speak, we are predisposed to think in particular ways. There have been many studies of this hypothesis, none producing very convincing results (see Rosch, 1974b, for a review). One aspect of this research, however, is particularly relevant. This research considered the way in which our vocabulary divides up the world — the categories of our perception and of our thought. To take an example, Brown and Lenneberg (1954) gave subjects a selection of small chips of different colours to name. They found that some were easily and rapidly given a short, high frequency name, by a large majority of the subjects. These colours were highly 'codeable'. Others received different names from different people, the names were often phrases rather than single words, and the time to give them was generally slow. These colours were of low codeability. They then measured the ease with which the two kinds of colour were recognized in a delayed colour memory test, and found that the highly codeable colours were better recognized. They argued that this result indicates the possible role of our verbal concepts in encoding memory for perceptual stimuli.

The interpretation of this result changed markedly, however, as the result of some research by Eleanor Rosch (for example, 1973). Rosch taught colour names to members of a primitive tribe, the Dani of New Guinea, who had no colour names corresponding to common words like *red* or *blue* in their vocabulary. She discovered that the colour categories were much easier to learn if the terms being taught corresponded to codeable colours in English, than if they corresponded to hues in between. She thus showed that the relation of recognition memory to colour naming is in fact dependent on a third more basic factor — the perceptual 'goodness' of particular colours. Red is given a high frequency name in our language for the same reason that it is easy to remember — it is in the perception of the colour that the answer lies, and not in the mere naming of it. She obtained similar results with teaching the Dani names for geometric plane figures. Concepts like equilateral triangles, circles and squares were easier to learn than arbitrarily distorted versions of them. For both colours and shapes, it appears that there are 'natural prototypes' around which concepts can easily be formed.

This analysis suggests that there should be a universal effect of particular colours being easily named, regardless of language. This is what Berlin and Kay (1969) in fact found. Analysing the colour wavelengths corresponding to the *best* hue for colour names across a range of languages, they found that the wavelengths clustered around particular points on the colour spectrum—corresponding to the primary colours of red, green, blue and yellow. In fact languages only have terms for secondary colours (pink, orange, purple, brown and grey) if they already have primary colour terms, and they only have primary colour terms if they already have names for black and white.

It appears then that colour terms do not provide good evidence for cultural effects of language terminology affecting conceptualization. Another popular candidate for such effects is the degree of differentiation in different domains of vocabulary across different languages. Thus Eskimo languages contain many words for types of snow, desert dwellers have many words for types of camel, Far Eastern languages for types of rice, and so forth. Surely having such a wide vocabulary for talking about a particular topic must lead to a better understanding of the domain.

In spite of the intuitive appeal of this argument, the direct influence of language is again unlikely to be strong. While it is clearly true that specialists in a particular field such as medicine or computer engineering have large vocabularies of specialized terms for describing and thinking about their areas of expertise, it is not the possession of the terms *per se* which leads to the understanding and depth of knowledge they have. The vocabulary can be seen as a necessary part of learning the domain of knowledge, but it is certainly not sufficient.

It is not language that leads to conceptualization, but rather the other way around. Consider the number of terms that we have in English for types of bird, tree, flower, fish and other categories of natural object. Now imagine how many words you have in your vocabulary for which you could not identify the named object. Most of us know the names of common English trees — oak, ash, elm, beech, birch immediately spring to mind—but if asked to point them out on a walk in the park, we would have real difficulty identifying which was which. Clearly the existence of a highly differentiated vocabulary does not imply a highly differentiated conceptual space.

For a systems designer then, various principles should govern the choice of terms, and the construction of their associated concepts. First, although existence of vocabulary does not guarantee depth of knowledge, one could certainly argue that it makes learning easier. For instance learning to identify trees may be a lot easier for the existence of common terms for them in our vocabulary. We do not have to learn the names — just the association of name to definition. From this notion, it would follow that using familiar English words (in an English-speaking community) will make an interface language easier to learn than if novel or technical terms are used. (Familiar terms will also aid friendliness from a purely motivational–emotional standpoint.) The danger of course is where interference may arise from the everyday understanding of the terms used. If, for example, the words CUT and PASTE are used for excising sections of a text and inserting them elsewhere, everyday connotations of the terms may lead to erroneous expectations (for example, that the CUT text will be removed and not merely copied, that a blank space must be created in which to PASTE the section, that one cannot CUT across page boundaries, and so on). Awareness of these prior understandings may greatly aid the designer in picking suitable terms, and aid the development of introductory documentation and training materials which can draw attention to the differences between the technical sense of the word, within the system, and the cluster of meanings with which the word may be associated in everyday usage.

A second principle may be taken from the fact that we seem to be able to have words in our vocabulary which although perfectly familiar, do not correspond to properly defined concepts. Miller (1969) refers to word meanings as possessing 'partial definitions'. So, as we saw above, we may believe that an elm is a deciduous tree, found commonly in Britain, growing to about the height of the average house. Our concept may not however be sufficient for us to identify one, or to know the suitability of the wood for carpentry, log fires, and so forth. From this example we can suggest that concepts are acquired *gradually* with more information and specification being added to them as their use requires. In the process of learning to use a system, it should therefore follow that concepts that have to be learnt should be constructed so that they can be used successfully at different levels of understanding. Depending on how much a particular user needs to know about a concept term, (s)he should be able to acquire, in a stepwise fashion, greater knowledge about it. Systems designed to allow the user to operate at different levels of understanding should be not only more widely attractive, but should actually be easier to learn to use.

Basic level objects

One of the most important results to emerge from the experimental study of concepts concerns the level of generality at which different words apply. Roger Brown (1956) pointed out that the words we most commonly use to name objects, and those which children first learn as names, are neither the most general, nor the most specific terms we have, but are at some intermediate level of generality. Research into the way in which conceptual space is differentiated at different levels was undertaken in further work by Rosch. Rosch *et al.* (1976) did a series of experiments in which they investigated hierarchies of concepts. An object such as the one I am sitting on can be called a number of things in English. It is a cane chair, a wooden chair, a chair, an article of furniture, a household object, an artefact, or a thing. Many of these terms can be organizied in apparent class inclusion hierarchies — wooden chairs are a subset of chairs, which are a subset of furniture, and so on. Rosch and her colleagues set out to investigate these different levels of categorization. What they discovered is that there is a particular level which can be called 'basic'. This is the level of generality which we most commonly use to name any object — in the above example the term CHAIR is the basic object level term. There are a large number of converging measures that all point to the basic level. Linguistically, it tends to be the most specific level at which the name is still a single lexical item, (CHAIR as opposed to ARMCHAIR), and also tends to be the term with highest frequency in the language. It has been found to be the term that parents use when naming an object to children (for instance, CAT not ANIMAL), and is consequently the term that appears first in children's vocabulary. Psychologically, the basic term has been shown to be the most general level at which one can form a single image of the object (Rosch *et al*. 1976), and the level at which one is fastest to match up a picture with a previously presented name (Murphy and Smith, 1982). It is also the level at which the number of properties that the objects in the class have in common reaches an asymptote — both in perceptual and in functional aspects (Rosch *et al.*, 1976). Tversky and Hemenway (1984) showed that basic level terms also categorize together objects that share the same kinds of 'parts', and argue that the parts structure of object concepts may form the basis of establishing the basic level in any concept hierarchy.

There are two interesting further developments of this basic object notion. The first is the idea that increasing expertise may change the basic level to a more specific level. Rosch *et al*.(1976) reported the case of an aircraft mechanic whose expert knowledge of aeroplanes led him not to treat AEROPLANE as the basic level. For him, a Boeing 747, or a DC10 were basic level objects, as unlike to him as aeroplanes and helicopters are to us. One can see how an intimate knowledge of the parts of different makes of plane would necessarily increase the perceived commonality of different models of the 747, and decrease the commonality between 747s and DC10s.

The second development involves a revision of the general theory of basic objects. Jolicoeur, Gluck and Kosslyn (1984), using a name–picture matching task, showed that whereas a highly representative member of a basic object class is most quickly identified with its basic object name, an unrepresentative member may be more rapidly identified with a name subordinate to the basic level. Thus, for example, a sedan car is more rapidly identified as a CAR than as a SEDAN, but a jeep may be better identified as a JEEP than as a CAR. Robins are identified as BIRDS more rapidly than as ROBINS, whereas penguins are more rapidly identified as PENGUINS than as BIRDS. We have therefore to revise the notion of basic object level. It seems that there is not a particular level of generality in a hierarchy which is identified as basic. Object names on the same level can be both basic and not basic. The correct way of conceiving of the effect is in terms of individual objects. Any particular object (or picture) has a particular name which is basic for that object. Such names will *tend* to be found all at a particular level in a concept hierarchy. However it is not the name *per se* which is basic. (BIRD is basic for SPARROWS, but not for OSTRICHES.) It is the object–name relation which is basic. Thus for every object or picture there is a particular concept term which is the most easily and readily used name.

To draw some tentative conclusions for the design of information systems, the basic object research suggests that where a set of functions or variables in a system is organized hierarchically, then one level should be chosen to be the basic level. This level should be given familiar common short words for naming the functions. It should maximize the degree of differentiation between concepts relative to the degree of similarity between subordinate terms within each concept class. When learning to use the system, people should be introduced to this intermediate level first, and become familiar with it before learning superordinate classifications or subordinate types. Basic object level terms should name disjoint sets of functions or entities, with no overlap between things named by one term and onother. For superordinate level terms, overlap is allowable — in natural classes superordinates (like PET, FRUIT, SPORT) tend to name objects that have common functional bases. Subordinate terms can also overlap — and should perhaps initially be given names that are two-word phrases indicating which basic concept they belong to. Finally, with increasing expertise one may expect the level which is basic to move down to more differentiated levels. The interface should therefore allow for shortening the names given to subordinate functions, so that people can develop a more specific level of basic concept terms, as they become more familiar with system operation.

Categorization based on similarity

Why should it be that penguins and ostriches have basic level names that are at a more subordinate level than sparrows and robins? The answer that Rosch would give is that categories are based on perceived similarity. Just as the aeroplane mechanic could no longer see 747s and DC10s as similar, knowing so much about the different layout and construction of their constituent parts, so we tend to put things together and give them a common name because of their similarity. The way in which Rosch demonstrated this (Rosch and Mervis, 1975) was by having groups of subjects generate attributes to describe a set of objects from a category such as FRUITS and from a contrasting category such as VEGETABLES. They then calculated the number of attributes that each item had in common with the other members of its own category, and with the members of the contrasting category. They called this measure the 'family resemblance score', after Wittgenstein's (1953) suggestion that concepts hang together rather in the way that members of a family tend to look alike. The family resemblance score for basic level objects was always considerably higher than for superordinate categories. Furthermore, if one looks at categories subordinate to the basic level, the internal family resemblance does not increase by much, but the number of attributes in common with contrasting sets does increase. Rosch therefore argued that given the attributes to which we attend (perceptual and functional), then the categories that we form and the level which is basic will be determined by the 'structure of the world'.

Family resemblances can then explain why penguins and ostriches have basic level terms below the basic level term BIRD. This has to do with the concept of *typicality* or goodness of example (see Chapter 5). Items in a category that possess the most attributes in common with the other category members (and least in common with members of contrast sets), are considered by subjects to be more representative, good, or typical members of the category (the terms are used interchangeably). They also tend to be more familiar and more commonly associated with the category name (Hampton, 1979, 1981; Hampton and Gardiner, 1983). On these grounds, penguins and ostriches are very atypical birds — they share relatively few of the attributes of typical birds like flight, song and small size. As a result the within-class similarity of penguins begins to outweigh the between-class similarity of penguins with other birds, and so PENGUIN is adopted as the basic level name for these creatures.

The use of similarity as a basis of categorization has been taken further with formal development of a similarity axiom. Tversky (1977) developed a definition of similarity as the weighted sum of the common and distinctive features between any two items. Thus the greater the number and weight of common over distinctive features, the greater is the perceived similarity. Tversky (1977) reported many interesting results in support of the similarity axiom. In particular, he was able to show that similarity breaks a number of constraints, so that it is not possible to represent the similarity relations among a set of items in terms of a spatial model, with similarities mapped onto a distance metric. For example similarity is 'asymmetrical', it does not obey the 'triangle inequality' (the similarity of A to B, plus that of B to C, does not constrain the dissimilarity of A to C), and it does not obey the 'corner inequality' (items that differ on two continuous dimensions are perceived as more similar if they have an exact match on one dimension, and a very poor match on the other, than if there is a fair match on both).

The implications of these results for theories of categorization based on similarity have not been fully developed. However they may serve to explain a number of curious inconsistencies in categorization that have been obtained experimentally (see, for example, Hampton, 1982). For instance, hierarchies of categories are only loosely based on class inclusion. Subjects are happy to agree that CHAIRS are a type of FURNITURE, even though they also agree that CAR-SEATS, CHAIR-LIFTS and ELECTRIC CHAIRS are all kinds of chair which are *not* FURNITURE. Research with categories of personality trait by Sarah Hampson (1985) shows very similar effects. For example 'talkativeness' is classed as 'a way of being extraverted', whereas 'being extraverted' is not a way of being talkative. However, this apparent hierarchical relation does not imply that one cannot be talkative without being extravert at the same time. Our intuitions about categorization are based on the overlap of conceptual meanings, and not on the distribution of examples of the concepts in the world.

Similar deviations from set logic occur with the use of conjunction, disjunction and negation. Hampton (1985a) showed that people will call CHESS a GAME WHICH IS A SPORT, although earlier they had judged that it was not a SPORT. To take another example, CRICKET PADS are considered PROTECTIVE CLO-THING, but not CLOTHING, even though most subjects agree that protective clothing is indeed a type of clothing. In some unpublished experiments, Hampton found that the negation of a set (for example SPORTS which are NOT GAMES) is equally overextended. Thus items may be both GAMES and NOT GAMES at the same time, if a majority opinion is taken as indicating class membership. In disjunctions too, membership may be either 'overextended' (CHESTNUTS are not FRUITS, and not VEGETABLES, but they do get included in FRUITS OR VEGETABLES), or sometimes 'underextended' (an electric toothbrush is a house-hold appliance, but gets left out of the class of HOUSEHOLD APPLIANCES OR KITCHEN UTENSILS). These kinds of curious inconsistency are in fact entirely consistent with the similarity based theory of concepts and categories. Tversky and Kahneman (1983) have found effects on probability estimation that exactly correspond to the overextension of conjunctive categories (see also Chapter 4). For example given that a girl was active in student politics, and reads the *Guardian* (to translate their example for an English audience), subjects tend to judge it more likely that she would be a bank teller who is a feminist, than that she would simply be a bank teller. This is of course impossible. Since anyone who is a feminist bank teller must also be a bank teller, one cannot be more likely to belong to the conjunction than to the set from which it was formed.

Tversky and Kahneman (1983) identify the root of this fallacy as the use of what they have termed the 'representativeness heuristic' for probability estimation. The representativeness heuristic is used as follows. To assess likelihood, we judge how typical the event is of the class of events to which it is being compared. Just as with categorization of objects, we determine typicality in terms of shared and contrasting attributes. If the item shares more attributes with the conjunctive set (as in the bank teller example) then we feel that it is more likely to belong to that set.

The conclusion to be drawn from this section is therefore that people *do* categorize on the basis of similarity, although this may not be optimal for logical thinking. The logic of natural concepts does not correspond to Boolean set logic (a point also made in Chapter 4). We prefer to classify on the basis of general similarity to some central *prototype* (to use Rosch's term), and find it difficult to keep sets of things consistently classified in mutually distinct classes. To illustrate, the basis of similarity by which we judge that chairs are a kind of furniture relies on their being wooden, used in homes for a comfort-related function, being heavy but yet portable, and so forth. The reasons for a car-seat being a chair are however quite different — relating to the structural design and the common function of being sat upon. When the two concepts (car-seat and furniture) are compared because the two categorizations depend on different shared features, there is not enough in common for categorization to occur. It is the use of similarity, and the use of prototype representations for concepts that lead, perhaps inevitably, to the logical inconsistencies found in these experiments.

Interestingly this is another example where what we do and what we think we do differ (see Chapter 4 for a more detailed discussion of this point in connection with explanations of reasoning behaviour). People in these experiments often behave as if they believe all categories are either hierarchically embedded, or else are mutually exclusive and non-overlapping. (In fact early models of semantic memory were based on this assumption — see Collins and Quillian, 1972). Having to decide if CRICKET is a SPORT, and then if it is a GAME, some subjects feel obliged to say that it is one but not the other. The assumption of mutual exclusivity is only a good fit to the reality of our concepts around the basic object level, where most categories are in fact non-overlapping. This may reflect in part a strategy adopted by children to learn vocabulary terms first for non-overlapping categories, and indeed to assume that concepts will be non-overlapping as they form hypotheses about word meanings (Clark, 1973).

Context dependency

A corollary of the inexact nature of our concepts, and their basis in perceived similarity is the fact that they are highly variable from context to context. Linguistically this is easy to demonstrate. For example the adjective RED has quite different typical values on a colour spectrum when paired with different noun concepts. Think of red wine, red hair, red cars, red beans. Each has a different characteristic colour which we loosely call red, since red is the closest primary colour name to the hue we wish to describe. To some extent these are conventional effects. However novel effects of context can also easily be shown. For example, Roth and Shoben (1983) asked subjects to read paragraphs in which a concept such as BIRD would be presented in different contexts (for example a farmyard or a seashore). As might be expected the normal effects of item typicality can be reversed when an expectation is set up for a farmyard or sea bird. Similarly, Hampton (1985a) showed that the concept FURNITURE is changed in subtle ways when placed in noun–noun compounds such as OFFICE FURNITURE, KITCHEN FURNITURE, or CHURCH FURNITURE. One effect already mentioned in the previous section is that some items such as photocopiers or filing trays may be considered to be members of the category OFFICE FURNITURE but yet are not considered to be in the category FURNITURE itself.

The prototype model of concepts allows quite readily for these types of effect. Context can operate to modify the weights attached to different features or attributes in the definition of the category. Thus OFFICE will modify the typical functions of FURNITURE in such a way that objects in the office which fulfil *in general terms* the same role for office activities as objects of domestic furniture fulfil for domestic activities, will become allowable members of the category. Smith and Osherson (1984) describe a simple model of how such modification of attributes may occur for adjective–noun conjunctions.

A more radical view of concept flexibility has been propounded by Barsalou (1984). In reviewing a number of studies in which subjects made semantic judgements of different types, he concluded that the intra-subject consistency of such judgements was often remarkably low, with correlations from occasion to occasion of around 0.7, and from subject to subject of around 0.4 to 0.5. From this instability in people's category structure, Barsalou argued that the structure may not in fact be a real aspect of memory storage for conceptual information. It is quite possible that the whole notion of concepts and categories as permanent stable entities stored in the mind is a purely fictional creation of the psychologist. Concepts may exist as ways of talking (and theorizing) about what we know, but may not be involved in the representation of that knowledge at all. The argument is taken further in some ingenious experiments where people were asked to make judgements of category typicality from different points of view (Barsalou and Sewell, 1985). In one experiment, people had to rate the typicality of birds, sports, crimes and so on, from their own point of view, and from the points of view of a redneck farmer, a Chinese peasant, or a middle-class housewife. The interesting result was that people were able to generate others' points of view with as much consistency as they did their own. Furthermore when students rated categories from the points of view of university faculty, and vice versa, the match between projected and actual points of view was surprisingly good. A student pretending to be a member of the teaching faculty was indistinguishable from an actual faculty member. This ability that people display to realign their conceptual categories to reflect the viewpoint of someone quite different is remarkable. It suggests that our concepts are not only unstable, but are also highly flexible. One could conceive of the point of view manipulation as another kind of contextual effect. In this instance the concepts are modified by introducing some stereotyped view of what other people are likely to find important and salient, and with what kinds of objects in the environment they are likely to be familiar.

One may not want to agree entirely with Barsalou that concepts are so unstable that they are created afresh to deal with each particular task as it arises. However there are particular kinds of concept for which this is almost certainly the case. Barsalou did some further experiments in which he studied two kinds of concept — *ad hoc* categories, and goal-directed categories (for a review see Barsalou, 1983). *Ad hoc* categories are novel concepts created by particular contextual specifications. For example one could form a category of 'things likely to fall on one's head while walking down Oxford Street', in which the category is defined by setting up a suitable scenario and then finding items that can play a particular role in that scenario. *Ah hoc* concepts are in general novel forms of another kind of concept — goal-directed concepts. A goal-directed concept is one in which category members are objects which fulfil a particular goal that one has. Thus 'birthday presents for my mother-in-law', or 'places where I might have left my keys' each form particular concepts which I may construct in the course of everyday planning of actions. Barsalou examined the semantic basis of these kinds of concepts and found that in comparison with 'natural' object categories, there was a far greater emphasis on the degree to which an object possessed some ideal value for particular dimensions. For instance 'things to eat on a diet' are typical to the extent that they have low calories (in addition to being familiar). The dependence on family resemblance structure and similarity is therefore not found in these kinds of concepts. The most representative items are those with extreme values, and not those reflecting the central tendencies of actual instances. Again, the interesting aspect of this research is its emphasis on the great creativity and flexibility of the conceptual system. We are apparently able to reclassify the objects in our world in an indefinitely large number of different ways, as different goals arise that have to be satisfied. Of course one should also remember that we do also suffer from inefficiency in constructing these novel goal-directed concepts — which is why it takes so long to find one's keys, or to buy a suitable birthday present for one's mother-in-law. Existing categorizations can also inhibit the free creation of novel classifications. For instance the gestalt psychologists' interest in 'functional fixedness' (Maier, Duncker, see also Chapter 3) concerned just this effect, where seeing an object as a pair of scissors made it much harder to use it as a pendulum bob, or for some other unusual function.

Concept definitions

To conclude this part of the chapter, let us turn to perhaps the most central question in the study of concepts — how are they defined? We have seen how in Rosch's theory, concepts are defined as a central prototype, around which members of the category are arranged according to their similarity, which in turn is determined by the relative number of matching and non-matching features the item possesses. This general model copes well with effects of context, since the weight attached to each attribute in the prototype can be varied in a continuous way to generate an infinite number of infinitesimally different versions of the same concept. What is still lacking is an adequate detailed mechanism for how context operates to change attribute weights. Some work has been done for concept conjunctions (Hampton, 1985b; Smith and Osherson, 1984), but a more general model will be required to demonstrate the value of the approach.

The standard prototype theory has also been called into question by a number of psychologists and linguists who have rightly pointed out that as it stands it is an insufficient representation of the schematic knowledge that we have of a domain. For example our understanding of BIRDS does not consist merely of a list of the common and typical attributes of the prototype bird. Rather we also know that the internal structures of birds form a complex and interdependent life-function system, that their behaviour has evolved to ensure their survival in a particular environmental niche, and so on. As Murphy and Medin (1985) argue, concepts are inseparable from our theories of the conceptual domain in which they lie. In part, this perspective fits with a view that Osherson and Smith (1981, 1982) have taken, that concepts may have two types of representation — a defining core, and a superficial recognition procedure. Whereas category membership depends on the core, the typicality and the speed of categorizing an instance will depend on how easily it fits a schema for identifying category members. The notion of a defining core accords with the idea of concepts as theories, and as parts of more general theory-like structures.

To capture the difference between the Roschian and the 'concept-as-theory' approaches, one can consider the origin of our everyday concepts. According to the prototype view, the world as we perceive it contains 'correlations' between various attributes across the objects within a domain. Thus flying, having wings, and having feathers tend to cluster or correlate. Knowing that an object has one attribute, one can reduce one's uncertainty about it having the other. In the extreme, for example, knowing that a creature has feathers, wings, eyes, and a beak, one can be certain that it also is hatched from an egg, has two legs and no gills. This model is basically a statistical model of concept formation. Prototypes are induced from following the statistical correlations in the world with which we interact. By contrast, the theory-driven view of concepts suggests that what links various attributes together to form a concept prototype is a theoretical schema of how and why they co-occur. Thus for man-made artefacts we have a schema of why chairs are built to have seats and backs, and of a material strong enough to support a person's weight, and of why they serve the particular need that they do. For natural objects we have theories of how they propagate, and of how their anatomy and behaviour are interrelated. Statistical correlation then becomes a much weaker influence on the centrality of an attribute for defining a prototype. It is the strength of the schemata linking an attribute with the other attributes that is more critical.

There is as yet no empirical evidence to decide between these two views. The theory-driven view has the advantage of allowing for a far richer representation of semantic knowledge. It may be that theoretical schemata develop later than the prototype concepts, and take them over. Keil (1986) has some very interesting data on the development of children's concepts. He finds that initially children may classify on easily perceived, salient features. Thus *uncles* are any jovial male adult who is a family friend and visitor to the home. For older children, he found a 'characteristic to defining' shift, with the emphasis on the surface characteristics declining, and the importance of the adult meaning (kinship relation) increasing. Keil also showed that for artefacts, such as coffee-pots, discovering something new about the object has no effect on its categorization, whereas altering its appearance did. Conversely for natural kinds (like animals) altering appearance left the animal unchanged, while making a discovery (such as that it was stuffed with machinery, and not with blood and guts) would change classification. Again, this was an effect that emerged with age between around 4 and 7 years. The difference between domains in the type of information treated as relevant to classification is entirely consistent with the theory-driven view of concepts. It seems that the youngest children's simple prototype classes are refashioned by the emergence of theories of the world, distinguishing biological from man-made domains, and changing the importance of superficial and underlying or internal properties of the objects.

It may well turn out that most of the concept terms used in the design of user–system interfaces will be quite strongly dependent on an underlying theory or 'mental model' of the system (see Chapter 4), which the user develops as (s)he becomes familiar with the system's behaviour. However, if the developmental trend described by Keil also applies to adult learning, we may well expect prototype effects to be common in the earlier stages of learning, when people have incomplete knowledge of the system and are operating under uncertainty about how to do things, and how the system will respond to particular inputs. Memory of previous interchanges, and generalization based on similarity of context may well drive the user's choice of commands for pursuing a goal. Research directed at the particular understanding of the system possessed by people at this early stage in training could be very helpful in leading to design principles for making the system easier to learn. An understanding of the concepts which users bring with them to the task of learning to use the system — the naïve model of the system with which they start — and the expectations of the meaning and uses of the terms used by the interface language, could also lead to more efficient and less stressful learning.

Conclusions

This section of the chapter has discussed recent research on everyday concepts, on their flexibility and the way in which they may be defined. The inexactness and instability of concepts seems best explained in terms of the prototype model of concept definitions. A modification to this model is to suggest that what holds the attributes of a prototype together is not so much perceived statistical correlation in the world, as the causal schemas that we construct to relate each attribute to the rest. The influence of causal schemas has been well documented in probability judgements as well. Tversky and Kahneman (1982), showed that a conjunction of two events (for instance an Arab oil embargo plus a US invasion of the Persian Gulf), is seen as more likely than just one of the events (a US invasion of the Persian Gulf), if the two events form part of a sensible scenario, or causal chain of events. In a number of demonstrations, they also showed that forwards causal connections are much more powerful than backwards, diagnostic connections in influencing perceived likelihoods. For instance people believe it should be easier to predict a son's height when fully grown from his father's height, than the father's from the son's. Causality is a most powerful conceptual connection. We may therefore take their work as additional reason to expect concepts to be held together by some form of causal 'glue', and not purely on the basis of statistical frequency.

A conclusion for the design of user–system interfaces which capitalize on this knowledge of conceptual structure is that one should try to map system terms onto natural concepts as closely as possible; that one should use concepts that are as distinct as possible from each other, and that are mutually exclusive, in order to build a basic level of concept terms; and that one should give this level the most common everyday language terms. Superordinate concepts can then be created for particular functions, and these may overlap. Subordinate concepts can be defined as overlapping subsets of the basic level concepts, and given two-word labels to reflect which basic level term they fall under. In tems of concept definitions, it is highly likely that being part of a logically structured system they will be less fuzzily defined than are natural concepts. However, it may be important in teaching people to learn and use the concept terms to identify the most *central* or typical examples of the terms used, and train users in these examples first. Simple causal explanations of the relation between different attributes of the concept may also help the user to build a coherent model of the concept more rapidly. Finally, there may be occasions where the peculiar nature of human concepts can be exploited to advantage. One is in the use of multiple aliases for different terms (Landauer, Galotti and Hartwell, 1983). It is natural for us to have ten ways of saying the same thing, and to use different expressions on different occasions. (Just consider the multiplicity of terms used by different computer systems to erase information—ERASE, DELETE, REMOVE, CUT, RELEASE, ZAP, RUBOUT and so forth — or to end a program — STOP, END, FINISH, TERMINATE and so on.) Some of the memory load on a learner can therefore be reduced by allowing similar flexibility in naming system terms. Another way of exploiting the nature of human concepts may be in the modelling of natural connectives to replace more strict set-theoretical operators. Thus people may be able to understand and use conjunctions or disjunctions of concepts more readily if they are based on the non-logical nature of natural language connectives. Hence some interfaces and systems may be easier to use if they incorporate prototype structure, and similarity-based classification in their knowledge base, or in their use of language-like terms.

LANGUAGE AS SOCIAL INTERACTION

The prevalance of the written word in much of our lives should not blind us to the fact that language is primarily a *spoken* medium. At an early stage in our evolution from ape-like ancestors, we developed a highly specialized speech apparatus, and highly specialized regions of the brain for hearing, comprehending and producing speech. If speech is the primary form of language, so conversation is the primary form of speech. There are many different social contexts in which we may speak, from delivering a lecture, or giving a radio talk, to performing in a play, or bellowing commands on a parade ground. The most natural context, however, is where we are face to face with an interlocutor and engage in conversation. There are many aspects of this activity to consider and describe. For further coverage of this material, the reader is referred to sources such as Bolinger (1975), Clark and Clark (1977), and Clark (1983).

Speaker's meaning

Let us begin by differentiating what we mean from what we say. In natural language, the relation between these two is far from straightforward. Imagine the following exchange:

> *John*: Do you know there's a union meeting tomorrow?
> *Gladys*: Yes, the revolution starts on Thursday week.

To analyse the processes involved let us start with John's question. Here we should distinguish what he utters — an enquiry about the state of Gladys' knowledge — from what he intends, which is to tell Gladys about the meeting (here we must assume that the context allows John to infer that Gladys may not know about the meeting, and that she may have reason to want to know about it). Gladys' reply is apparently a *non sequitur*, and is also apparently the assertion of a falsehood. Gladys here is using *irony* to convey her attitude to the activities of the union. (Actually several attitudinal beliefs are conveyed by the single remark.) The interesting problem that this example illustrates is the question of how John and Gladys are able to understand what each *intends* their words to be taken by the other to mean, over and above what they are literally saying.

To understand how we may mean something by an utterance, Grice (1975) argued that we must analyse the *intention* of the speaker. (Indeed we often use the word 'mean' to signify intention as in 'Did you mean to do that?') A speaker communicates successfully by getting his or her listener to recognize his or her intention. The means by which (s)he does this is through uttering words which (s)he believes will count for the listener as signalling that intention. What is more, a speaker can only know that his or her attempt to communicate is successful when (s)he knows that the listener has recognized his or her intention. This feedback must in fact be continued indefinitely in a recursive fashion, to the point where speaker and listener each know that the other knows, and that the other knows that they know, and so on, what the speaker's original intention had been. This paradoxically endless recursion of acknowledgement in fact proceeds very rapidly to a point sufficient for the normal purposes of a conversation, and it constitutes what we mean by *understanding* one another when we converse. Unlike most computer systems which respond purely to the literal utterance that the user enters through the keyboard, human listeners make an effort (usually) to understand what the speaker is trying to say, and will be prepared to go beyond (and even to ignore) the literal form.

The state achieved when an utterance has been successfully received is one of mutual or shared belief. It is possible partly through a crucial aspect of human language, which is its *reflexivity*. Language can be about the world, but it can also be about itself. In indicating our understanding to a speaker we are in fact commenting on his or her utterance as an utterance, while at the same time going beyond the words to agree with him or her on what his or her intention had been in making it.

Examination of some simple exchanges will illustrate this point. For instance:

> *George*: Get me a cloth.
> *Kenneth*: You mean a floor cloth?
> *George*: Something has spilled under the table.

George's utterance is insufficent for Kenneth to comply with his request. As a result Kenneth proposes a resolution of the ambiguity. In answer, George provides clarification not directly, but by telling Kenneth something new, which George intends should count as (a) confirming Kenneth's presupposition of what was requested, and (b) justifying the original request.

Conventions

Both the examples we have considered so far illustrate an important fact of conversations. We assume that other persons' utterances will be relevant, and we can use this assumption in order to draw many inferences about their intended meaning. This assumption is one of a number of *conventions* which we shall see later govern normal language behaviour. The example of George and Kenneth also reveals the way in which a single utterance can serve multiple functions. The analysis of the functions of speech is called *Speech Act Theory*. In a book entitled *How to Do Things with Words*, the philosopher J.L. Austin (1962) defined three levels of function or 'force' that any utterance can have. The first he called *locutionary force*. This is the actual content of an utterance — for example the proposition expressed in the sentence 'Arsenal are playing at home this Saturday'. The second he called *illocutionary force*. This is what it is that the speaker is doing *in* uttering the words (that is to say, what kind of act (s)he is performing — what the words count as). Thus the speaker may be making an assertion, performing an act of warning, or requesting information. Finally, Austin defined the *perlocutionary force* of an utterance as what we intend to achieve *through* making the utterance. Thus the speaker may intend to change the listener's state of belief, or may intend the listener to take a particular action (such as avoiding the Highbury area where the football match will take place), or (s)he may even be saying that (s)he intends to go to the game.

We can see that in speaking, the speaker may generally be doing many things at the same time. Planning and uttering a (reasonably) syntactic sentence, usually with some propositional content, performing one of a small set of conventionally accepted speech acts, such as promising, warning, threatening or questioning, and intending his or her words to have some number of obvious or less obvious effects on the listener's present state and future behaviour. The picture becomes more complex still when we consider that a single utterance may have several of these functions simultaneously. While clearly true for perlocutionary force (the speaker may intend his or her utterance to yield several consequences), it turns out to be equally the case for illocutionary force — what kind of an act the utterance should be taken as counting as. We very often use utterances whose conventional canonical form is of one type of speech act, in order to make a quite different speech act. To see how this works, we must distinguish between 'direct' and 'indirect' speech acts. If we ask somebody the question 'Do you know the time?', our direct speech act is an enquiry about that person's knowledge, to which (s)he may legitimately answer 'yes' or 'no'. Direct speech acts reflect the *literal* meaning of the sentence used for the utterance. The speaker's 'real' intention or meaning, however, is to request that the listener tell him or her the present time — to the nearest minute or five minutes (the expected exactness will depend on the context). This request is termed the *indirect* speech act. Much of our conventional dialogue involves these two levels of speech acts, and various factors determine the degree to which we process both levels.

Clark (1979) performed an experiment to investigate this, in which 100 restaurants in the San Francisco area were telephoned, and asked one of two questions:

(1) Do you accept credit cards?
(2) Do you accept American Express cards?

For those who responded in the affirmative, if asked question (1) the majority went on to answer an indirect implied request to list those cards they took. If asked question (2), the respondents only responded to the direct speech act, saying 'yes' and nothing more. Clark (1979) also found that the more conventional the indirect form of the request (in the sense of how commonly it is used to make a request in normal speech), then the less likely people are to respond to the direct speech act, and the more immediate perception of the intended indirect speech act is (see also Gibbs, 1981). Thus people use both the context in which an utterance is made, and conventions about ways of making indirect speech acts, in order to guess the intention of the speaker and answer him or her appropriately.

The foregoing discussion highlights something that should be emerging as a central aspect of communicating with language — that language depends on *conventions*. A convention is something which two or more parties agree to observe, in order to coordinate their actions successfully. (For example we shake hands with our right hands, we arrange the pages in a book so it can be opened with the spine on the left in English, but on the right in Hebrew, and so on.) Grice

(1975) made an analysis of the most central conventions which a conversee must follow if his or her contribution to a conversation is to be effective and easily understood. He described these conventions in terms of a number of *maxims*, which can be summarized as follows:

(1) *Maxim of Relation*: Be relevant. We saw how this maxim was used in order to allow a hearer to draw an inference about the speaker's meaning. In general, irony and 'insinuation' may take the form of stretching the maxim of relation so that the hearer has to fill in the links in the chain of relevance between the utterance and the context in which it is made.

(2) *Maxim of Quality*: Be truthful. One does not normally (that is, conventionally) make false statements, or assertions for which one has no grounds at all. This convention is obviously crucial if we are to trust one another enought to ever communicate anything at all. When it is flaunted in conversation then this may be taken as a signal of irony or sarcasm — but only when the speaker knows that the addressee has sufficient evidence not to take him or her seriously.

(3) *Maxim of Quantity*: Be informative. In making a contribution, one should provide as much specific detail as the current goal of the conversation requires, neither more nor less. This convention may then allow a hearer to infer that if the information provided is insufficiently detailed, then this is because the speaker has no more to give (for instance if the speaker asks someone the time and that person says 'It's some time after six').

(4) *Maxim of Manner*: Be clear. The final maxim should be obvious. When we speak we try to take account of the knowledge and understanding of the listener. Thus we avoid obscure terms, if we have reason to suspect the hearer will not know them. We avoid terms that will be ambiguous in the context of the utterance. We try to present things in an order that will be easy to follow (for instance telling a narrative in chronological order), and try to be neither too terse nor too repetitive in the telling.

These maxims are particularly interesting, because although one can show that so much of our successful communication relies on us not only obeying them, but also assuming that our fellow speakers are obeying them, yet we are able to flout them in creative ways to generate a range of interesting and amusing effects. At first it may appear that our conversations are hedged about with so many conventional constraints that this would surely limit our ability to express ourselves. However, paradoxically, just as the greatest classical artists and composers used highly constrained rule-bound forms to enhance their creative expression, so the very fact of these conventions increases the creativity and flexibility possible in human language use. Furthermore it is often just this creativity and flexibility which may be notably lacking in conversations conducted with electronic systems. Computers are notorious for taking a very dim view of creative rule-breaking in conversation.

Let us examine just how the conventions permit rapid and efficient communication. Take again the first example of John, Gladys and the union meeting. To understand Gladys' retort, John has to be able to relate it to the ongoing topic of conversation. John knows Gladys, and has no reason to suppose that she does not follow the Maxim of Relation in her conversation. (That is she shows no sign of psychotic breakdown or drug dependence.) From assuming that Gladys is being relevant, John must therefore also infer that there is some additional missing utterance which context alone will allow him to construct, in order to make Gladys' utterance relevant. John therefore infers that Gladys sees some connection between the union meeting and the imminence of revolution. However John is then in further trouble. Knowing Gladys as he does, he also notices that she is breaking the Maxim of Quality — she is not being truthful, since John has reason to believe that she does not *really* think that the revolution will start next week. In fact Gladys was able to break this maxim simply because (and *only* because) she knew that John would *know* she was being untruthful. We can be untruthful (or irrelevant, or obscure, or verbose and so on) in those contexts where we know that the hearer will easily recognize that such was our intention. It is the result of this involved process of inferences based on detailed mutual knowledge of each others' beliefs and intentions, that we are able to say one thing and know that it will be taken as *counting* as something else.

Conventions therefore allow us to communicate smoothly and efficiently because the communication channel is set up with a large number of 'defaults' which both parties can safely take for granted. But at the same time we can deliberately flout the conventions — break the defaults — in order to add interest and humour to our conversation. Provided the context allows our intention to be unambiguously understood, we can use words with tremendous freedom. If on stubbing a toe a person shouts 'Curtains' in an aggrieved tone, that utterance will be interpreted by all present in just the way it was intended.

Cooperation

We have seen how as speaker and addressee we must follow the same conventions (and know that the other is doing likewise, and that the other knows that we are, and so on), in order to converse. We must agree to follow the maxims, and in fact can only successfully understand one another by assuming the cooperation of the other. One revealing way in which cooperation in involved in conversation has been described by Clark and Wilkes-Gibbs (in press). They described how when a speaker fails to find the right word for his or her utterance, the hearer will very commonly make helpful suggestions, or even complete the utterance. (The similarity to menu selection is interesting here.) Some people even make an annoying habit of finishing other people's sentences for them, given the smallest opportunity. Clark and Wilkes-Gibbs rightly point out that this kind of language behaviour in which two or more people actually *collaborate* in the taking of each conversational turn, renders incomplete theories of language behaviour according to which one person composes a message which is sent out to the other person, who decodes it, works out a reply and sends it back in turn (rather like a conversation by telex). Communication in natural speech settings is not simply one-dimensional with the channel direction being reversed at the end of each turn (as in the use of the word 'over' in radio communication). Rather, as a speaker speaks, the hearer immediately begins the task of finding the speaker's intention, and is quite prepared to offer words which (s)he feels may help express the intention which (s)he believes the speaker has in mind.

As part of this process there is also a 'back-channel' of reponses from the hearer which coincides with the speaker's utterance. This back-channel of facial expression, 'Uh-huh's' and other simple noises can also play an important role in modulating the speaker's utterances as they are being formed. If the addressee appears bored we speed along with what we are saying, planning ahead to find what we believe (s)he will find interesting, and lending it extra emphasis. If the addressee appears puzzled we speak more slowly, and try to find several ways of expressing the same intended message.

Structure of conversations

Conversations as we have seen follow Grice's maxims of relevance and truth. As a result each utterance must generally be connected to the same ongoing *topic* of the conversation. At the sentence level this is achieved by what Clark calls the *Given–New* contract. Each new proposition contributed to a discourse (by either speaker) will contain two parts — a 'given' which identifies some referent in what is called the 'common ground' of the discourse, and a 'new' part which attaches some further information to that referent, and so adds to the common ground. In this way as a conversation proceeds, so a constant topic is maintained, to which different parties make contributions, in order to build up a set of beliefs (plus perhaps a knowledge of who in the conversation holds which beliefs) which will be represented in the minds of all those in the conversation (including bystanders).

The process involved was illustrated in an experiment by Clark and Haviland (1977). Subjects were timed while reading short paragraphs of text. In one condition they read the following:

They took the food and the beer from the car. The beer was warm.

Time to read the second sentence was measured and compared with another condition in which the food and beer were not previously mentioned, as in:

They took the picnic from the car. The beer was warm.

Clark and Haviland found that extra time was required in the second condition, as subjects were forced to set up an inferential step — that the picnic included beer — in order to identify the referent of 'the beer' in the second sentence. The common ground is central to the analysis of discourse and conversations. It consists of all the topics and domains which any of the speakers have introduced into the conversation. Once in the common ground, an item can be referred to using definite reference ('*the* beer' rather than '*some* beer'), and where context permits easy disambiguation, by pronouns like 'he', 'it' and 'her'.

There are various devices for marking deliberate changes in the general topic of conversation, but such changes must usually be explicitly marked. Conventional devices are expressions like 'By the way', or 'That reminds me'. Even so, one normally tries to bring a conversation round to a desired topic, by some route of associated topics, perhaps in order to avoid wiping clean the common ground that has been established. Common ground eases the planning of our contributions, and one of the more difficult skills a conversationalist needs is that of steering the direction of the topic without any abrupt changes of direction that will leave the other with no contribution to make. Perhaps the closest analogue to common ground in electronic systems is the notion of the 'current' file or line. If both user and electronic system know that a particular piece of data is the given, then communication proceeds much more rapidly.

There are also devices for embedding topics within other topics, just as programs may be accessed and run within other programs in an electronic system. While discussing what to make for dinner, we may introduce a subtopic of the price of eggs, which may lead us into a discussion of the EEC common agricultural policy. Eventually we will 'pop' back up to the top level concern of dinner. Such diversions will generally be embedded (as opposed to merely chained together) if the conversation is goal-directed. That is, if we have information to exchange, a decision to reach, or a difference of opinion to resolve, then we will attempt to control the embedded diversions, and keep track of the different levels in our conversation. (In planning, the embedded levels may be subgoals, which must each be reached in order to achieve the main goal.) There are special markers in our language — phrases like 'anyway', and 'so', said with the right intonation — which are used to indicate return from an embedded topic to a higher level.

A similar type of structure is found in the themes of narratives — extended utterances in which a sequence of events is described. Speakers typically use linguistic devices to mark information as *foreground* (pertaining to the central theme or storyline), or *background* (setting the scene in which the story unfolds). In written language we commonly use devices like parentheses or footnotes to background comments. Another common device is to prepose clauses containing background material ('while the others made ready for bed, Jeremy set out to find a tall tree'). The foreground–background distinction permits the main thread of the argument or narrative to be followed, without ambiguity about the direction in which it is going. The common ground is therefore structured in the sense that we cooperate as speakers and hearers in keeping a main storyline, or goal-directed path, distinct from other diversions, be they embedded subgoals or asides, or incidental information supplementary to the main action. (Thriller writers rely heavily on deliberately *backgrounding* information, which later proves crucially important to the foreground plot development.)

The system as a social animal

The aim of a system that will be more human must then depend on devising procedures that will explicitly begin to comply with these general principles of our language behaviour. This will mean a system that has a representation of the state of knowledge of the particular user — perhaps knowing the degree of experience with the system that the individual has, or inferring such knowledge from the user's speed and skill in using the system. The system may also represent the typical errors and difficulties experienced by the individual in the past — which help requests have been most often used, which error messages most frequently given. Most difficult will be the design of systems that build a representation of the user's intended request or command, using the contextual cues and the conventions of social interaction in order to perform the kinds of inference that we as humans make continually and with no apparent effort. Online help systems may be one area for development here — if the system has a model of the user's likely goal, advice can be offered on the best ways to achieve it, and warnings issued if wrong paths are chosen.

On a more psychological level, there may be considerable advantages to a system that obeys the more ritualistic aspects of language communication. The amount of effort people are prepared to expend on learning to use systems (or the speed with which learning occurs, if they *have* to learn them) may depend in part on the way in which the system treats the user. The early systems with their terse 'error messages' — often giving just a code number that had to be looked up in a reference manual, where one was lucky to find any comprehensible explanation — were often seen as technically minded, jargon-ridden, intolerant and rude individuals — rather like the worst stereotype of the technologists who invented them! There is still a real gap between the introductory manuals that take a user carefully and slowly through their first paces with a system, and the technical manuals containing complete specifications in a language that only experts can follow.

If one is conversing with an electronic system, then the system will necessarily have attributed to it characteristics of a person. With few exceptions people interact with electronic systems in a goal-directed way. We wish to give them something to remember, ask them a question, ask them to do something or learn something from them. All of these functions are ones which we would ordinarily perform with other people, using natural language. The scope for improving the humaneness of user–system interfaces, by incorporating language-like processes must therefore be great. We want machines that will cooperate with us in telling them what we require, that will try to read our intentions, and use the context of the topic, the common ground, and its knowledge of our own state of knowledge to allow us to be as vague or elliptical as we would normally be in speaking to one of our fellow kind. Above all we want systems that will be more tolerant of inaccurate and ambiguous inputs, such as typically occur in natural speech. The machine should be able to use all the contextual and conventional aspects of the discourse to select the most likely interpretation of ambiguous or vague inputs, and to provide a back-channel confirming the way in which the speaker's intention has been interpreted.

Many of these goals are doubtless very long-term, if not futuristic. They would certainly require large memory capacities, fast and powerful processing, and highly sophisticated programming. However, there is certainly no harm in trying to point out the direction in which we should aim, and a truly conversational computer system is a highly desirable goal for the future.

SUMMARY PRINCIPLES

1. Being a speaker of a language gives the user a strong set of expectations about how conversations should run.

   1.1 The meanings of concepts are inseparable from users' expectations and knowledge of the concept domain in which they lie.

   1.2 Users have expectations of what category members should look like, what they should do, and how they relate to other objects in the environment. The speed with which users identify other category members, or assign typicality judgements to them, increases with the match between the new category members and those expectations.

2. In everyday conversation the meaning attributed to utterances, concepts, ideas and names is highly context-dependent, unstable and ill-defined.

   2.1 The reference of a term (the class of objects, events or processes which we can use the term as a name for) is neither fixed across contexts and domains, nor is it well defined.

3. Learning involves assimilation of new learnt material to existing schemata.

   3.1 Existence of a vocabulary of common names for given sets of concepts facilitates learning: it requires only that associations be learnt between the names in the vocabulary and their definitions in real life.

   3.2 The existence of a vocabulary of common or familiar names also aids acquisition of a positive attitude toward the learning situation and increases motivation to learn.

   3.3 The existence of specific terms in a vocabulary does not necessarily entail complete knowledge about the concepts to which they refer.

   3.4 In interaction with a system, users have to relate the technical use of the terms used to the cluster of common everyday uses and meanings that they may have. Learning may be impaired by conflicts between the common or normal usage of terms and their different usage in a given context.

    3.5 Concepts are acquired gradually, through an iterative process of adding information and specification to initially learnt concepts

4. Objects differ in their level of generality: they can be at a superordinate, basic or subordinate level. The basic level normally reflects (a) the most commonly used names for the object, (b) the level at which one can have a single image of the object.

    4.1 Basic level membership leads to

        (a) fast matching of pictures of the basic level object to its previously presented name; and

        (b) greater overlap between the given object and other objects at a similar basic level within the same set.

    4.2 Increasing expertise may change the user's perception of the basic level for objects in a given set. This change will be reflected in a tendency towards treating more specific (subordinate) levels as basic levels for the set.

5. Objects or concepts are grouped together in sets or categories on the basis of the perceived similarity amongst the objects or concepts concerned. Perceived similarity is determined on the basis of perceptual (what the objects or concepts look like) and functional (what they do or can be done with them) attributes.

    5.1 Perceived similarity can be conceived as the weighted sum of the common and distinctive features between any two items. The greater the number and weight of common over distinctive features, the greater the perceived similarity.

    5.2 Perceived similarity is context-dependent and does not necessarily follow the dictates of logic.

6. The likelihood of an item being seen to belong in a given set is dependent on the context in which the judgement is made (the representativeness heuristic defines this probability in more detail).

    6.1 To assess likelihood, users judge how typical the event is of the class of events to which it is being compared. This typicality is defined in terms of shared and contrasting attributes. The probability of inclusion depends on the number of shared and contrasting attributes. The probability of inclusion depends on the number of shared attributes over contrasting attributes.

    6.2 Context can be used to modify the weights attached to different features or attributes in the definition of the 'rules' that dictate category membership.

7. Family resemblance or similarity as a basis for categorization does not apply to decisions of category membership where the categories are created for a specific purpose (goal-directed categories). In these categories, the emphasis

is more on the degree to which an object possesses some ideal value for particular dimensions which also reflect the rules for forming the category.

8. Items in a category that possess the most attributes in common with the other category members (and least in common with members of contrast sets) are considered to be more representative, good, or typical members of the category.

   8.1 Typical items tend to be more familiar and more commonly associated with the category name. (See also principles 31.1 to 31.6 in Chapter 5, for additional information about the consequences of typicality for behaviour measured in a variety of ways.)

9. It is natural for users to use several ways of saying the same thing, and to use different expressions on different occasions. Flexibility of this kind tends to reduce memory load.

10. A speaker communicates successfully (fast and efficiently) by getting his or her listener to recognize his or her intention. Recognition of the correct intention is aided by adherence to known conventions of speech and knowledge of the features of the context in which an utterance is made.

    10.1 Known conventions include relevance, truthfulness, informativeness (with little redundance) and clarity. Clarity is aided by
       (a) taking account of the knowledge and understanding of the listener;
       (b) choosing terms which match that knowledge and understanding;
       (c) presenting arguments in an order which relates to the intended effect; and
       (d) avoiding redundancy and repetition (while providing enough information for successful transfer of the meaning and intention of the utterance).

11. Successful communication requires cooperation between the parties engaged in the dialogue. Cooperation can take the form of
    (a) supplying potentially relevant items of information where the communicating party appears to be unable to retrieve the correct item;
    (b) providing immediate, unobtrusive feedback on the progress of communication; and
    (c) matching the tone, verboseness and speed of communication, and the emphasis placed on given items, to the feedback received from the listener.

12. Successful communication also depends on the degree to which each new proposition contributed to a dialogue will contain two separate parts:
    — a 'given', which identifies some referent in the common ground (the topic as discussed up to that point in time) of the dialogue; and
    — a 'new' part which attaches some further information to that referent, and so adds to the common ground.

    12.1 Establishing and maintaining contact with the common ground helps in planning later contributions to the dialogue.

13. In order to communicate successfully, parties in a dialogue need to have a representation of the state of knowledge of other parties in the dialogue.
14. Dialogues need to be structured if they are to succeed in their communicative role.

    14.1 Structuring is helped if changes to the topic of conversation, or temporary diversions from it, are explicitly marked.

    14.2 Structure is also highlighted by marking information as 'foreground' (pertaining to the central theme or storyline) and 'background' (setting the scene in which the dialogue unfolds). Maintaining clear differentiation between foreground and background information reduces ambiguity and facilitates communication flow.

15. The amount of effort people are prepared to expend on communicating with another person or with an electronic system may depend on the feedback received from that other person or from the system in the course of the dialogue. Unhelpful, terse reactions lead to lower motivation to proceed.

THE NEXT CHAPTER

The last four chapters considered the user from a variety of different viewpoints. They discussed features of human thinking and problem-solving, outlined the structure and process of human memory, described the process of skill acquisition and, finally, looked at how people communicate with each other through language. At the end of each chapter, key summaries of the research reviewed were presented, as summary 'principles' aiming to provide the reader with relatively short and unambiguous statements of the structure, capabilities, processes and limitations of the human cognitive system.

We have now concluded our presentation of the theoretical foundations for the application chapters that follow. The next chapter starts the process of application of the knowledge we have just finished reviewing. In it we consider the summary principles listed at the end of the last four chapters and, through a structured process of interpretation and combination, produce an initial set of guidelines illustrating the potential of cognitive psychology research for the design of interfaces to electronic office systems.

PART THREE:
TOWARDS APPLICATION

Design guidelines

Chris Marshall, Catherine Nelson and Margaret M. Gardiner

INTRODUCTION

This chapter presents a compilation of guidelines for the design of the user inter-face to complex computing systems. The emphasis is on the cognitive aspects of interface design, the so-called software psychology or software ergonomics. As such the chapter follows a well-established route for transferring knowledge to designers. What is different about the guidelines presented here is that they are built directly, in a structured manner, from the theoretical bases which had been largely untapped until now. Very few of the design guidelines which are cur-rently available have been derived directly from research on high-level cognitive processes, along the lines described here. In previous chapters, psychological theory was distilled into broad 'principles' or summaries. These principles are now taken through a process of simplification and turned into guidelines which are as jargon-free and explicit as possible. Finally, we cast these guidelines into a framework of concepts. These concepts are introduced as 'sensitive dimensions' in human–computer interaction design. The aim is to demonstrate an approach which may prove increasingly useful, as our understanding of human cognitive psychology continues to broaden and deepen, rather than to provide a tool which is fully tested and ready to go. In any case, as we discussed in Chapter 2, the issue of using guidelines as a design tool needs to be approached in parallel with issues concerning the methodologies associated with the design process as a whole.

The purpose of this chapter

The purpose of this chapter is threefold:

— To demonstrate that principles derived from an empirical basis in cognitive psychology can be used to generate guidelines for the design of user interfaces to computer systems. To this end, examples of the methodology are provided which show how such principles can be interpreted and illustrated in terms of current system designs and problems, gradually building towards specific guidelines.

— To provide an 'opening' set of guidelines derived, in the above fashion, from the principles of cognitive psychology presented earlier in this book.

— To arrange this 'opening' set of guidelines into a category framework of relevant concepts or 'sensitive dimensions'. This framework will, it is hoped, provide a useful forerunner of an application tool for system designers and will help structure the information to assist the thinking of other interested parties.

The concepts which form the basis for our design-tool framework can be thought of as 'sensitive dimensions'. That is, they are the dimensions along which it may be useful to think of the design process and along which specific design actions, relevant to human perception of and performance with the interface, can be taken. These sensitive dimensions have developed naturally as a consequence of grouping together related guidelines derived from cognitive psychology until robust and useful categories emerged. In time, the boundaries and relationships among these categories will be more clearly understood so that they may provide both a description of user interfaces and a prescription of how they should be designed which is stronger than the current thinking in this area. With this in mind, there appear to be some advantages to the approach we have taken here:

— The framework is essentially modular: it can grow and change emphasis as the need for new categories is recognized. There are many dimensions of human–computer interaction which are not included in the limited framework provided here (perceptual and physical issues are completely and deliberately excluded, for example). Collecting principles from a greater depth and breadth of psychology, and other sources, would help to flesh-out and crystallize existing categories and drive the need for others.

— Once it is more refined, the framework could be used selectively to help optimize designs along specific dimensions. For instance, a designer may recognize the importance of getting a specific area of the design right for a particular group of intended users. A prototype might have revealed damning inconsistencies in the design leading to slow learning and many user errors and complaints. It is not enough for guidelines to tell designers to 'be consistent', as is sometimes the case with existing guidelines. Designers intuitively recognize the value of such advice, just as they quickly recognize its naïvety. What they need is information on 'how to be consistent'. These guidelines take initial steps in this direction on most of the sensitive dimensions.

— The framework helps to organize thinking about the concepts, complexities and subtleties of designing systems which ensure good user reaction and performance. Compromises, tradeoffs and relationships between the contributory factors (as embodied in the sensitive dimensions) are usefully brought out.

A word about guidelines

It is worth stressing again in this chapter — just as we did in Chapter 2 — that user-interface design guidelines generally, and these are no exception, cannot provide an automatic solution to the design problem. They do not tell the designer how to do exactly the right thing and they do no tell him or her exactly when to do it. They are remote from the design process and many commentators have noted that they are either too specific or too general (see Chapter 2). In order to make genuinely useful statements they must be context-free. This unfortunately reduces their power in any given application. All guidelines in this complex area are therefore dependent on their user for sensitive and intelligent interpretation and application. They are not a stand-alone tool and they cannot provide a substitute for effective evaluation and iterative refinement of a design. They can however provide complementary and helpful advice at all stages in the design process.

Our aim here is not to review the complexities of human–computer interaction or the debate about the effectiveness and use of guidelines. We feel that the previous chapters have more than adequately highlighted the many issues which must be borne in mind in this particularly intricate and rewarding domain. Rather, we wish to concentrate on presenting relevant information in what we hope is a novel, simple, structured and potentially useful form. To this end we ask that readers accept the deficiencies as a penalty for clearer communication of the concepts involved.

Having said this, it is worth considering a few general issues about guidelines. Guidelines have been the traditional medium for transferring specialist information to designers. But the process of deriving them is not entirely straightforward. A somewhat idealistic view is presented by Granda (1980) who states that 'Effective guidelines must be specific and quantitative in statement; they must indicate their relative importance with respect to other guideline statements; they must be based on valid user attributes, cognitive, behavioural, physiological and psychological. Finally they must be interpretable and usable by a population of designers and other computer personnel with no extensive background in behavioural science.'

On the other hand, Gould and Lewis (1985) take a more pragmatic view, and highlight the difficulties and limitations that can occur when using design guidelines alone to achieve an effective design:

. . . a guideline cannot recommend that special purpose keys be used instead of typed commands because the choice depends on whether or not users are touch typists, whether or not it is possible for the system to distinguish commands from other entries if they are typed, whether or not the command set is extensible, and many other aspects of the situation. Existing guidelines are often based on informed opinion rather than on data or estabished principles . . . We feel, at present, that guidelines should be viewed as an informal collection of suggestions, rather than as a distilled science. Designers will have to make many choices on their own, and be prepared to test their work empirically.

These comments reinforce the statements we have already made and emphasize the need for understanding the intended user population and the tasks which are to be carried out, the need to adopt an iterative design process with empirical measurement of user performance, and the need for careful consideration of how context-free guideline statements can be applied in specific situations.

Nevertheless, the benefits which accrue from developing and disseminating design guidelines should not be underestimated. They are an accessible medium; they provide valuable reference material to help with design decisions which crop up during the design process; they are a springboard for ideas, a checklist for omissions, an educational tool and a testing ground for human factors and psychology principles. Used with the proper respect and in context, they are a valuable adjunct to relying on designer intuition alone to solve human interface problems.

Given that we now have a reasonable basis of knowledge about human psychological attributes (as expanded in earlier sections), the time is now due when an attempt is made to cast this knowledge into a useful framework so that the issues are put into a coherent perspective for designers, users and researchers. In the following sections we discuss one method for doing this.

DERIVING GUIDELINES FROM PSYCHOLOGY PRINCIPLES

Not all the principles listed at the end of the psychological foundation chapters have proved suitable for interpretation as guidelines. Some are descriptive and do not translate to directives, others are very limited in scope, whilst some are too abstract or ill-defined to convert to guidelines which might be readily applied in practice. This aside, the great majority of principles could be translated to guidelines, though with varying degrees of success.

The derivation process

The general method used to derive the guidelines from their embodiment in the principles of cognitive psychology is one of 'showing-by-example'. Successive levels of simplification are presented to bridge the gap between the psychology and the guideline.

Principles which have face validity and which seem robust enough to stand the process are taken, either by themselves or grouped into related sets, and are interpreted into a more or less jargon-free format. This makes the principles more immediately accessible to a non-expert in that particular area of cognitive psychology. These jargon-free principles are then interpreted in terms of a concrete example from current system design practices. The examples are tailored to non-psychologists with a reasonable knowledge of existing technology. These examples either demonstrate the principle(s), or highlight typical problems that non-application of the principle(s) can cause, or suggest how a current design might be improved by adhering to the principle(s). The type of example used depends on the nature of the principle(s), the existence of meaningful illustrations from existing systems, and the concepts which it is most important to convey. In theory several types of example should be used to illustrate each principle so that a designer can get a view from different angles of how the principle can and should be applied. In practice this is not so easy for every single principle and is also an extremely time-consuming process. Generating at least one example is very useful though, both from the point of view of a potential user of the derived guidelines (to provide a specific illustration of how to use it) and from the point of view of the people who are generating the guidelines (since it forces careful thinking about the nature of the underlying psychology principle and how it can be interpreted in a practical situation. This in turn leads to a consideration of how a guideline can be specified.) The provision of concrete examples wherever possible helps to minimize the effects of the generality of the guidelines presented.

Having thus set the scene for the design guidelines to follow, each applicable principle is then 'unpacked' into its consequences for system design. The language used at this, lowest, level of description does not assume any knowledge of the relevant psychological concepts. After this stage, though a large number of guidelines have been generated, there is still little structure to help in relating this mass of information to the achievement of specific design objectives. The next stage in our process is to 'tag' each guideline outlining its system-related area of application. When enough guidelines become consistently tagged with the same label, a category or 'sensitive dimension' in human–computer interaction has been created. As stable categories develop, so an increasing number of new guidelines begin to fall into one (or more) of these existing categories. Almost all guidelines have one primary area of applicability and at least one secondary area. Some have secondary applicability in several areas. This then gives birth to the design-tool framework discussed earlier. The final stage of the process is to attach *caveats* and supplementary information to each guideline or set of related guidelines, and to make explicit any assumptions and relationships to other guidelines.

The design-tool framework thus generated should allow its potential user to identify those primary and secondary guidelines that are needed. Hence a designer wanting to find out about principles to do with, for example, the use of metaphors (such as the electronic 'desktops' currently so popular) can be easily referred to the appropriate guidelines from the super-list provided, to read not only about how to develop a suitable metaphor, but also where metaphors are useful, what hinders the use of metaphors and what to do if a metaphor is being used. This guideline derivation process is illustrated in the schematic diagram below.

Principles from cognitive psychology

↓

Filter and group principles

↓

Interpret as jargon-free principles

↓

Translate through examples

↓

'Unpack' guidelines

↓

Add relevant comments

↓

'Tag' guidelines and categorize

↓

Generate design-tool framework

A bonus of this approach is that the guidelines which are eventually presented can be traced back to the research findings on which they are based. This allows for their easy updating as the knowledge base improves. In contrast, the sources of information used to derive other currently available guidelines are not always divulged. A further bonus is that the interested reader has a means of backtracking to these relevant sources and reasoning through their application. Thus the need for education is also fulfilled in a practical manner.

CATEGORIES OF DESIGN GUIDELINES

Illustrating how each principle of cognitive psychology presented earlier has been translated into guidelines, through the process mentioned above, fills a small book in itself. Thus it is not practical to demonstrate each guideline derivation here. Our purpose, it will be remembered from the introduction to this chapter, is to provide both the guidelines themselves and to demonstrate the process by which they were generated. We have already made the derivation process explicit, so we turn now to summarize the categories which have developed from over 100 principles processed to date. In most cases, as we discuss each category, we shall provide a 'sample' of the full derivation process which has led to the generation of a guideline or guidelines whose primary area of application is within that category. In this fashion we shall fulfill our first purpose in writing this chapter. It is not possible to provide a fully derived sample for all categories. Some sensitive dimensions have emerged on the basis of only a few guidelines, and thus the underlying cognitive psychology has not tackled these areas completely. They represent areas where more effort is needed and are included here only to demonstrate the possibilities for a more complete framework in future.

The key categories or sensitive dimensions

Only time and use in applied situations will prove the value and robustness of the various categories presented here. A division of the rich context of human–computer interaction into a number of discrete categories or dimensions may seem a simplistic approach. However, since little structure exists at present in this field, any such attempt may have value and certainly warrants exploration. It will be noticed that for some categories a lot more information is given (for example, in the introductory statement describing the domain addressed by the dimension) than is the case for other categories. This reflects largely the extent of relevant knowledge reviewed in this book, and the robustness and direct applicability of such knowledge. Some categories also appear to apply more widely to different design domains than others, and hence require more text to cover these same application facets. The amount of text allocated per category does not necessarily correlate with the importance of that category. Categories are presented in no particular order of importance.

1. Design of procedures and tasks

For effective human–computer interaction, the procedures involved in achieving a given task should be compatible with the known cognitive characteristics of the user. Cognitive psychology has given us a wealth of knowledge concerning the way that people manipulate and utilize information. To improve user performance this body of knowledge needs to be taken into account in the system design process. The guidelines which have been placed in this category suggest ways in which tasks and procedures could be implemented to make maximum use of the knowledge at our disposal and engender good user performance as a result.

Tasks and procedures should be structured logically and consistently but, more importantly, in a manner which is acceptable to the users and meets with their existing knowledge expectations. Expectations will be many and varied depending on the users' experience in both the electronic and non-electronic world. Therefore, computerized tasks and procedures may benefit from close correspondence with the ways that similar tasks and procedures are carried out in the non-electronic world (though we must be careful not to ignore the extra power and flexibility that an electronic system can offer).

Sample

Principle(s)

A sequence is unlikely to be automated if it crosses a major boundary in the users' goal structure.

Interpretation

When using a system, users develop a hierarchical structure of goals and subgoals associated with performing any given task. If a sequence of actions required by the system crosses from one subgoal to another, or from one branch to another in the hierarchy, that sequence is unlikely to be automated.

Example(s)

In a system for document preparation, a hierarchy of goals might be (from top down): format a document, set margins, set tab positions, etc. It is unlikely that automatization will cross the boundaries between such subgoals. Therefore, the overall task, made up of those separate entities, should be treated as a non-automated task (for example, it will be time-consuming to perform and will load the user's working memory).

Guideline(s)

Tasks which are best performed quickly and easily, such as tasks which are intellectually low-level and are a means to an end, should be made up of actions which build sequentially towards that end. Action sequences should not take excursions into other tasks or task elements which are intended to achieve different ends.

Comment(s)

Sequences which cross major boundaries in the users' goal structure will be likely to give rise to capture errors, where the user ends up completing the wrong task or mixing actions in a useless combination. Also, tasks which require conscious attention will require careful consideration of ways in which the load on human working memory can be reduced to a minimum (for example, screen layout considerations).

2. Analogy and metaphor

Metaphors such as the 'desktop' concept first used in the Xerox Star and later in Apple's Lisa and Macintosh have caught the imagination of system designers, and have been taken up by many of the major manufacturers of electronic office systems. The general idea behind the use of metaphors is that they make the system appear to be 'like' the non-electronic world. Interaction is facilitated because even naïve users will know what to expect from the system, and will have previous knowledge of what to do in specific situations. Having encountered those situations before in the non-electronic world, they can generalize to their electronic counterparts. Metaphors are also particularly useful for training naïve users in the use of a complex system. In addition, analogy and metaphor are powerful ways of presenting information simply and intelligibly when the information relates to concepts which the user may find difficult to understand. For example, using a postal system (mailbox, envelopes, addresses, post offices, etc.) as an analogy is an effective way of demonstrating how a computerized mail system works. The user can visualize an electronic mailbox (into which mail is put) more easily than a section of electronic storage space which contains a set of character strings.

Effective human–computer interaction relies on the user being able to develop an accurate mental model of the way that a system functions. Models are constructed by the continual assimilation and organization of relevant information. If the information presented is familiar and comprehensible the model is constructed more easily. A system which uses the power of analogy and metaphor makes use of the user's existing knowledge in a particular area. The user can bring to the computer system a body of knowledge which has been obtained in a non-computerized environment.

Many benefits come from encouraging users to utilize their existing knowledge through metaphors. For example:

— users will tend to know what is happening when the system gives them certain types of feedback;
— they will tend to know how to respond to that feedback;
— they will tend to know how to plan their tasks better; and
— they will tend to be able to generalize from known, already encountered situations, to new and unknown ones.

All of the above will in turn encourage the user to try out commands and system operations which would otherwise possibly not be used. If the users feel that the system is 'like' well-known, familiar things, they will feel more inclined to use it for everyday tasks, and their feelings towards the system will be more positive than if the system requires the adoption of completely alien ways of working in order to perform any given task.

Metaphors depend for their efficiency on the *schemata* we all have for behaviour within given contexts: the templates which tell us how things interrelate and function in a given situation, and how we are expected to behave in that situation. A familiar environment facilitates access to existing templates. New templates can also be acquired. To create a new 'template' the user needs to have consistent information which follows certain optimal 'rules'. Here, appropriate forms of training and tutoring are particularly important.

However, using metaphors for system design can entail the danger that by tying an interface to concepts which prevail in non-electronic environments, one is not taking full advantage of the benefits that can accrue from using the electronic medium. Functionality must be matched to the ease of use that the metaphor may engender. For example, a 'filing cabinet' metaphor can be as restrictive as the real-life filing cabinet.

Giving users the means to learn quickly *about* a system, or to be able to generalize from one system mode to another, also means that users can become particularly unforgiving of any 'system quirks' which in other systems would not acquire quite as much importance. Users will also become 'experts' very quickly, and interfaces need to be able to cope with these rapidly changing levels of user skill, probably more so than the more conventional types of interface need to. One criticism of some closed environments based on the 'desktop' metaphor is that they do not cater adequately for expert users. (The section on Adaptation (p. 244) addresses this problem in more detail.)

Sample

Principle(s)

— If when an anology or metaphor is first introduced in a dialogue no information is present to identify (a) those task domains in which its use is appropriate, and (b) those task domains in which its use is inappropriate, then the power of the analogy or metaphor is reduced.

— If when an anology or metaphor is first introduced in a dialogue no information is present to identify (a) those structures and functional relations that are essential, and (b) those structures and functions that are incidental to the analogy or metaphor, then the power of the analogy or metaphor will be reduced.

— If no information is present in a dialogue to identify when a structure or functional relation in a system or subsystem departs from what is conventionally the case (in the analogy or metaphor), then the power of the analogy or metaphor will become a negative power for each occurrence of that case.

Interpretation

The power of an analogy or metaphor will be increased if examples of where it holds true, and where it does not, are given.

Where an analogy or metaphor holds true, there will be incidental structures and functional relations added in order to create the necessary illusion and continuity. Essential structures and functional relations need to be highlighted against those which are incidental or cosmetic.

Where there is a mismatch between the analogy in use and the specific procedures or labels of the system in question, users will have difficulty understanding why that is so, or may be 'led down the garden path' to an outcome which is unexpected on the basis of their internal knowledge. They may even abandon using the analogy or metaphor altogther (if they have the choice). This could have serious consequences for performance on the system in question and on other systems. Where the mismatch occurs, these serious consequences may be avoided if information is provided to highlight or explain the mismatch.

Example(s)

In the increasingly popular 'desktop type' systems, an electronic clipboard should allow a number of items to be clipped together, just as a real, physical clipboard does. It should not throw an old item away everytime a new one is 'clipped in'. If it does, users may stop thinking about it as a clipboard, and may start wondering whether other objects used in the metaphor have the same deviations from what is commonly the case. They may also ignore the desktop metaphor altogether, because it does not seem to hold up in practice.

Guideline(s)

— Make use of analogies and metaphors which are in common usage and especially those with readily anticipated characteristics.
— Provide information to delineate the boundary of application of the analogy or metaphor within the dialogue.
— Provide information on which characteristics of an analogy or metaphor are essential in the dialogue, and which are incidental or cosmetic.
— Make explicit the nature of any mismatch between the actual system functions and the objects and features of the analogy or metaphor being employed to assist system users.

Comment(s)

Analogies and metaphors are concepts or devices which have potentially much to contribute to the design of the conceptual model by which the system is described. It follows that, generally, guidelines which apply to the choice and usage of analogies and metaphors apply equally well to the choice and usage of conceptual models. (Conceptual models are seen as tools that can be used for the teaching or understanding of physical systems.)

3. Training and practice

In most systems, but particularly when a system is to be used by infrequent users, or by users with different levels of expertise, it is essential to provide some form of guidance and training, which may also include allowing practice at given tasks before the system is used 'for real'. This helps to compensate for the natural forgetting process between intermittent sessions. It also helps new users get to know the system's functionality. Guidance of this sort can take the form of either specific HELP information, or of online tutoring facilities, or a combination of the two, and it can also be in the form of paper-based manuals. It can also be system feedback of various sorts.

Online guidance is a valuable tool in helping novice users get to know a system and use it to its best advantage. It is far superior to paper-based forms of training, in that it shares features of the *system* the user is trying to learn to use, as opposed to those of a totally different medium (like paper-based user manuals).

The objectives of effective training are to promote smooth, error-free performance and a good conceptual understanding of the system model. This can only be achieved if the interface design, independent of the training material, is of an equivalent standard. Particular design features contribute to a reduction in training needs. Consistency within and between procedures reduces the volume of knowledge that has to be assimilated. If a task is performed in several contexts care should be taken to ensure that the procedures used are the same. (If this is not possible, as is sometimes the case, the procedures should be significantly different and that difference made clearly visible.) Similarly a simple model or one based on analogy or metaphor reduces the learning demands by helping the user to develop an effective mental model; one based on existing knowledge.

One objective of a training programme is to produce task automation where it is appropriate. Guidelines are given which suggest design features known to promote the rapid attainment of this level of skilled performance. Where systems are used to support important intellectual tasks, the development of automaticity for support tasks is particularly important; for instance, CAD systems, word-processors or databases. Automated performance of the secondary task allows the user to concentrate the maximum cognitive attention on the primary (decision-making, problem-solving or planning) task.

Sample

Principle(s)
　　Existing schemata are automatic transferable thinking processes from the user's general knowledge.

— If no familiar examples are available, new schemata are required.
— Induction of new schemata requires practice.

Interpretation
　　If a particularly new and unusual concept is being introduced into the design of a user interface, it helps users to get to know the system faster and operate it more efficiently if they are allowed, step by step, to try out different

approaches to complete a task, gradually gaining practice in the different operations of the interface.

It also helps if users are allowed to recover easily from errors so that practice can proceed smoothly.

Example(s)

Many facilities provided in current office systems lie idle or are rarely used. Part of the problem is that they may not be required as frequently as other facilities, or that it is possible to make do without them. Users make do because the effort of remembering how to use these facilities can be great. If it is always possible for users to escape to a harmless practice or learning mode, in order to rehearse these less favoured facilities when they are needed, then it is likely that a far greater proportion of the system functionality would be exploited.

Guideline(s)

— Allow users to practise when introducing unfamiliar methods, tasks, or concepts into the dialogue.

— Ideally, a practice mode should be context-dependent.

— Allow users to make repeated passes at a new task without demanding a high cost or sacrifice in terms of the work accomplished.

Comment(s)

For novice users, everything will be unfamiliar, even if the concepts behind the interface are in common usage.

A well-structured and simple programme of practice will help and encourage users to 'get to know the system' more quickly. However, many situations can only be adequately described in unstructured, complex terms, for which users have no previously acquired knowledge. In such cases, it may be better to allow users to build up new knowledge gradually from simple concepts right through to a more powerful yet generalizable system model. Training and practice system modes should aim to adopt this approach.

Besides having a context-dependent practice mode, there are other approaches to interface design which can be considered with respect to this problem. Including with the system a readily available interactive tutorial is useful, as is allowing users to choose their preferred skill level for interaction with the system. In this case the interface would change to match the user-defined skill level (commands may take over from menus for example, as the user gains confidence). A more ambitious solution is to make the interface adaptive to the needs and skills of its users (this approach has yet to be satisfactorily demonstrated).

4. Task–User match

The structure and arrangement of tasks and procedures should be compatible with known cognitive abilities. These can be abilities relating to experience as well as those known to apply universally. The more information that the designer has available concerning the potential users of the system, the better position (s)he is in to be able to match the demands placed on the user with the user's known cognitive characteristics. In the absence of such information, allowances have to be made for a range of user types. Much is known about cognitive processing — the way people think — that is relevant to the design of effective interfaces. A task procedure which the user understands, and is fully capable of performing, will be performed better and learned more easily than a procedure which causes difficulty. The guidelines related to this category contain information concerning cognitive characteristics which if incorporated in system design will help ensure that the user is not required to perform beyond his or her limitations.

Sample

Principle(s)

> The older the user (>55 years of age), the less information (s)he can hold in working memory at any given time.

Interpretation

> This principle is fairly self-explanatory. Working memory is a buffer store in which current information is held while it is operated upon or integrated with information retrieved from the user's store of 'knowledge'.

Example(s)

> A computer-based public service which will become more popular is the transaction-processing system used in electronic shopping for example. There may, in future, be an increasing amount of older users who wish to make use of such services to make purchases without venturing out of the house. This principle should be heeded to ensure, for instance, that lengthy or complex product-ordering codes are avoided with which users cannot easily cope.

Guideline(s)

> — Where it is anticipated that a significant number of older users (>55 years of age) will have cause to use the system:
> — Reduce the amount of information that has to be kept in mind in order to carry out subsequent actions.

— Make use of the display as an external working memory, in other words, keep relevant information present or allow it to be easily accessed.

Comment(s)

This principle is part of a general class of principles associated with human ageing. It is not just working memory that degrades with age, but also most aspects of cognitive, perceptual and physical performance. The effects of ageing on performance can nearly always be reduced if the user maintains frequent practice at a high level of performance. Where the older user is infrequent in his or her use of relevant faculties, like memory, degradation of those faculties will be greater than it would be for a younger person.

5. Feedback

Feedback is essential for effective user performance. The type and amount that is required varies, depending on the experience of the user and the nature of the task being performed. There are essentially two types of feedback discussed with respect to interface design: Required feedback, which is needed during task performance; and confirmatory feedback, which is needed on task or action completion only. The type of feedback that is necessary depends first on the experience of the user and second on the nature of the task. Complex tasks will usually warrant required feedback even though the user is familiar with the task. Whereas for simple tasks even the most inexperienced user will only need feedback on completion.

The guidelines in this section refer to the type of feedback that is necessary in different contexts and they give some recommendations for its presentation.

Sample

Principle(s)

Controlled sequences need confirmatory feedback (both required and redundant); automated sequences only need required feedback during the automated sequence.

Interpretation

Controlled sequences are those which a user cannot perform automatically, that is without thinking. As a rough check: a controlled sequence is one which a person cannot usually continue to carry out if (s)he is required to divert attention to another procedure simultaneously.

Users need to know that a controlled sequence is being or has been successfully completed, and such information should be conveyed in several complementary forms where practical.

For an automated sequence it is only necessary, as a minimum requirement, to provide feedback during the task sequence and to provide it in one form only.

Example(s)

The ability to touch-type is an obvious example of automated processing. Usually the noise of the key-press or the feel of the keys is enough to tell the skilled typist that words are being typed correctly. It is not necessary to switch attention from the copy in order to see what is being typed. For a novice typist, on the other hand, it is essential that the text that is being created be clearly visible at all times and that feedback on correct or incorrect actions be conveyed in many forms.

In a different context, such a sending an electronic message, experienced system users do not find it crucial to know that a message has actually been forwarded. They have confidence in a good system and their own actions. Novice users, on the other hand, will be extremely worried that their message never even left the terminal if they do not receive confirmatory feedback that the message was sent out to the named recipient when they issue the 'send' command. Unfortunately, many electronic mail systems make no effort to provide such information and many more do so in a manner which assumes a large degree of system familiarity and which gets information to the user in only one form.

Guideline(s)

When a procedure, task or sequence is not automatic to users (either because they are novice users or because the task is particularly complex or difficult), provide feedback in a number of complementary forms. Feedback should be provided both during the task sequence, to inform the user that things are progressing satisfactorily or otherwise, and at completion, to inform the user that the task sequence has been brought to a close satisfactorily or otherwise.

Comment(s)

This does not mean that a skilled user or a simple sequence should not have the provision of required and confirmatory feedback in a variety of forms; just that this is not absolutely essential is such cases. In practice the best solution is to allow the more experienced user to select the amount and type of feedback which is most desirable for certain sequences.

6. Selecting terms, wording and objects

Dialogues are composed of text, speech and visual images. In this category some rules for the provision of these dialogue elements are given. The physical presentation of information is critical to human–computer communication (see also Screen design, p. 239).

However good the 'concept' behind an interface, it will lose its value if its features are obscured by ineffective communication. The language of interaction, that is, command language, menu design, icons, synthetic speech messages, etc., must be selected to be comprehensible, easy to learn and compatible with known user characteristics. Communication skills are learned and developed according to a wide ranging set of rules. When selecting the terms, exact wordings, and graphical designs which will constitute a dialogue, we must be careful not to violate these rules (which are know implicitly but are only partially available in explicit form) or the dialogue will be less efficient and may break down entirely, leaving the user frustrated and dissatisfied and the job undone or, perhaps worse, done incorrectly.

Sample

Principle(s)

If the sentences used in a dialogue contain negatives, then they are read more slowly and less accurately than comparable sentences phrased in terms of affirmatives.

Interpretation

Negatives slow down users' understanding of what a sentence means. The sentence may also be read incorrectly, perhaps being interpreted for an affirmative statement if the user reads it quickly without a great deal of attention. Clearly, in some circumstances, this could have catastrophic consequences where a crucial action is wrongly taken.

Example(s)

When a user is receiving help on how to use an acoustic coupler, from a system or a manual perhaps, the instruction 'Do not replace the receiver until you hear the carrier signal' would be better written as 'When you hear the carrier signal, replace the receiver'.

Guideline(s)

When presenting instructions, feedback, etc., use affirmative sentences. Use negatives as little as possible.

Comment(s)

Obviously, this guideline should not be applied pedantically in all situations. There will be occasions where the convolutions necessary to avoid a negative would be counterproductive. For example, it can be very hard (and it could also be misleading) to try and say what should not be done by being affirmative about what should be done. The directive 'You may press all buttons except button B' may not be as relevant or powerful as 'Do not press button B' in a given circumstance. This guideline should therefore be applied generally but with sensitivity to specific cases.

7. Consistency

Consistency is fundamental to effective interface design. It contributes to usability in a number of ways. For example, it facilitates learning, lessens the number of errors made and helps the user to develop an accurate system model. It is rarely possible to be completely consistent within and between the applications of a system. So the designer will often have to determine the priorities of the system and make tradeoffs accordingly. For example, should the designer be rigidly consistent if the result is a slow and inappropriate procedure when an inconsistent procedure would achieve the goal more efficiently? The decision has to be made based on the function of the system and the users for whom it is intended.

The guidelines in this category emphasize the importance of consistency in certain domains, and identify areas where tradeoffs could be made; for example, it is suggested that consistency within an application should take priority over consistency between applications.

Sample

Principle(s)
— If the scoring between a system's dominant functional characteristics and those of other systems is low, then the probability of the user making the correct assumptions about the dominant functional characteristics of each of the major features and operations of the system will be reduced.
— If the probability of the user making the correct assumptions about the dominant functional characteristics of each of a system's major features and operations is low, then the probability of capture will be increased.

Interpretation
   If there are large inconsistencies between the different modes, application programmes or versions of a system, then the user's ability to generalize from one to another is reduced. If users assume that system aspects are similar, they will be prone to 'capture', that is errors in which they overgeneralize and assume that actions taken in one system mode will have the same effect in other, related, system modes.

Example(s)
   If most of the systems in the office market employ the 'desktop metaphor' and an apparently similar interface is introduced in another product or context, but this interface contains different types of command and consequences of those commands, and different relationships between elements in the interface, then users will find it particularly difficult to use and learn. (Possibly because they have different stored knowledge for what

desktop systems are all about and the new interface breaks all the rules stored with such knowledge.)

Guideline(s)

— If the intended interface is functionally different from other extant interfaces make it look different.

— Within the same system, ensure that different modes, application packages or versions either share common operational attributes or that they look sufficiently different from one another that users will not be tempted to overgeneralize.

8. Screen design

The quality of the physical interface, that is, the point at which information transfer occurs, is critical. It will have a significant bearing on the efficiency of human–computer interaction. A good conceptual stystem will be wasted if the physical interface is not an adequate medium of communication.

Screen design is concerned with the way that information is presented to the user: the spatial layout and properties, the information organization and format, the shape(s) and the continuity of presentation. Collectively these have been called the syntax of human–computer communication by some researchers. Performance can be maximized if attention is paid to known cognitive and perceptual characteristics which relate to these variables.

Sample

Principle(s)

If the items on any screen of information are independent of one another then the probability of comprehending the dialogue will be reduced.

Interpretation

Comprehensibility of a screen, and hence of the dialogue as a whole, depends on how the objects, images, text, commands, etc. which are present on a given screen relate to one another. If they are all logically related, then it is easier for users to understand where they are in a system and what the system can do.

Example(s)

Some typical systems currently available provide, as part of an editor menu, a screen of information containing the number of blocks of information available on disk, a number of mode options (for example, mathematics mode, interactive mode), a number of editing commands, a clock/date indicator, etc. There is almost no logical relation among the items displayed and the screen is particularly difficult to navigate through and use.

Guideline(s)
— Maintain logical and functional relationships between the items on any given screen.
— If some items on a screen are independent of the others or cannot easily be related to them at the same level of abstraction, then consider moving them onto a different screen or separating them clearly from the other elements of the screen (possibly using borders or boxing techniques).

9. Organization

System organization covers a range of concepts including structure, functionality, status and consistency. One can think in terms of organizing commands into structures, to help the users learn and remember them; organizing tasks such that they can be achieved easily and in the optimal order; organizing user directories to encourage efficiency, and so on. Features of organization hence span both the specific design of the interface and its language, and the design of procedures which will allow users to create and maintain efficient data stores. Optimizing organization in system design is subject to the priorities and intended purpose of the system, and is thus context-dependent. An effective design can only be achieved if the designer has clear objectives and a well-defined target user group. If (s)he does not, the system may be developed for a universal population and risk being inappropriate for many user types — that is, too simple and not powerful enough for experienced users but too complex for the inexperienced.

Sample

Principle(s)
    Assuming that items can be categorized according to some rule, a cue presented at recall that is effective for gaining access to one particular item will also facilitate access to other items in the same category. It will not facilitate access to other items in other categories presented at the same time (that is, it will obtain access to the category concept).

Interpretation
    Human memory is an organized entity. Appropriate prompting will allow access to certain categories of concepts and will assist retrieval of information from them, but it will not assist retrieval of information from categories not relevant to the prompt, even when that information was initially present together with the relevant information. This means that prompts may not work across category boundaries.

Example(s)

Filenames in a directory can be pointed to by a prompt, such as the directory name. If files in a particular directory relate to those in other directories, the designer should ensure that facilities exist that highlight this, or allow the users to 'flag' this when they are filing. The mere presence on screen of those files at the time of filing will not necessarily be sufficient to remind users later on that there exist relationships amongst them. Similarly, browsing will be facilitated by the provision of these facilities.

Guideline(s)

Categorize, or encourage users to categorize, information which must be recalled later. To assist recall from these categories of information, provide prompts, processes, labels or names which are relevant to those categories. Where information must be or might benefit from being retrieved across category boundaries, provide facilities to create prompts relevant to all the categories involved or to make use of 'pointers' or 'flags' to these categories. (It may be necessary to encourage users to provide these themselves.)

Comment(s)

This principle is particularly useful in designing systems that allow for browsing. If it is possible to categorize items, or if the system encourages this categorization process at storage, then it should also allow for easy browsing by increasing the context information provided. This may have implications for how the database is organized, so that users can easily go across category boundaries and retrieve documents this way.

10. Multimodal and multimedia interaction

There exist a variety of forms of communication that can be utilized in human–computer interaction. Information can be conveyed using text, speech or visual representation (icons). The guidelines in this section make recommendations about the most effective ways of using them, and the advantages to be had from using one form rather than another. Text is the most commonly used medium. Usually it is less open to ambiguity than pictorial information, and can be processed at the users' chosen speed — which speech generally cannot. In other words, users can control the speed at which they read but they cannot usually control the speed of a spoken message (nor would this necessarily be advisable). An advantage of both visual media over speech is that the information display is semipermanent: assuming the user can control how long the image is retained on the screen, the user can continue to reread the message (or look at the icon) until (s)he is sure that it is understood. The choice of media ultimately depends on the task requirements (and such elements as cost, technology, etc.)

Sample

Principle(s)

The presence of irrelevant speech sounds will impair recall regardless of their source.

Interpretation

This is self-explanatory.

Example(s)

Systems using voice synthesis or recognition (voice messaging systems, inventory order systems, etc.) should not require that users listen to or utter commands or messages while holding information in memory which must be carried forward to another context.

Guideline(s)

If the user has to remember information, eliminate any non-relevant speech sounds from the dialogue.

Comment(s)

A problem with adhering to this guideline is that in most work environments there will inevitably be many irrelevant speech sounds generated from natural sources. The designer should at least aim to ensure that the computer system does not add to the problem.

11. Navigation

If the user is to develop an accurate model of the system, his or her position in the system must be clear. It should be obvious at all times exactly where (s)he is and where (s)he can go. This type of status information is required to identify the system application and mode, for example, insert or write-over in a word-processor. Navigation can be facilitated by developing a simple and logical structure which the user can understand easily, and by providing location pointers and status information. These could take a variety of forms depending on the context. For example, the system could provide a different-shaped cursor to differentiate between modes or give the name, size and directory of a file that is being used. It is also important for the user to know the relationship between his or her present position and the location of other files and facilities. There should be a clearly defined route between related entities and an easy access system which allows the user to move around easily.

Sample

Principle(s)

— If sentences 1, 2 and 3 of a new screen of information do not specifically relate that screen to the previous screen of information, then the probability of comprehending the dialogue will be reduced.

— If the consequences of the possible user responses to any screen of information are not given explicitly, in terms of the information to be encountered in the next screen, then the probability of comprehending the dialogue will be reduced.

Interpretation

Developing a useful understanding of any system is helped if continuity in the dialogue is preserved. This can be achieved by providing information relating a current screen to past screens and possible future screens, or the consequences of future actions. Without such information, users may find it difficult to keep track of how far along their mental 'plan' for accomplishing a given task they are, and may be less confident of their actions. This may in turn affect their efficiency and make them more error-prone. Information which preserves continuity should come at the beginning and end of each screen.

Example(s)

If users are in 'editing mode' in a menu-based word-processor, then screen options should be headed 'editing mode' (that is, 'you are here'). Also the system should specify how to leave editing mode (that is, 'do this to get out') and where users will be left if they do leave that mode (that is, 'this is where you will end up').

Similarly, HELP screens should indicate where the users are, how they got there and what they can do to progress.

Guideline(s)

— Place orienting information at the top and bottom of each screen relating it to those preceding it and those following it respectively.

— Orienting information should relate the current screen to the preceding screen, identifying what the preceding screen was and why the current screen is being presented.

— Orienting information at the bottom of the screen should relate it to the choice and consequences of actions available in the following screen.

12. Adaptation

A system is rarely intended for a highly specific and static user group. Individual users will bring to the system a variety of skills and experience levels, and will develop these at differing rates. Adaptability and flexibility refer to the ability of the system to act appropriately in a given context, to suit a particular user's needs and preferences.

One can conceive of at least two kinds of adaptation in interfaces:

— adaptive in the sense that is adapts to a user's preferred *style* of work and information needs. The emphasis is on developing an 'active' system that takes some of the decision-making away from the user;
— adaptable in the sense that it can respond differently to different levels of user expertise. The emphasis is on developing an interface that is capable of moulding itself to the feedback, help and dialogue needs of different user types.

The art of building adaptability and flexibility into an interface must rely on the careful matching of features in the electronic system such that they allow the human to have free 'processing capacity' to concentrate on the things (s)he is good at. It is also important to bear in mind that user needs from an electronic system are swayed by the current task and work environment and the level of expertise or frequency of system use the user has. The ideal adaptable or flexible interface should be able to support a variety of users, with differing needs in different situations. With the current technology, one can only hope to go part of the way in that direction. However, a lot can still be done even within this limited domain, by allowing the system to be personalized by the user, or by utilizing user feedback and simple monitoring devices to automatically change task descriptions and system reactions.

By and large, if a given environment is likely to involve.

— variety of tasks,
— variety of problem-solving strategies,

there is a need to create an interface that adapts or is flexible enough that it can be adapted.

Interfaces with built-in flexibility create an illusion of adaptiveness. The interface can be customized by the user, who is free to combine facilities, options and commands to suit his or her particular task requirements or problem-solving strategies. Whether a flexible (as opposed to fully adaptive) interface is enough depends primarily on what the user is trying to do with the system, and on the levels of user skill and task frequency.

User tasks fall into two broad categories:

— closed tasks, where all parameters and 'allowable' routes are predefined;
— open tasks, where not all — if any — parameters can be predefined. In this type of task (for example, graphics creation), preferred styles of work

and task requirements mean that it is not possible to defined a single 'ideal' route through the system in order to achieve the task. Many are allowable.

Overlaid on these two types of task are considerations of task frequency and user level of expertise, such that:

— Novice users, or infrequent (closed) tasks need systems that specify a clear task structure, display available options and explain how each option is implemented. For these systems, the dialogue needs to be fully explanatory and should not contain cryptic references which require the use of a manual. A moded interface that can be set to different 'levels and contains suitable help facilities can go a long way towards satisfying many of these needs.
— Frequent (closed) tasks or experienced users do not need fully explanatory dialogues (in fact, this irritates an experienced user) and not all options need to be visible at any given time in the interaction. In this case the user can be given the larger share of control and should be given ample and appropriate feedback (for example, menu short-cutting and creation of macros). Again, appropriate moding can achieve significant gains.
— Open tasks and frequent or experienced users require systems that encourage and support 'navigating' through the system, so the user can plot his or her own course to achieve a given (open) task (for example, present all options available, or provide an audit trail). Such systems should also allow the option of combining different utilities and resources and create personalized interfaces.
— A combination of an open-ended task and an infrequent user is possibly the most challenging from the system design point of view. It will also be one of the best application domains for truly adaptive interfaces, if they are seriously developed. In the meantime, one possible solution is to consider incorporating intelligent front-ends into the system, to act as a buffer between the user and the existing interface. These can monitor the responses of the user and translate the messages from the system so that specific types of user can understand them.

13. Error management

Dealing with errors is crucial to interface design. Two approaches need to be taken. The first to prevent or reduce errors, and the second to recover from the errors which will inevitably occur. Erroneous performance can be made less likely but it cannot be prevented altogether. An interface which professes to manage errors needs to evaluate the validity of input, only executing if validity criteria are met. These criteria should relate to the suitability and consequences of the action. If the criteria are not met the system should provide the user with information which would allow him or her to re-evaluate the input. This is a difficult task for current systems which have no real way of determining the user's intention, and so cannot always make a sensible evaluation of the suitability of the action. Grammatical or syntactical errors can be detected easily and the user should be able to make the corrections with the minimum of effort. For example it should not be necessary to retype a full line when only a single character is incorrect.

There are a number of design features known to reduce the likelihood of errors. These should be incorporated when possible but the consequential effects and interactions should be assessed before implementation. For example reducing all command names to single characters will reduce the likelihood of typing errors, but may make the command language difficult to remember. All such interactions need to be considered and design choices made based on system priorities. For example, is speed or ease of use more or less important than the occasional error?

14. Locus of control

In human–computer interaction the locus of control can reside anywhere along a continuum ranging from total system control to total user control. The optimum point for the locus is dependent on a number of factors. The major determinants are user experience and the purpose for which the system is being designed. The varying demands of a task may mean that the locus of control should ideally shift within some interactive sessions. For the inexperienced or occasional user the initiative for interaction needs to come from the system. A considerable amount of assistance should be available. As the user gains experience the locus needs to shift. The user will need less help from the system and will wish to bypass many of the formalities intended for naïve users. For example, the switch from a menu-driven interface to a command-driven interface represents just such a shift.

There are two levels on which the question of the locus of control needs to be considered. The first is whether the locus is fixed or variable, and the second is how the locus is determined. At one extreme is the single task system which is designed with a particular user in mind, and usefully serves only that user and purpose. At the other extreme is the self-adapting system which evaluates user performance and detects changes, making appropriate alterations to the locus as a result. Unless the designer has a considerable amount of information about the potential users of a system some flexibility needs to be built in. One example of how this can be done is the provision of experience levels (similar to computer games) where the user can select a level ranging from very inexperienced through to very experienced.

GUIDELINES

Framework for guideline application

The following matrix identifies the application domains of the guidelines. Primary guidelines are those which directly address the category subject. For example, guidelines 1 to 24 are specifically concerned with the 'design of procedures and tasks'. Secondary guidelines are those which have an indirect or less important contribution to make to that category or sensitive dimension.

Many more sensitive dimensions could be added and discussed as more of the cognitive psychological foundations are explored and more guidelines are generated. Some categories could grow and subdivide; others could perhaps be subsumed into a more holistic category for a particular concept. For now, though, we have hopefully provided enough dimensions and explanation to serve as a useful framework into which the current guidelines can be placed. We turn now to consider the specific guidelines in greater detail in the following section.

The guidelines

Reading the list of guidelines may prove interesting but it is not necessarily a useful activity in its own right. The framework is provided as an attempt to assist the guidelines user in organizing the information which is relevant to particular design problems. Any use of the guidelines in a design context will perhaps be best directed through the framework. At the present time it has ben possible to generate only a relatively small number of guidelines. This is due to the limited coverage of cognitive psychology from which guidelines have been derived so far. It is also due to the large number of questions about human cognition that still remain to be answered. For this reason there are many gaps in the guidelines presented here as well as many inconsistencies in their level of application. Some, for instance, are very general, others quite specific. It is envisaged that a great deal of work has to be done yet — not least testing in design contexts — before the categorized lists of guidelines can be synthesized into more formal design 'rules' with established methods for their application.

As the reader will soon note (from looking at the guidelines in isolation), it is perhaps more useful and educational to be able to see the full derivation of each guideline from the underlying psychology, with examples from system design, as illustrated in the 'samples' in the last section. Therefore the following sections should be treated more as an illustration than as fully usable guidelines. The numbers in square brackets after each guideline refer to the summary principles of cognitive psychology which are listed at the end of Chapters 4 to 7. The number in italics identifies the chapter number, the second number identifies the summary principle.

Category	Primary guidelines	Secondary guidelines
Design of procedures and tasks	1–24	33 37 42 50 53 55 61 64 68 70 72 73 75 80 82 84 86 89 90 94 98 116 127 136 140 146 152 153 154 155
Analogy and metaphor	25–56	15 17 19 61 65
Training and practice	57–82	1 23 24 25 28 52 83 88 96 104 112 113 114 156 162
Task–user match	83–93	1 3 4 8 9 10 14 17 18 19 20 21 22 23 24 25 27 61 62 74 98 104 106 111 112 113 114 125 127 136 146 156 160 162
Feedback	94–98	7 13 29 71 74 102 104 122 144 147 148 149 157 158 159
Selecting terms, wording and objects	99–115	7 12 13 15 19 31 32 38 51 93 117 128 136 141 145 150 151
Consistency	116–122	14 15 56 130 133 136 142 149
Screen design	123–130	40 77 79 81 84 85 87 92 93 103 109 110 136 147 148 149
Organization	131–142	2 16 70 85 87 92 105 123 124
Multimodal and multimedia interaction	143–146	125
Navigation	147–149	37 97 137
Adaptation	150–156	53 66 75 76 77 78 92
Error management	157–160	3 4 18 24 42 43 44 45 46 47 48 49 57 63 102 107 119 120 121
Locus of control	161, 162	156 160

1. Design of procedures and tasks

One of the aims of good design must be to devise appropriate ways of representing tasks and procedures such that the system's functionality can be fully utilized, while placing a minimum of load on the user. A number of factors can contribute to loading the user in this respect: length of the total task sequence, the ease with which the user can abstract meaningful blocks of transactions which together, in proper combination, lead to the achievement of the task as a whole, and so on. The following guidelines refer to the choice of appropriate task structures:

(1) Task sequences should be kept short (to encourage automatic, effortless performance). Keep the number of user actions in a sequence to a minimum. [6-8]

(2) Break up long task sequences into sub-sequences. [6-8]

(3) Tasks can be combined in the following ways: simple + simple, or complex + simple. A user should not be asked to perform two complex tasks together. This is especially true for novice users. [6-11]

(4) Action sequences for different tasks should be unique. Try not to have similar opening actions. Where this is unavoidable draw the users' attention to the point at which the sequences diverge. [6-9]

(5) If formally equivalent procedures (that is, procedures having a similar logical structure) are shared between different task domains or systems it is important to make those procedures explicit in each context. [4-1]

Having selected a suitable task structure, it then becomes essential to consider how to inform the user of the characteristics of the structure selected. The aim is to devise appropriate ways of showing to the user, as clearly as possible, how tasks can be accomplished using the system. There are a number of ways in which the task structure can be made visible to the user:

(6) Consider adding extra, redundant information about key components of the task to help make the task structure as explicit as possible. [4-3]

However, to avoid confusing the user, ensure that (s)he is aware of what is simply 'background' information, and what is 'foreground', and hence important, information:

(7) Make important information explicit. [4-17 and 7-14]

(8) Do not present information which is *irrelevant* to the task that users are trying to perform. [4-3]

(9) If the user has to remember and then use information, do not fill the time between these tasks with irrelevant distracting information or activity. [5-5]

In addition,

(10) Avoid introducing distractions when it is important that users remember visual abstract patterns. [5-13]

Completeness of the information the user receives from the system is also an important determinant of the probability of the user developing a good understanding of the way the task can be accomplished electronically. It allows the user to build up a consistent and coherent 'picture' of the ways of achieving the task. The following guidelines should be considered:

(11) Enclose all information relevant or necessary to the completion of a task within the task-associated dialogue. [4-14]
(12) Define all terms relevant to the completion of a task early on in the interaction. [4-14]
(13) Ensure that objects or entities to which a command, label, message, etc. refers, have been defined elsewhere in the dialogue [4-14]
(14) Ensure that users can utilize well-learned, generic (system-wide) commands for routine or repetitive actions or sequences of actions. [4-2]

Another way to make a task structure visible to a user is to capitalize on the user's own previous knowledge. This approach is addressed in more detail in the next section, on analogy and metaphor, but the following guidelines are appropriate here:

(15) Ensure that the common or natural structure and labelling of the different elements that make up a task are preserved in the electronic versions of those tasks [4-3, 4-7, 4-8 and 4-9]
(16) Present information in the order in which it will be used. [4-11]

Familiarity with the information provided by the system (for example where system design capitalizes on existing knowledge structures) has certain implications in terms of the processing mode which the system induces in the user. Users can operate in at least two processing modes: low-level and high-level. These modes reflect the amount of attention that the user dedicates to the mechanics of achieving the task at hand, as well as the strategies that are used for task achievement: heuristic strategies and direct memories for low-level processing, problem-solving behaviour using existing knowledge for high-level processing. Features of the information present in the environment lead to the adoption of these different modes of processing, and can be utilized to actively promote one or the other mode, depending on the task characteristics:

(17) Make use of familiar material and familiar methods of manipulating that material when the required performance is low-level (that is, to accomplish tasks which are routine, repetitious or simply a means to an end). [4-4]
(18) When it is desirable for users to think about what they are doing, in

non-routine or critical parts of the task, ensure that the features of the electronic situation are not too familiar. [4-4]

(19) When it is desirable for users to progress rapidly through a series of transactions, because they are routine and non-critical parts of a task, use familiar or well-practised labels or sequences of actions. [4-4]

(20) To engender quick and accurate performance of tasks such as decision-making, reasoning and planning; encourage the user to complete one task at a time. [5-15]

(21) To engender quick and accurate performance of tasks such as decision-making, reasoning and planning; avoid using nested loops within them. [5-15]

(22) To engender quick and accurate performance of tasks such as decision-making, reasoning and planning; provide linear task structures, that is, avoid parallel, branched or nested task elements. [5-15]

(23) If it is desirable for a task to become automatic then define the most appropriate way of performing it and allow only that method to be used. [6-5]

(24) Tasks which are best performed quickly and easily — for example, tasks which are intellectually low-level and are a means to an end — should be made up of actions which build sequentially towards that end. Action sequences should not take excursions into other tasks which are intended to achieve different ends. [6-6]

2. Analogy and metaphor

One can do a lot towards improving the ease of use of an electronic system by allowing users to capitalize on their existing bodies of knowledge about procedures and tasks in the non-electronic world. The following guidelines cover some ways of ensuring that user knowledge is accessed and/or utilized:

(25) Use familiar procedures when introducing new concepts so that existing bodies of knowledge can be used. [6-1]

(26) Use text materials as instructions to invoke relevant domains of user knowledge [4-6]

(27) Use familiar material, situations, working methods and relevant analogies to engender good user performance. [4-5]

(28) In complex or unfamiliar contexts, remind or prompt users to think about the kinds of model or plan that will be useful. (This can be done using a suitable analogy.) [4-2]

(29) Use text material to supply useful analogies and to help users to understand what they have done and how effective it has been. [4-6]

However, making a system approachable to even naïve users, has implications which extend beyond the immediate domain of improving user–system cognitive compatibility. In particular, one must ensure that the system's functionality at least matches the expectations the user will have, on the basis of previous knowledge of similar situations in the non-electronic world. For example, a desktop metaphor may lead a user to expect to be able to have drawings as well as text on a piece of electronic 'paper'. That is a common feature of the non-electronic desktop. If the interface does not deliver that expected functionality, user reactions may be more negative than if a more conventional interface is used; the user expects more and may be less forgiving of even small system limitations.

Similarly, encouraging novices to gain hands-on experience, by making the system accessible through a metaphor means that efforts should be invested in ensuring that the system is robust enough to cope with the types of experimenting behaviour which computer-naïve users are likely to inflict on the system. For example, allowing the user to put the operating system in the 'wastebin' of a desktop-based system can have disastrous consequences in terms of a user's willingness to experiment with the system ever again.

The power of a metaphor depends on a number of features, mostly to do with the influence that context and content have on human reasoning within a knowledge domain. For example, we know that context can determine whether an item is seen to be a member of a category or not, and how similar different objects are perceived to be. We also know that categorization helps reduce 'mental load'. Good implementation needs to take account of as many of these recommendations as possible, within the constraints of the particular system development under consideration:

(30) Do not mix metaphors. [4-1, 4-3 and 7-13]
     Even if more than one metaphor is actually being used (such as office work and desktops), efforts should be made to ensure that the desktop appears to be like an 'office' desktop, not a school or shop desktop. Terms should be chosen from within one domain only.
(31) When electronic metaphors of common situations or contexts are used, ensure that the terms used to give the illusion of the metaphor refer to typical items in the common, real-life situations or contexts. (In this way the user will be prompted to think in terms of the metaphor.) [4-6]
(32) Ensure that the tone of the metaphor matches the attitude that the user should have towards the system. [7-15]
     For example, if the intention is to encourage users to use an office system, comparing the deleting of files to cremation will not encourage a positive attitude towards the system. Similarly, 'jokey' metaphors or 'jokey' labels for items within a metaphor can suggest to the user that the system is not a

'serious' system which can be used for real work. This may put some users off the system altogether.

(33) Ensure that the metaphor matches the type of work the system will be used for. [4-3]

For example, the metaphor of a digital kitchen (as outlined, for example, by Houston, 1983) would be of little practical use in helping a user navigate through an office system. A typewriter metaphor may not be adequate to promote word-processing skills. The typewriter does not allow many of the functions the user should know about in word-processing. It would lead the user to expect *different* things from the word-processor, and suggests that the limitations of the typewriter apply to the system as well.

(34) Make use of analogies and metaphors which are in common usage and especially those with readily anticipated characteristics. [4-7, 4-8 and 4-9]

(35) Provide information to delineate the boundary of application of the analogy or metaphor within the dialogue. [4-7, 4-8 and 4-9]

(36) Use metaphors that are clearly defined, well-bounded entities. [4-7, 4-8 and 5-29]

For example, a vague metaphor such as 'office work' will be more open to misinterpretation and variation than a more restricted metaphor such as 'desktop', 'diary', 'index file'.

(37) Preserve in the metaphor the order of the actions that are common in the non-electronic situation that serves as a basis for the metaphor. [4-11]

(38) When using a metaphor, use the *same* terms for the electronic version as are commonly used for the non-electronic situation. [4-18, 7-1 and 7-3] This may also include allowing the same object or action to be called by different names (for example, file, save, put away, store tend to mean the same type of thing in the 'real' world). Different people prefer different names. The same person may use more than one name.

(39) Provide information on which characteristics of an analogy or metaphor are essential, in the dialogue, and which are incidental or cosmetic. [4-7, 4-8 and 4-9]

(40) If a metaphor is only applicable to *part* of a user interface, those situations where it does *not* apply should be clearly identified (for example, by making the screen look different, introducing a warning sound signal, etc.) [4-7]

(41) Make explicit the nature of any mismatch between the actual system functions and the analogy or metaphor being employed to assist system users [4-7, 4-8 and 4-9]

For example, if certain 'rules' normally associated with the non-electronic situation have to be broken in its electronic translation, warn the user about those deviations from the norm using screen design or other techniques. (For instance, use unusual terms to label operations which will not behave as expected, or present options in a different format, to alert the user that something is different and encourage the user to think about what (s)he is doing. Or use messages of the kind 'You are now in command mode. To return to the desktop mode press the control key', to alert the user that a significant change has just taken place. It is also appropriate to simply inform the user that 'Option X does not utilize the metaphor on which the rest of the system is based', so long as the user is also given information about how to get *back* to the metaphor before and after implementing that option.)

It was stated above that it is important to match the interface to the natural 'ways of doing things' in the non-electronic world, as this helps reinforce the metaphor. (Although this may conflict with the user's image of the computer's 'way of doing things'.) It is equally important to match the metaphor to the requirements of the task the user is trying to achieve using the system. In particular, using a metaphor tends to make the user adopt a certain type of processing 'mode'. It is necessary to make sure that this processing mode matches the requirements of what the user does using the system. (See also the related comments and guidelines contained in the section on design of procedures and tasks, p. 248)

Metaphor-based interfaces may encourage 'automatic' modes of operation in users: situations are so familiar that the user stops thinking about what (s)he is doing. In some cases, such as log-on procedures, assessing often-used utility packages, this automatization of behaviour can be desirable; it is a fast, smooth mode of user–system interaction that leaves the user free to plan the task ahead, think, etc. However, there are situations where it is highly desirable that users be kept fully aware of what they are doing, even if this involves slower, more effortful interaction.

(42) Take steps to avoid automatic interaction:
   (a) where the consequences of inappropriate actions (brought about by automatic interaction) are 'fatal' in some way (for example, files are destroyed, clearing signals are issued, etc.); [6-9]
   (b) where the user needs to keep track of long series of operations, or needs to remember what was done in a given situation (for example, when copying files, storing information, performing long sequences of operations); [6-9]
   (c) where sequences of actions have similar starting points but very different consequences (for example, log-off and leave-utility operations; certain cut-and-paste and copy-and-paste operations, etc.). [6-9 and 6-12]

The following procedures are appropriate to encourage the use of 'controlled', rather than 'automatic' processing from the user, without destroying the power of the metaphor:

(43) Require a confirmatory input prior to major 'fatal' operations. Couple the request with an unusual or unexpected event (a beep, reverse video or flashing). [6-5]

(44) Require confirmatory input which is random and demands that attention be paid to the current screen (for example, 'type "x" if that is really what you want to do' — where "x" changes in an unpredictable manner). [6-5]

(45) Provide a long (4 seconds or more) pause before action or command implementation, with the option to cancel the operation at one stroke. (This procedure is also useful where it is desirable that the user read something presented on screen which is nevertheless not essential to completing the task, such as a copyright notice.) [6-5]

(46) Space out the individual elements of a given sequence of operations, and ensure that the user cannot simply enter a long string of advance commands to be held in a buffer until required (for example, when copying files, deleting files). [6-4 and 6-5]

(47) Require the user to acknowlege the completion of each stage in a sequence, and allow full cancellation of the sequence at any stage. [6-5]

Choice of which of these procedures to select depends on the task the user is involved in, and the particular system characteristics. In addition, because at least some users like to 'think by doing' [4-5 and 4-6]:

(48) Provide a powerful and consistently used 'undo' key or function key.

(49) Provide an equally powerful 'redo' key, in case the user changes his or her mind.

(50) Minimize the use of default procedures at fatal points in a dialogue, or where the user would benefit from thinking about information currently being removed from screen (for example, during filing, for better subsequent recall).

The task of alerting the user to the fact the system is based on a metaphor needs to be approached with care. The context in which information is found affects the way that information is interpreted, so:

(51) Consider using highly evocative names for the first few items the user will encounter after logging-on [4-5, 4-6 and 5-32]
For example, 'desk', 'clipboard', 'wastebin' are highly evocative of an office environment; 'carpet', 'window' and 'door' are not, and 'pen', 'bin' and 'telephone' are too general or ambiguous.

(52) Be aware that verbal labels *alone* are not sufficient to make people think to best effect in terms of the metaphor. An initial online tutorial demonstrating the *key* features and interrelations used in the system metaphor is almost essential. [4-5 and 4-8]

Metaphors make systems easier to use because they draw on the users' existing knowledge of techniques and optimal procedures. But it is important to recognize that not all users have the same styles of working even in the non-electronic world. This means that:

(53) Wherever possible users should be given flexibility in the input type they can use to enter commands. [5-1 and 6-7]
For example, expert users may prefer to group selections together in macros, if need be ignoring any metaphors used in system design, rather than choose options from pull-down menus all the time, or manoeuvering icons around the screen. Or, for keyboard-based interactions, the user may prefer to enter commands via the keyboard; for mouse-based interactions (for example, graphics) the user may prefer to select from menus, using the mouse, to effect the *same* procedure.

Note, too, that flexibility should be built into the choice of input media used as well, particularly where speech is used to enter commands or effect selections. Both these considerations are dealt with in greater detail in the sections on adaptation, selection of terms, wording and objects, and multimodal and multimedia interaction (pp. 272, 264, 271).

If a metaphor cannot be used consistently throughout a given user interface, the following tradeoffs and remedial steps are appropriate:

(54) If it is difficult to develop a metaphor for a particular type of interface, then encourage the user to develop a good system model in other ways. For example, provide suitable online tutoring which covers the *key features* of the dialogue. Aim to provide a framework for using the system, rather than trying to teach the user every single system feature. [4-5 and 4-8]

(55) If it is not possible to preserve in the metaphor the order in which operations are normally performed in the non-electronic analogue of the metaphor, then consider delegating control to the *system* at the start of each major sequence of operations that deviate from the norm. [4-11]
For example, a given system may require that certain formating operations, including setting up the printer, be carried out before creating a document. Normally, the task of creating a document and producing a final copy tend to be treated separately, and in that order. In this case, it is better to have the system prompt the user for *all* required items of

information before the user is allowed to start, rather than expect the user to remember to feed in all the information unprompted.

In all cases above, however,

(56) keep inconsistent information well separate from other information which does not break the rules implicit in the metaphor. [4-9 and 6-7] (See also the section on consistency, p. 266).

3. Training and practice

For a novice user, an electronic system tends to appear as a complex, unfamiliar environment, whose rules are unknown or difficult to grasp. There are several ways of helping the user over the many hurdles of learning to use a system effectively. In the previous section we looked at the role that analogy and metaphor can play. Here we consider the role of adequate training materials and of system features aimed directly at allowing novices gain a reasonable understanding of the system in the most 'cognitively compatible' way.

(57) For systems incorporating particularly novel concepts, provide online tutorials which allow the user to experience the interface without catastrophic effects, and which provide (textual) information step by step on what is happening and why. [4-6]

(58) In complex or unfamiliar contexts, where there are no existing relevant or useful models to assist thinking, allow users to develop new plans (for example, by providing 'optimal route' suggestions, audit trails, etc.). [4-2]

Text instructions — such as those often provided in system HELP facilities and many system tutorials — are useful to allow the user to gain access to the relevant knowledge domains (s)he already possesses (for example, knowledge about the non-electronic equivalent of a given metaphor). But they are not enough, by themselves, to promote the kinds of thinking skills and strategies which help a user get to know the full capabilities of a system. And this is true even of tutorials which take the user through the solution of a particular example, whilst blocking user access to the system while the tutorial is running. There is no substitute for hands-on practice.

(59) Do not use text instruction as a short cut to skill acquisition. Practice is essential. [4-6]

(60) Provide comprehensive online tutorial programmes for the novice user. [4-16]

(61) Pay attention to 'standard and conventional' procedures or models when

confronting users with unfamiliar information so that they can make use of previous experiences and existing knowledge to plan how to tackle the task at hand. [6-1]

Providing a learning 'mode' which the user can enter in order to practise the new skills can nurture the formation of such plans. A moded interface is one which can be 'set' to different levels of user skill and requirements. Within the context of training and practice, moded interfaces refer mostly to interfaces which provide exploratory environments for the novice user, allowing him or her to learn by doing, not by being told. The following general guidelines apply to the design of training modes for user interfaces:

(62) Allow users to practise when introducing unfamiliar methods, tasks or concepts into the dialogue. [4-5]
    In other words, allow users to learn by *doing*: do not require them to go through screen after screen of text instructions with no facilities for trying out for themselves the implications of those instructions.

(63) Training modes should, as an essential requirement, protect the user from the consequences of errors: fragile training-mode interfaces can be counterproductive. [4-5 and 7-15]
    (As we discussed in the section on metaphors, a system's response to a user can be critical in determining the attitude the user has towards the system. System feedback is used to gain an overall view of the situation, and antagonistic contexts will lead to antagonistic attitudes.)

(64) Training modes should use realistic tasks, that is, tasks the user is likely to encounter in normal use. Skills gained in one domain do not always generalize to another domain. [4-1]
    In addition, if the user feels (s)he can do 'real' work within a short period from logging-on, this may increase his or her motivation to learn further and reduce resistance to novelty.

(65) Training modes for systems adopting a metaphor approach should aim to provide the user with the *key* features of the metaphor. They should not attempt exhaustive description of all features of the metaphor. [4-2, 4-5 and 4-8]

The emphasis should always be on encouraging the user to *think* through the learning process, by providing the right framework, suitably error-cushioned, in which discovery and trial-and-error can take place. The following guidelines refer to features of the system which may contribute to providing such a framework:

(66) Ideally, a practice mode should be context dependent. [4-5]
    In other words, if users can escape to practice mode when they encounter

difficulties in handling the 'real' system, they should be allowed to practise using the kind of task they are trying to achieve, not just be given high-level, task-irrelevant help.

(67) Allow users to make repeated passes at a new task without demanding a high cost or sacrifice in terms of the work accomplished. [4-5 and 7-3] For example, ensure that while experimenting with the system, in a training mode, novice users cannot command themselves into 'blind alleys'.

(68) Consider restricting the initial options novice users can access to a few *basic* choices that are sufficient for a user to achieve simple tasks. [4-5, 4-8, 6-9 and 7-3]
For example, one could consider barring access to higher-level (for example, directory maintenance, document manipulation, queuing facilities) system functions in the training mode. *However*, in the interests of allowing users to capitalize on their facilities for incidental learning:

(69) Do not eliminate the *mention* of the other options — simply alert novice users to the fact that those facilities are not accessible in the training mode. [5-27 and 7-3]

(70) Make clear the functional structure of the system by giving explicit feedback on all necessary preliminary work before certain options become accessible. [4-3 and 6-10]
For example, if a novice requests a printing option before all necessary editing or document preparation operations are complete, the system should provide clear feedback on what needs to be done (as a minimum) before the option is accessible. Under no circumstances should the system just ignore the request or damage the previous user work.

(71) Make the feedback *positive*, not negative. [4-12]
For example, say that the option required *is* available *after* certain required work, not that the option is not available or, worse still, that a syntax error has deen committed. This will help give the user a positive attitude towards the system. For a similar reason, avoid pairing the feedback with loud noises, flashing lights, etc. which may intimidate the user or embarrass him or her in front of his or her colleagues.

Context-sensitive HELP can also be used as a teaching facility, particularly if users are allowed to learn through practice, using realistic tasks, and with no fatal consequences.

(72) Consider combining the HELP function with some kind of computer-assisted learning which allows the user to try out the different available courses of action using his or her *current problem* and then allows the user to port the 'solution' to his or her working 'space'. [4-5]

In all cases, however,

(73) The match between the HELP information and the user interface to the system; and between training modes and the 'real' system, must be as exact as possible. [4-1]

The above guidelines have implications for the type of processing mode that will be induced in the user during the performance of the task. Specifically,

(74) If users have to wait for system feedback before completing a task, do not assume that the task will become automatic (that it will be performed quickly and without thinking). [6-5]

With suitable practice and training procedures, the user will progress to more sophisticated forms of interaction with more confidence. This progression needs to be handled with care, if the benefits of training and practice are to be capitalized on. The following guidelines apply to this progression from the training to more sophisticated modes:

(75) Start gradually and encourage users to try out more complex facilities only as they gain experience. [5-1, 6-9 and 7-3]
(76) Progression to more advanced facilities should be under user control. [5-1 and 6-9]
(77) Ensure that the user can progress from one skill mode to the next easily, and make those options clearly visible [6-9]
(78) Consider making it an option to proceed to a more advanced level and back again at key points in the dialogue. [6-9]

Defaults can be useful to help users progress from lower to higher levels of sophistication in system use. Used in a traning mode, they allow users to achieve quasi-sophisticated outputs without requiring sophisticated knowledge of system syntax and procedures. Used in more advanced modes, they allow fast, effortless completion of often-attempted tasks. However, bear in mind the following factors:

(79) Where default values exist for certain system parameters, make it obvious to the user (through appropriate screen design) that a default exists and what it is. [4-9 and 4-21]

Novice users unfamiliar with the concept of defaults often try to specify unfamiliar parameters and are likely to get lost in unknown system paths which may not be essential to the work they want to do.

(80) For certain defaults and tasks, consider blocking access to the re-specification options, with a clear message to the user to the effect that an option is not available in the training mode. [4-5, 4-8 and 6-9]

(81) Make the default look more prominent than any options to do with specifying *non-default* parameters. [*4-9, 4-21* and *6-7*]

(81) Make the process of specifying a default, or of specifying new parameters, as clear and simple as possible. [*6-8*]

4. Task–user match

Normally, users do not come to a system — even a new system — totally 'cold': they will have some experience (however minimal) of other systems, and they will have some knowledge of the general task domain (electronic or non-electronic). Though a certain amount of generalization does occur across systems and between the electronic and non-electronic knowledge domains,

(83) Do not assume that users will make a perfect connection between the requirements of an unfamiliar system or task domain and a system or task domain that they already know, even when many of the procedures are structurally or logically similar. [*4-1*]

In other words, ensure that HELP, training and practice are available which present, clearly and unambiguously, the key concepts of the new system. And if these deviate in significant ways from similar concepts in existing systems, or existing task procedures, highlight these deviations to the user.

System design involves developing a suitable way of breaking down the tasks that will be performed electronically, such that they 'fit' the requirements of the system. Attention should also be dedicated to ensuring that the task breakdown fits the requirements of the user. This concerns both the amount of information which needs to be held in memory in order to perform the task, as well as the nature of such information (familiar, unfamiliar), and features of the presentation of that information for the first time, when it is to be stored in memory for subsequent use. For example,

(84) Reduce the amount of information that has to be remembered to help the user quickly and accurately carry out tasks such as decision-making, reasoning and planning. [*5-15*] For example.

(a) minimize the number of actions, commands, objects, properties, rules, etc. that the user needs to remember in order to perform efficiently in a given task or application. [*4-19*]

(b) if users have to remember information for some time (for example, to complete a task) make sure that the total number of items that need to be held in memory (commands, transactions, etc.) does not exceed five. [*5-6*]

(85) If information has to be rememberd and used after it has been removed from the display, but has been presented in no particular order, then keep

related elements together to form meaningful chunks, do not display more than five chunks. [5-1]

(86) When presenting unfamiliar information do not put any unnecessary memory demands on the user. [6-3]

(87) When groups of items have to be accurately recalled (for example, in the same order), if possible present those items in meaningful groups of up to three items. [5-1]

(88) When the user must remember information, present it slowly and well spaced out. [6-5]

(89) If a task requires feedback then try to minimize memory demands; let the users concentrate all their attention on that task. [6-5]

(90) If a task is intellectually demanding let the user concentrate fully on it. For example,
    (a) eliminate unnecessary information and distractions. [6-11]
    (b) when users have to remember information from one screen to another or one system state to another, ensure that the minimum irrelevant information is presented and the least redundant actions required. [5-7]

(91) Guidelines which apply to the memory of text and speech will also apply to the names of pictures. [5-14]

Users are not all the same: they differ along dimensions of skill, age, style of thinking (for example, how much information they like to consider at any given time when engaged in problem-solving behaviour), etc. The above guidelines need therefore to be qualified by consideration of these variables. The following considerations are appropriate:

(92) With expert users, 'super chunks' (hierarchies of chunked information) can be used to convey a lot of information quickly. [5-1]

(93) When it is anticipated that a significant number of older users (>55 years of age) will have cause to use the system:
    (a) reduce the amount of information that has to be kept in mind in order to carry out subsequent actions;
    (b) make use of the display as an external working memory, that is, keep relevant information present or allow it to be easily accessed. [5-33]
    This latter guideline also applies to the design of interfaces meant to accommodate different styles of thinking — not all users have the same attention span, and not all of them like to bear in mind the same amounts of information.

A consequence of these latter two guidelines is that the system should be built for flexibility. This is a question discussed in more detail in the section on adaptation, p. 272.

5. Feedback

The nature of the feedback the system gives the user is in many cases the user's key source of information on what to do to complete a task. In order to be effective, feedback needs to be presented at the proper pace and to be tailored to the processing mode that factors such as skill and the nature of the task have induced in the user. The following guidelines concentrate on generic aspects of feedback. The sections on training and practice, error management and adaptation contain more specific guidelines to do with feedback, and should be consulted as well.

(94) Alert the users to specific courses of action, system 'rules' and particular dependencies amongst dialogue elements as they become relevant to the task. [4-19]

(95) Give feedback in the most usable form. [6-5]

For example, aim to provide the user with necessary information *in the format in which it needs to be used* — that is, without requiring computation prior to use. If necessary, allow the user to convert easily one type of data into other possible formats, such as numerical data (accurate calculations), graph data (trend computation), bar and pie chart (broad comparisons), task-based or resource-based planning (project scheduling), etc.

(96) If it is desirable for a task to become automatic then provide feedback which does not require the users' full attention. It should be presented immediately in a familiar, consistent and appropriate form. [6-5]

(97) Feedback should tell users

(a) what effect their action has had on the system;

(b) any possible consequences of that action;

(c) the new system state; and

(d) their new location in the system. [6-10]

In addition, the needs of novice users and infrequent tasks need to be catered for carefully:

(98) When a procedure, task or sequence is not automatic to users (either because they are novice users or because the task is particularly complex or difficult),

(a) provide feedback in a number of complementary forms;

(b) provide feedback both during the task sequence (to inform the user that things are progressing satisfactorily or otherwise) and at completion (to inform the user that the task sequence has been brought to a close satisfactorily or otherwise). [6-10]

6. Selecting terms, wording and objects

The system communicates with the user, and allows the user to manipulate data, through specific commands, menu names and menu options, icons, concepts and so on; and complements this communication process through messages of various kinds (error and HELP, for example). The quality of the choices made with regard to these system features is critical in determining how well dialogues are comprehended, how easily and smoothly the user can interact with the system, and also the overall appearance the system can have to the user (particularly in the case of icons). The guidelines that follow are meant to guide those choices. Note that no guidelines are given concerning such important perceptual features as design of lettering, use of colour, and so on. Guidelines and standards do exist in these areas, and they should also be consulted.

First of all, guidelines concerning the use of text-based concepts, such as menu labels, menu options, system messages, etc.:

(99) Avoid using prefixes which qualify the meaning of sentences within a dialogue. [4-10]

For example, do not ask a user 'how inexperienced are you?' in order to find out to what skill level to set a moded system. The critical dimension here is 'experience' — a better question would be 'what is your level of experience?'

(100) When prefixes are essential (to clarify the meaning of a command for instance) use suitable coding or conventions to make it clear to the user which part of the term involves or initiates an action, and which part is redundant. (That is, differentiate the command from the terms used to prefix it.) [4-10]

(101) The natural use of negation is to 'signal a change in meaning' (that is, to deny an explicit prior assertion or an implicit presupposition.) [4-12]

(a) When presenting instructions, feedback, etc., use affirmative sentences. Use negatives as little as possible. [4-12]

For example, avoid telling the user 'option x is not available'. It is more informative and infinitely more approachable to say 'option x is available only after parameter y has been set'.

(b) Never use double or nested negatives. [4-12]

For example the seemingly helpful message 'The printer will not print edited files unless these are not tagged as edited' normally requires a certain amount of mental debate before understanding finally dawns.

(102) Construct sentences which are open to only one interpretation. [4-13]

For example the menu option 'Cases must not agree' is ambiguous: does it mean that when specifying a 'search' option, letter cases in the search string and in the string being searched for should not agree, or that they *need* not agree? To a novice user, possibly not too familiar with the notion of searching for information, the first interpretation might be more apparent, since it conforms more closely to normal conversational usage, though in the system context it is incorrect.

(103) Simplify as far as possible all dialogues which contain or convery important information. (If necessary 'unpack' a screen into several related screens to ensure that all the important needs are attended to.) [4-17]

(104) Highlight the important information when verbose dialogue cannot be avoided. [4-17]

For example, embolden parts of text which contain detailed instructions and present in normal format all other explanatory information.

(105) If it is essential for an item to be remembered, flag or display it in a highly unusual or meaningful way. [5-21]

For example, animation may call attention to an item on a screen which might otherwise not be noticed; or colour could be used to signal 'pay attention'. However ensure that colour is not used for other purposes in the same screen, or that the whole screen contents are not being moved about at the same time: A feature (such as colour) only really works when it is distinctive, and it can only be distinctive if it is rare or unique in that particular context. [5-21]

(106) When information is presented as words or pronounceable non-words, and must be recalled immediately, use short strings or sentences of monosyllables. [5-2]

Graphics, and in particular icons are also valuable means of facilitating user–system interaction. Their use in metaphor-based interfaces, for example, contributes very significantly to inducing in the user the illusion the metaphor seeks to provide. Generally, icons also tend to take up less space and, if appropriately drawn, can be very quickly recognized by the user as generic indicators of a particular object or function. Obviously, an icon should only be used when it provides a representation which is clear to the *user*, not just the designer. User tests prior to implementation are recommended.

(107) The chances of fatal consequences through selecting an icon should be minimized. Warning dialogues are appropriate, and users should be told that experimentation is safe. [6-9]

For example, it should not be possible to delete a file simply by pointing to the 'delete' icon. A request for confirmation should follow selection of the icon, and the system should not allow the user to proceed until confirmation or cancellation has been entered. Though this applies generally to other types of interface object as well (such as words), the guideline is particularly important in the case of icons because they can represent collections of items and because they are often more accessible than similar text items.

(108) Capitalize on the user's knowledge when using icons: map the icon to a conceptual representation of an item, not to a specific piece of hardware. [5-32]
For example, an icon of a filing cabinet will stand the test of time, and will be understood better and faster than an icon of the specific hard-disc used for a given system.

(109) Use meaningful icons to display background information that is essential to system operation. [5-13 and 5-26]

(110) Do not use icons or pictures to represent abstract items or concepts; in other words, icons should be nameable. [5-13 and 5-26]

(111) Do not expect users to remember the detailed appearance of a novel, visual abstract pattern presented in iconic form, even over a short period of time, such as a few seconds. [5-10]

(112) Use simple, familiar concrete pictures to represent information and to act as memory prompts. [5-10]

(113) When it is important that users remember and make associations with a visual pattern, keep that pattern simple. [5-11]

Graphics can be used in a number of guises in interface design. For example, they can be used as feedback to the user of how well the interaction is proceeding, or as means of representing unambiguously to the user relationships amongst objects and tools the system offers:

(114) Diagrams can be used to highlight associations between items so long as the diagrams are kept simple. [5-11]
For example, a Venn diagram is a simple and effective way of indicating which system tools can be accessed from which other tools.

Whether they are icon-based or text-based, or hybrid, it is important to ensure that the structure of command languages is understandable to the user. Importantly:

(115) Command languages should have the syntax of normal speech. [6-3]

7. Consistency

The learning process associated with becoming a skilled user of an electronic system is facilitated if the user can grasp easily the relationships between commands and system actions, objects and their consequences, and so forth. Consistency can be expressed in many ways. The following guidelines highlight some of these features of consistency:

(116) All procedures and component elements in a dialogue should have consistent properties, names and relationships with other elements; and be used consistently throughout the dialogue [4-15]
For example, consistent use of <RETURN> would involve <RETURN> always leading to the same, or the same type of outcome, and that outcome only being achieved through pressing <RETURN>.

(117) Give each action, command, object, etc. one name and use that name consistently throughout the dialogue. [4-18]

Features of the display can be used to indicate consistent relationships amongst items which are otherwise not related (in terms of their place in the task struture, for example). Such features include colour, blinking, movement, size, and so on. It is useful to cue the user to these generic consistencies. For example:

(118) If an item of information has to be used within a short time of being removed from the screen (for instance, <30 seconds) provide at least one distinctive feature associated with it and make that feature common to other items of information which are used in that way. [5-18]

Consistency need not be restricted to within-system design. Users normally see and interact with other systems, and they will usually try to utilize their knowledge about other systems when interacting with the current one.

(119) If the intended interface is functionally different from other extant interfaces make it look different. [4-23 and 4-24]
For example, if an interface is outwardly based on the 'desktop' metaphor, but deviates from normal intepretations of the 'desktop' metaphor, efforts should be made to at least warn the user of the differences. Preferably, the interface should be made to look as different as possible from other systems based on the traditional view of the metaphor.

Similarly,

(120) Within the same system, ensure that different modes, application packages or versions either share common operational attributes or that they look sufficiently different from one another that users will not be tempted to overgeneralize. [4-23 and 4-24]

(121) When consistency is not possible throughout the interface be consistent within the immediate domain (for instance, task, application, etc.) [6-2]

(122) If an action or procedure has to be used inconsistently, the user should be warned of the inconsistency of the situations where it holds. [6-7]

8. Screen design

Screen design guidelines are possibly the most common type of design guideline in existence today. Mostly, they concern features of screen design such as the use of colour, contrast ratios between lettering and background, design of fonts for easy legibility, etc. Guidelines to do with the use of screens to help the user navigate through the system, or to promote efficient memory use are less common. This section considers this latter domain. But, of course, for optimal design both domains should be considered. We start with guidelines concerned with optimizing the use of memory.

(123) Maintain logical and functional relationships between the items on any given screen. [4-22]
For example, ensure that all items in a given screen of information relate to a particular aspect of accomplishing the current task.

(124) If some items on a screen are independent of the others or cannot be easily related to them at the same level of abstraction then consider moving them onto a different screen or separating them clearly from the other elements of the screen (possibly using borders or boxing techniques). [4-22]

(125) Items which must be recalled from memory some time after being removed from the screen should be surrounded with supporting information to which they are related, and should be immersed in a visually rich environment — with colour/shading, movement, shapes, texture, etc. [5-17 inc. 5-18]

(126) If information is scrolled off a screen, make it easy for the user to access the top of the scroll or leave important information tagged on the screen. [5-5]

(127) There is more chance of remembering the last few items in a list. Capitalize on this by placing important information, or summaries, at the end (though this does not mean that the summaries are not useful at the start). [5-9]

Ease of navigation is an important determinant of learning, and depends in part on providing appropriate context information ('you are here' types of information) which helps the user gain access to the relevant knowledge domain. However, care should be taken to ensure that providing context imformation does not detract from user performance, for example by cluttering the screen. Similarly, context information needs to tell the user where (s)he is in the path that will lead to accomplishing a task. The following guidelines relate to this aspect of screen design:

(128) When a system displays options that cannot be selected (for example, to provide context information to help users create a good model of the system) ensure that they look different from options that can be selected. [4-3]

(129) Keep all relevant information and choices in view or place them where they can be accessed easily, but avoid cluttering the screen unduly [4-19]

(130) Give each type of information in a dialogue of consistent screen position. [4-18]

9. Organization

As with consistency, organization can cover a multitude of sins. One can think in terms of organizing commands into structures which make sense and are easy to remember, organizing a task such that all the actions necessary to achieve it can be accomplished easily and in the optimal order, organizing user directories in systems which support information storage and retrieval, and so on. Features of organization hence span both the specific design of the interface and its language, and the design of procedures which will allow the user to create and maintain efficient data stores. We consider first the interface-specific features of organization.

Commands can be grouped together in hierarchical structures which refer to the different stages of implementing a task. The size of these categories and subcategories needs to be kept within bounds, however:

(131) Keep the number of items subsumed under a single label, prompt or name as low as possible. [5-20]
For example, an interface which contains 50 different commands for editing and similar numbers for other similar functions would be difficult to use. Breaking down the editing function into smaller domains, with smaller numbers of commands associated with each domain will improve efficiency.

(132) If you have to subsume a large number of items under a prompt, label or name then choose items which vary in complexity and/or style. [5-20]

(133) Generate categories and rules for categorizing items. Apply those rules consistently to items which the user should see as related. For example a rule might be that items must look or behave in a similar way. [5-30]

(134) If it will help the user to think in terms of which commands belong in which category, then help the user by providing information about the 'essential' features of the category. (That is, those features without which an item cannot be included in a category.) [5-30]
For example, information such as 'all printing commands have the extension '.prt', or 'green icons are created by the system and cannot be deleted or moved' helps the user learn about the different concepts that make up the interface.

(135) Use prototype or archetype examples to help the user determine categories. In other words, give an example which obeys all the rules for category membership. [5-31, 5-32 and 7-8]

For example, presenting a very good example of a given category will prompt the user to think in terms of that category and determine which other items present on screen are of the same type.

Efficiency is determined to a large extent, too, by how easily users can access information which has been stored and which now needs to be reviewed or integrated to create new documents or new information. Support for effective file management needs therefore to be considered carefully. Many of the guidelines presented above can also be interpreted to apply to this particular aspect of interface design. Others can be developed as well:

(136) If users have to remember how information was stored, or remember information otherwise removed from the screen, make the process of storage and presentation, and the environment in which they are done, as memorable as possible. This can be achieved by making the user consider the meaning of an item of information and its relationships with other items at the moment of storage or presentation. Or by using a large number of, and similar, dialogue elements, such as prompts, processes, labels, names, etc. in both environments. (This is not so important where there is only a short time lapse before recall.) [5-15 inc. 5-18]

(137) Categorize, or encourage users to categorize, information which must be recalled later. To assist recall from these categories of information, provide prompts, processes, labels or names which are relevant to those categories. Where information must be retrieved across category boundaries, provide prompts relevant to all the categories involved and make use of 'pointers' or 'flags' to these categories. (It may be necessary to encourage users to provide these themselves.) [5-19]

(138) In the absence of more sophisticated, system-wide file-management procedures, encourage users to structure their directories such that the number of files tagged to a single directory or prompt does not exceed the limits of human memory. [5-20]
For example, this can be achieved by limiting the size of a prompt's storage space, encouraging users to limit the number of items they put under one prompt or warning the user if (s)he tries to use too many. Usually, tagging more than about six items to a single, superordinate label reduces the chances of good recall.

(139) Allow the users to create and easily cross-reference personalized directories for filenames, keywords, etc. [5-19]

(140) Allow (and encourage) users to name items that are to be filed — in other words, avoid default filing. The user should be warned that items given a default filename will be harder to remember than items they have named themselves. [5-23]

(141) Make items interact dynamically if it is important to remember them. [5-25]

For example, manipulating discriminable icons of documents into different directories, creating a graphical representation of a directory structure and tagging items to different points in the representation, etc. all capitalize on features of human memory which promote good recall.

Organization of the processes required to perform a given task is also important. It allows users to plan ahead and hence facilitates creating a good system 'model'.

(142) If a task cannot be performed consistently throughout an interface, group together the different procedures into system modes. These should be easy to discriminate from one another. For example, create a different visual environment, different cursors, different control keys, etc. [6-7]

10. Multimodal and multimedia interaction

The ease with which a user communicates with a system depends to a large extent on the creation of appropriate electronic analogues of the traditional ways of communicating or manipulating similar information in the non-electronic domain. This goodness of match between the electronic and non-electronic domains also facilitates the development of automatization, freeing processing resources in the user for thinking and problem-solving.

(143) As good a match as possible should be obtained between 'natural' input means and the input media used in the interface. [6-7]
   For example, if users are used to pointing to something to indicate selection, then the electronic analogue should allow similar types of input. As a rule of thumb,
   — hand-held devices, such as a mouse, light-pen or digitizing-tablet-and-stylus combinations lend themselves ideally to drawing, pointing, selecting and moving tasks — in other words, spatial and visual tasks.
   — keyboard-based commands are particularly appropriate for word-processing applications, where the task itself is also keyboard-based. Similarly, numerical data entry is best served by a keypad;
   — mainly verbal or logical tasks may benefit from some form of speech command (for example, menu option selection, selection of retrieval keywords from suitable menus in information retrieval tasks);
   — sound, or speech, is a natural medium for alerting others of danger or of changes to the environment. This means that speech is an appropriate medium for conveying status messages to a user. This is particularly important when there are response delays between inputting a command and obtaining a response from the system, when the user's attention may be diverted elsewhere.

Isomorphism of this kind among the task characteristics, the input devices and the 'natural' way of doing things in the non-electronic domain helps ensure fast and effortless system use. In addition,

(144) Use speech synthesis and voice annotation to reinforce items which have to be remembered and carried forward in a dialogue. [5-24]
(145) If users have to select objects without having them fully displayed, use multimedia presentation. for example, voice and text or text and icons. [5-25]
(146) If the user has to remember information, eliminate any non-relevant speech sounds from the dialogue. [5-4]

11. Navigation

Getting a useful understanding of any given system is helped if continuity in the dialogue is preserved. One way of achieving this is to provide information relating a current screen to past screens and possible future screens, or to the consequences of future actions. Without such information, users will find it difficult to keep track of how far they are along their mental 'plan' for accomplishing a given task, and will be less confident of their actions. This will in turn affect their efficiency and may increase the number of errors incurred. The following steps facilitate navigation through a system:

(147) Place orienting information at the top and bottom of each screen relating it to those screens preceding it and those following it respectively. [4-20 and 4-21]
(148) Orienting information should relate the current screen to the preceding screen, identifying what the preceding screen was and why the current screen is being presented. [4-20 and 4-21]
(149) Orienting information at the bottom of the screen should relate it to the choice and consequences of actions available in the following screen [4-20 and 4-21]

Features of screen design, organization and the selection of terms, wording and objects also need to be considered here, in order to apply these guidelines effectively.

12. Adaptation

In the section on training and practice we discussed the possible uses of a moded interface to accommodate different levels of user skill, concentrating on the needs of novice users. In this section we consider features of the interface which can contribute to the flexibility with which a system can accommodate different styles of work as well as more experienced users. Where full — intelligent — adaptability is not possible, for whatever reason, it is possible to make significant gains in usability by simply building in flexibility. In this case, the following basic requirements should be met:

(150) Allow users to express the same message in more than one way. [5-1, 6-2, 6-7 and 7-9]
(151) Allow for verbose and less verbose dialogue. [7-9]
    For example, have the system search for keywords in otherwise irrelevant input. The 'irrelevant' input may help the user keep track of what (s)he is doing.
(152) Allow the user to create suitable macros of commonly used command combinations and support this activity with clear on-screen reminders, under user control. [5-1]

People are, by nature, error-prone; it is often said that they can be very fast at being almost correct, but are particularly slow at being exactly accurate. In information retrieval systems, for example,

(153) Program for partial recall of key identifying information. [5-19 and 5-34]
(154) Do not require the user to have to specify exactly certain fields of information (for example, complete author names and years, all the keywords tagging a document) about a required item to be retrieved. [5-34]
(155) Given only partial recall, display the matches obtained and consider allowing the user to edit and reformulate the original query on the basis of such feedback. [5-34]
(156) Build into the interface the ability to work at several levels (for example, novice mode might give the user access to a small set of options which are always displayed; expert mode might have more options and display is optional). [4-19]

See also the section on error management for guidelines to do with the types of error message which are more appropriate to novice and experienced users.

13. Error management

Different types of users need different types of error feedback. These needs are tied in with the differences in the amounts of declarative ("what") and procedural ("how") knowledge which different levels of user skill entail. A well-designed error-monitoring device could take account of user skill levels and tailor error feedback accordingly:

(157) Often, expert users only need to be alerted to the fact that an error has occurred and where: the nature of the error is information of secondary importance. [6-1]

(158) Frequent system users need to be told the nature of the error that has occurred, and also to be reminded of the proper syntax. Alternatively, a list of available solution options could be presented. [6-1]

(159) Novice system users need the most information, including full explanations of possible commands to repair the error, and the syntax they require. [6-1]

Finally, the consequences of possible errors also need to be considered and appropriate actions taken to ensure that the system supports the user as much as possible. Specifically,

(160) It is important that critical tasks, or tasks that may have dangerous consequences, do not become automatic. Ensure that a disruptive element is introduced to guarantee that users think carefully about what they are doing. Disruptive elements may be: introducing a wait, randomness, mental computation, calculation, thinking or reasoning, precise perceptual analysis, asking the user for confirmation of an input or using complex combinations of characters. [4-2, 4-4, 6-5 and 6-9]

14. Locus of control

Whether an interface has built-in adaptability or not, at certain points in the dialogue it is important to consider whether to delegate control to the user or to the system in order to ensure that both are working to best effect. We discussed before, in the section on training and practice, the use that can be made of system defaults to encourage system use by naïve users. In this section we consider two other possible situations where appropriate choice of the locus of control may facilitate task achievement.

(161) Consider allowing the interface to take the initiative in guiding users through an explicit task structure. [4-3]

For example, a graphical representation of the key task features and optimal task subdivisions could be presented to the user for approval, after which the system prompts the user for suitable inputs. The graphical representation could be obtained in a number of ways. For instance it could be built into the system as an 'ideal' structure from the start, or it could be derived as a result of monitoring of system use by experienced users.

(162) When the user must remember information let him or her control the speed at which it is presented. [6-5]

(This will also help the interface accommodate different styles of work and different user ages, with their concomitant differences in their levels of attention.)

LIMITATIONS AND COMPARISON WITH EXISTING GUIDELINES

There are obvious parallels between the guidelines we have produced here and existing interface design guidelines. This section explores the relationship in more detail.

Paper-based guidelines are the most commonly used way of providing the interface designer with useful human factors knowledge. Many sets of guidelines are already available, derived from and based on a combination of empirical and theoretical research, but they often rely heavily on the skill and intuition of the designer. The guidelines presented in this chapter have certain important attributes:

— They are based on findings from areas of cognitive psychology research many of which have not been applied in the form of guidelines before. They represent a significant increase in the knowledge-base to which designers may have access.
— They have been derived directly from pure cognitive psychology research. By contrast many existing guidelines are based on specific empirical methodologies, which are powerful in specific contexts but do not generalize well.
— Their derivations are clearly traced, therefore they can be easily updated as advances in research are made. (Some existing guidelines are vague and evasive about their sources of information.)

Complementary application

The attributes listed above have a number of implications for the way in which the approaches can be applied. The guidelines presented here cover a broad range of cognitive issues in human–computer interaction and can be generalized to many contexts. However, they are limited in some respects. Specifically, they require interpretation before being applied. Conversely, existing guidelines are typically more context-specific but better supported empirically.

The two approaches complement each other since they provide the designer with a broad strategy for concept development as well as offering specific examples of good design.

Scope of the guidelines presented

These guidelines are intended as forerunners to a design tool, and as a general contribution to the philosophy of interface design. They are not meant to replace the human factors specialist. Their aim is to provide knowledge and information in a readily digestible form in areas which until now have been poorly addressed. The exponential growth in cognitive psychology research and the diversity of the subject means that no one person can be an expert in all fields. The guidelines need the skill and expertise of the specialist if they are to be interpreted and implemented effectively. In return they allow the specialist to make design recommendations in a field in which (s)he may not be well versed.

Importantly, too, human factors specialists and cognitive psychologists working in industry are few and far between. They are not available 'on tap'. Yet a designer's work must go on, and in the absence of a specialist these guidelines give him or her direction and some examples of good design practice.

One of the principal advantages of the guidelines presented here over many other sets of guidelines is that they are context-independent. In other words, they can be applied to a range of system types and applications. As a consequence some skill and experience is needed to interpret and implement them effectively. It is the examples used in the derivation process from the cognitive psychology basis which help to target the guidelines in a particular domain. The examples also assist in interpretation and are therefore strictly essential for serious application of the guidelines.

Of course, this 'opening' set of guidelines cannot cover all the ground. Much additional work, refinement and validation will be required. The following points are examples of areas where the guidelines are seen as deficient at present.

The designer should not 'skip over' these areas, rather (s)he should look for guidance from other sources.

— *Functionality* Functionality is an important issue not addressed by these guidelines. There are certain functions that users will expect from a particular type of system. Determining what these are and how they should be provided is as much to do with market research as with system and human factors engineering. The designer must think about the types of task the system is intended for, and consider the facilities that the user will require. The type and number of functions provided will, of course, have implications for the nature of the interface design.

— *User support* The guidelines give some recommendations about providing tutorials and practice opportunities but no systematic attempt is made to deal with user support. User support in this context refers to the user having access to HELP facilities, explanations of system functions, manuals, etc. These may be online or offline.

— *Interaction and coherence* It is clear that some interaction takes place between guidelines and that tradeoffs need to be determined. In extreme cases direct contradictions can be seen. These reflect the context-free nature of the guidelines and the diversity of human cognition. These conflicts can be resolved by further research in cognitive psychology and experience in applying the guidelines practically.

It is important to realize that these guidelines cannot and do not have much to say about syntactic, perceptual, device and environmental issues in human–computer interaction. It is not clear what is the best way to use guidelines to tackle all these issues; which order they should be tackled in, how guidelines should be most powerfully combined, how guidelines dealing with different issues interact, where the most important overlaps and gaps are, etc. This situation can only improve but for the moment coherence is poor.

CONCLUSIONS

This chapter presents a set of guidelines based on research findings from key areas in cognitive psychology. Thimbleby (1984) has demonstrated an interesting approach with some parallels. In this he develops 'Generative User Engineering Principles' based on the evaluation of the concept of a user model in which providing principles to influence thinking about the interface is as important as providing specific guidelines (see also Chapter 2). The kinds of approach adopted by Thimbleby and ourselves to tackle the difficult design problems at the user interface, would seem to have something to offer. Here, we have only been able to demonstrate a crude first attempt to exploit research findings about human cognition. In as much as such findings represent the sum of our scientifically explored and validated knowledge about human cognitive processes, it is valuable and necessary that ways are found in which such knowledge can be usefully captured and applied. That there is a certain value in the method we have demonstrated is beyond doubt, but it is unlikely that this is the only or best method especially since we have barely scratched the surface of all relevant knowledge. At the same time, the gaps in the knowledge base we have used are large and ill-defined.

In some respects these approaches complement the more traditional approaches which have their roots in empirical methodologies. They provide a means of addressing higher-order cognitive processes in a structured domain-specific manner. Eventually they may form part of a wider-ranging human factors 'toolkit' which, when used in a well-balanced design team, will make an important and specific contribution. It is important to recognize their limitations as well as their potential contributions, and to identify other sources of knowledge which can fill the gaps that they leave.

In providing a conclusion to this chapter, we are acutely aware that we have only provided a whistle-stop tour of a massive amount of information, interpretation and discussion. A lot more information exists which will eventually need tackling. This is unfortunate but predictable within the space and media constraints of a book. We can only hope that we have exposed some of the critical issues in some detail, and provided a starting point for other researchers in the field.

THE NEXT CHAPTER

In this chapter we considered in detail one vehicle for applying the cognitive psychology research findings reported in earlier chapters: paper-based design guidelines. In Chapter 10 we will consider other ways of applying the same information; in the context of an electronic 'design support environment' for the evaluation and development of user interfaces that meet cognitive-compatibility requirements. Before we go on to discuss the components of this electronic environment, however, we will first consider the trends in user-interface technologies and techniques which will determine the domain in which the design support environment will operate. Identifying key trends in technologies and techniques for human–computer interaction will allow us to isolate areas where more research (pure and applied) may be needed in the future, in order to allow for the development of a suitably 'future-proofed' design support environment. In addition, in keeping with the general approach adopted for this book, we will also look at those trends in terms of the research findings reported, providing an assessment of the desirability or otherwise (in terms of cognitive compatibility) of what we can see coming our way in the near future.

Chapter 9

Assessment of trends in the technology and techniques of human–computer interaction

Chris Marshall, Bruce Christie and Margaret M. Gardiner

INTRODUCTION

This chapter reviews key trends in user-interface technology and techniques for human–computer interaction, and discusses their potential impacts in terms of the cognitive psychology reported in the earlier theoretical chapters. The intention is to assess these trends in terms of their potential human–machine cognitive compatibility within the office systems area, and to highlight areas where more 'pure' research might be necessary in the future.

A historical perspective

Growth and development in the computer industry seem to be on a never-ending exponential rise. But 40 years ago there were no computers in the modern sense; then came the large and clumsy machines constructed from rooms full of valves. These systems were limited in their power and an academic degree in electrical engineering was arguably the most relevant qualification for interacting with the machines. There were no storage technologies as such and inputs and outputs were made quite literally with switches and plugs. Applications were severely limited, mainly to number-crunching and code-breaking, and machines remained dedicated until John von Neumann introduced the concept of 'stored programs'. The prevalent attitude of the time towards computers can be assessed from the old story that after the Second World War, the British government reviewed its position on computing and saw a potential market of just two machines worldwide. It has been suggested that America now dominates the industry because the United States government saw a market for three.

Things have happened fast. The invention of the transistor by William Shockley revolutionized the industry, but only until it was completely changed

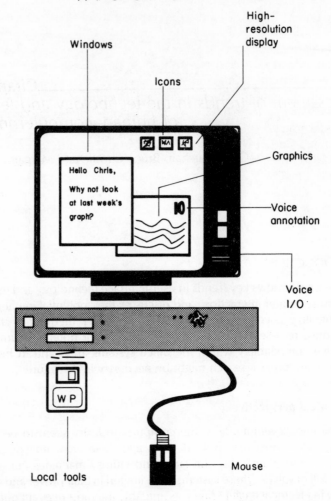

Figure 1.   Features of an advanced workstation.

again with the coming of the large scale integrated circuit in the 1960s and the addition of powerful storage media, courtesy of Dr. Wang and others, In economic terms these technical developments have had incredibly far-reaching effects, not only on the computing industry, but on every aspect of the developed nations. Robert Noyce, a founder of the microprocessor industry, produced a very famous series of graphs to illustrate the trends in modern computing (Noyce, 1977). With each wave of development, the cost per logic gate has fallen, whilst the number of components that can be squeezed into a given surface area has risen. The effects have been dramatic to say the least. The rise in computing power has been rivalled only by the fall in its cost. Cheap and powerful computing resources are, or very soon will be, universally available.

Powerful functionality is continually migrating towards the individual user workstation and most systems now offer a variety of useful office 'tools' or 'services' (for example, document preparation, spreadsheet calculations, project planning, information management, electronic mail, and many others). Coupled with this, there has been continual innovation in the kinds of input and output techniques employed.

An impression of what is rapidly becoming the norm in modern electronic offices is provided in Figure 1. This illustrates the key technologies which are currently employed at the human–machine interface. High-resolution (bitmapped) displays are increasingly common and allow good definition and character legibility. They also make the use of innovative dialogue elements, such as icons and windows, more practicable. Improvements in hardware architectures, processor speeds and power, and in software management techniques have converged to allow the presentation of information from a combination of different sources (and the direct interchange of information between them) to be managed (using windows) directly on screen.

Multiple modes of interaction are increasingly employed. There is the possibility of voice input to a speech recognizer which can handle spoken commands, file names, etc. Information which is short, transitory or requires redundant encoding can be output to the user via a speech synthesizer. Documents and other screen-based information can be multimedia in nature. For instance, text can be annotated with digitized voice messages, which can be played via the synthesizer when required. The manipulation of displayed items is increasingly accomplished by the use of pointing devices, especially the mouse. These are examples of the kinds of innovations that have emerged in recent years.

INPUT AND OUTPUT TECHNOLOGIES

Input technology

Punched cards for data input are now almost obsolete (just ten years ago they were quite common). Today, even though the necessity for keyboarding as a data entry technique has not been superseded, a variety of additional input devices have become available which supplement the keyboard in various ways or in some contexts replace it. Figure 2 presents a broad classification of current input techniques and devices.

Input methods to computer systems have always been based on muscular control actions of the hands, arms, legs, eyes, and vocal system. By and large, they have followed the trend in computers themselves: as systems have become more interactive, so the immediacy of the input devices available has been fundamental to the trend. This has been assisted by other developments such as

NATURAL	KEYING
handprint	keyboards
speech	punched cards
vision	

POINTING

DIRECT	INDIRECT
light pen	mouse
touch screen	touch pad
	tablets
	pressure pad

CONTROL	OTHERS
rollerball	tactile (prosthetics)
joystick	psychophysiological
	thought

Figure 2.   Classification of input techniques.

the ability to detect cursor positions on-screen, the need to manipulate screen based items and not just enter data, and more fundamentally by the change from teletype to VDU as an output device.

Keyboards

At present a typewriter-style keyboard is essential for inputting large quantities of alphanumeric data, and some feel that the conventional type of keyboard will be a primary way of communicating with computers for a long time to come (for example, Bailey, 1982).

Efficient operation of a conventional keyboard requires operator training. This is not necessarily helped by the fact that the standard layout — QWERTY — has a long history but an unclear origin which does not represent the ergonomically optimum arrangement of keys. For the most part the QWERTY layout elicits acceptable performance levels and it has the advantage of a widespread and long history of usage, that is, a large user population. However, there are many problems associated with it which stem mainly from the poor relational positioning of keys and uneven hand/finger loads. Acquiring typing skills at a high performance level has a long shallow learning curve, requiring heavy, frequent practice so that the process becomes automated. This mean that office workers for whom rapid alphanumeric data entry is not the primary task (and this may be the majority) rarely achieve high typing speeds. Typing remains a slow, clumsy activity demanding controlled processing. Many casual users do not rise above the break-even point where typing speed overhauls writing. Thus they either do not use the computer, or they do so through a human intermediary. It might be better, in some situations, for such people to have access to handwriting systems (machine recognition from a sensitive surface) so that they can make inputs in this fashion. After all, handwriting is a well-practised skill for most people. This might also be more compatible with input methods like the stylus.

An early attempt by Dvorak, circa 1932, to redesign the standard keyboard, so that most of the problems associated with it were reduced, was only one in a long line of redesigns which have claimed performance advantages. But even the most modern ergonomic designs, such as the PCD-Maltron (Malt, 1977), have not been shown conclusively to produce great improvement in keying performance, though some improvement is indisputable. For example, Massengill, Gordan and Henry (1975) carried out a comparison of a standard keyboard and six modified keyboard configurations. They found that typists tend to maintain their relative level of typing speed and accuracy regardless of the type of keyboard they are using. Similarly, Michaels (1971) was able to demonstrate that an alphabetic keyboard layout shows no significant improvement over QWERTY for naïve users. All this implies that excessive concentration of effort on optimizing keyboard designs is perhaps unwarranted in the light of the more global problems in human–machine interaction.

Chord keyboards Chord keyboards offer enormous speed advantages but examples of them are now very rare and include the stenograph and the palantype for shorthand. Their decline is not due to increased operator training times (although training is a necessity) but more to the increasing use of other techniques and a cultural resistance to learn chord keying. This highlights a general trend in office systems. As more applications become available, they are attractive to a wider range of users, and do not all demand high data input rates. This is especially true because they tend to emphasize the higher-level mental skills such as thinking, problem-solving and decision-making, rather than those associated with automated skills like copy-typing.

We cannot ignore the inertia which arises from the universal adoption of the QWERTY keyboard but at the same time there is no doubt that controlled processing of keyboarding does add to mental load, and therefore reduces the capacity which remains to be devoted to other cognitive aspects of interaction with computers. The unsatisfactory resolution of this problem is that users should learn to type or else wait uncomplainingly until other developments provide better solutions. The issues are as much social and economic as they are technical.

Function keys

These can be hardwired keys which only allow access to a specific command, action, function, etc. (hard function keys), or they can be reconfigurable in software to provide a variety of possibilities (soft function keys). They may be used in association with a full alphanumeric keyboard but they often provide advantages when used alone for a specific application, such as a parts order system. Here, all relevant information remains explicit and displayed, demands on memory are reduced and a simple, consistent mental model, in which separate items are designated by separate names, is engendered. Also, fewer keystrokes are required and errors tend to be lower. Of course, there are disadvantages in that a larger keyboard may be required, and because function keyboards are less flexible, their applications are restricted. They may also cause confusions with multifunction keys and they are generally expensive to produce.

It is a short step from having a soft (yet physical) function key to actually displaying and selecting the function from a screen. Many systems have started to take advantage of display innovations and input devices which make this very easy to do. They mean that the user does not have to shift attention from the keypad to the display so frequently. There is no doubt that this approach can have many advantages if used in the right context. Thus we may begin to see hard function keys falling out of favour when a display is also present, and their use being reserved for hardware selections or the like. This is an excellent example of the general trend to move the majority of action onto the interactive display surface.

Controls and pointing devices

It is assumed that the reader has at least a passing familiarity with the types of input and selection devices shown in Figure 2, and with the broad methods of operation of those devices. Those who wish to know more are referred to Ritchie and Turner (1975) for an early yet comprehensive account and analysis of most of the major devices.

A worrying mythology has grown up around the choice of selection device. The results of some research have been too readily interpreted by many commentators to mean that certain devices or techniques are better than others and should always be preferred. This is a simplistic approach and ignores most of the factors which impinge on any design choice. This is not a fault of the research itself, but of how it has been interpreted. The following examples illustrate the point.

Card, English and Burr (1978) were able to demonstrate superiority of the mouse over the joystick, step keys and text keys for text selection, but this was in the context of deriving models for the prediction of human performance; they were not so interested in coming to general conclusions about the particular devices themselves. In a similar vein, Goodwin (1975) demonstrated the superiority of the light pen and the light gun over a badly designed keyboard on a variety of screen-based tasks. Goodwin's work is a pointer to one of the main problems: that user performance is ultimately dependent upon the quality of the particular devices, tasks and environmental conditions which are in force — and upon the characteristics of the particular users themselves. An indication of the complexity of the situation is the recently reported work of Karat, McDonald and

Anderson (1984), where the mouse was shown to be a worse device than the keyboard which was worse than the touch panel on some typical office tasks.

Karat, McDonald and Anderson illustrate how the touch panel can be a useful device in some circumstances. However, although it might have some performance advantages stemming from its low demands on cognitive processing (touch pointing is a well-practised and undemanding activity) it can have many associated disadvantages such as the physical demands on the user's arm, the necessity to be close to the screen and the imprecise nature of the selections. In addition, whilst extolling the virtues of touch screens, Harrison (1983) fails to make any mention of their unsuitability for precision graphic inputs.

Haller, Mutschler and Voss (1984) used the more realistic task of correcting erroneous letters, that is, a text-editing task, and compared several devices: the light pen, graphic tablet, mouse, tracking ball, cursor keys and a voice recognizer. The light pen proved to be the fastest device and it is suggested that this is because it is more compatible, giving feedback in visual, tactual and proprioceptive modalities. Both the user's hand and the screen are visible simultaneously and all feedback is instantaneous. Voice input proved to be the slowest method of all. There was not too much to choose between the other devices.

Haller, Mutschler and Voss state that voice input, though not suited for cursor positioning may be better suited to alphanumeric input. Its potential advantage is its use when integrated with manual co-devices. The mouse and the tracker ball do appear to be devices that allow good performance, take up relatively small amounts of space and do not need to be picked up. Cursor control keys were shown to be inefficient, at least on the task used. Although the light pen came out best in the cursor positioning task, it would be unwise to assume that it should be unquestionably adopted. It cannot be grasped or put away quickly and requires the user to extend an arm towards the screen for what might be long working periods. Clearly these problems can cause discomfort and reduce the efficiency of the device in real terms. Also, where complex graphical input is necessary, it may prove to be more accurate to use a device like the graphic tablet which sits in the horizontal plane and allows the arm and hand to be supported in delicate operations.

The complexity of the problem posed for device choice by all these interacting variables is great and is further compounded by social, political and economic constraints. In a recent study by the senior author (Marshall, 1985) it was found that integrated circuit designers using a computer-aided design system preferred a puck to a mouse. This seemed to be principally motivated by the fact that all the designers had considerable past experience of design systems which provided a puck. Thus there was a resistance to change and not just a technical objection. The puck and mouse are very similar in most respects.

There are many examples of socio-economic constraints. For instance, joysticks and tracker balls have proved themselves very suitable for amusement arcade video games (and have supplanted the use of 'paddles'). Equally, it is unthinkable that a light pen or touch panel would be provided without a keyboard in the modern office, or that a high street bank cash dispenser be accessed via a light gun or stylus.

Heaped on top of these complexities are countless other issues which embrace such questions as 'how many buttons are best on a mouse?' It may be better to have more buttons on the mouse than to have more clicks on one button: the single-button method may invite problems of determining the system state. This would be supported by the cognitive principles considered earlier, which suggest that different system states should be clearly discernible to the user in appearance and in the action they require.

In conclusion, we would concur with Whitfield (1983):

> It is obvious that devices can vary in their capabilities. However, no single device is well suited to all of the input functions, due partly to the differences between information input tasks and selection tasks. Pointing is a technique well suited to the latter, and the need for this is likely to increase as graphic displays capable of supporting multi-tasking processors become more common. Users will increasingly select among displayed tasks rather than input commands to change tasks. The use of sets of complementary input devices will increase in new systems, and pointing devices will be an important member of this set. The selection of the most appropriate subset in any instance will of course be heavily dependent on the nature of the tasks to be performed.

Speech recognition

The natural medium of speech appears an attractive proposition for text, command and other inputs to computer-based systems. Preliminary studies suggest that error rates will be about the same as for keying whilst there will be reduced training requirements and increased input speed for most users. The problem at the moment, though, is that the technology does not allow these claims to be easily verified, since speaker-independent recognition of continuous speech is still at the stage of research and development. With current technologies there is a tradeoff between recognition performance and vocabulary size. Those who wish to know a little more about the underlying technology, methods and applications for speech recognition (and synthesis) will find a useful introduction in Schofield (1985).

It is not clear that all users and tasks would benefit from voice input. Bailey (1982) cites two relevant studies. The first, by Braunstein and Anderson, compared reading digits out loud (as if being spoken to a computer) with keying of those same digits. Most of the subjects had no prior experience with keypunching. The reading rate was approximately twice as fast as the keying rate. However, an interesting finding was that most of the subjects preferred keying to reading the digits and all the subjects found reading the digits a tiring task. For an experienced key operator, voice input did not offer speed or accuracy advantages over the keying input. In the second study, by Welch, which used actual voice recognition equipment, it was found that moderately experienced key operators could key digits almost twice as fast as they could read them.

In an interesting paper, Peckham (1983) asks the question: 'Is speech recognition technology a gimmick or a solution in search of a problem?' He hypothesizes that lack of user demand for the limited systems available over the past 15 years suggests that potential users regard anything less than automatic dictation as irrelevant. Peckham suggests that speech recognition should be applied only if there is a direct user benefit, for example, if hands or eyes are freed or mental encoding is reduced. Most of the benefits which can be derived from speaker-dependent, limited vocabulary systems seem to apply in domains outside the office, for example, in warehouses, weapons launching, robot control. Visick, Johnson and Long (1984) support this view, stating that any superiority of voice input over keyboard input is strongly dependent on the nature of the overall task. They suggest that voice input will only be faster if the task has sufficient manual content to effectively 'swallow' the relatively long response time required for speech.

In word-processing, it does seem that direct dictation would be faster for most users but that editing of the inserted text is unlikely to be optimized by voice control. Here, no successor to the keyboard and selection device is immediately apparent. Empirical evidence for this statement comes from the study by Haller, Mutschler and Voss described earlier, and from another study, by Green *et al.* (1984), who tested a speech-driven text editor design and found that subjects preferred the keyboard-driven version. This study relates well to the skill acquisition component in cognitive processing, since it suggests that optimum recognition accuracy requires voice pattern training and recognition tasks to be as nearly identical as possible.

However, text editing may be a stiff test of speech. Using speech for entering *subsidiary* information, whilst the main information is keystroked, may have advantages over keystroking all input. For example, Damper, Lambourne and Guy (1984) examined speech as a medium for the entry of style information as an adjunct to typed text for television subtitling, and found great advantages. Gould, Conti and Hovanyecz (1983) produced a laboratory simulation of a 'listening typewriter' with a typist acting as a speech recognition machine. Results suggested that there is the potential for a system which is at least as good as traditional methods of handwriting and dictating. On a more cautious note, Newell (1984) concluded that speech is not the universal solution to improving human–machine interaction, and suggested that more valid justifications than that 'it is natural' must be found before speech is chosen as the modality for any particular situation.

The issues concerning the application of speech recognition (and the close links this has with speech synthesis) are not simply stated or resolved for any given situation. Perhaps the most easily discernible trend with regard to speech input is also the simplest to understand. In a survey of user acceptance, Marshall (1982) found that there was urgent anticipation of a time when machines could be freely spoken to and would answer back with similar freedom. This suggests that the market will pull the technology into a variety of applications, which it may or may not support well, but only when systems really are intelligent and do not just sound it.

Other techniques

One technique which may assume more importance has already been touched upon: it is handwriting, or more precisely, online cursive script recognition. The improvements in processing speed and power, and the reduction in costs of microprocessor systems now available make cursive script recognition a viable proposition, especially in the area of office automation (cf. Higgins and Whitrow, 1984).

Many of the recognition problems and issues in cursive speech recognition are similar to those for speech. For example, as with speech, feedback (in terms of displayed verification of input) should be immediate. Whilst this technology is at present a very attractive proposition for certain tasks and users, it seems likely that the potential market in future will be squeezed increasingly between the forces of increasing keyboard use, skill and acceptance and the penetration of speech recognizers.

Psychophysiological input methods have not yet been extensively explored and, along with other techniques such as knee control, intuitively would seem to offer only limited potential within the office environment.

Lamb and Buckley (1984) suggest that there is much to be gained from employing auditory, visual and kinaesthetic modalities in harmony to assist effective human–machine interaction. They propose the development of more gesture-based dialogues. There is no doubt that humans make extensive use of gesture in their communication, and the ability to take account of this in communication with computers may offer some advantages. This topic is wide open for research and cuts deeply into the related area of software interface design

Another possibility is that of visual input. The visual selection of displayed items (achieved by tracking eye movements precisely) is more likely than direct visual input — for example, the user will select an item for deletion and will hit a delete key or speak the command 'delete' to a voice recognizer. There is promise in this technique and technically it is possible, at least for large targets. Current devices, however, are very costly and are mainly limited to military applications, requiring the user to wear clumsy headgear and being difficult to control in terms of visual distractions. If these problems can be overcome, there is very real potential for a pointing technique that would be as fast, in theory, as that which could be achieved by almost any other means, even closely rivalling direct control by thought in this respect.

Though possibly the 'ultimate' communication mode for human–computer interaction, communication by direct thought exchange is likely to be very difficult to achieve in the foreseeable future, and even if it could be demonstrated the actual operational problems would be enormous. In the keynote address to CAL '83, the computer-assisted learning conference held at Bristol University in 1983, Professor A. Bork advanced the brain wave input idea in all seriousness and stated that, 'From the computer's point of view, the problem of decoding brain waves is vey similar to that of decoding the human voice. We tend to assume that it would be harder but the computer doesn't share our prejudices.'

This is an interesting viewpoint but one which, so far, is backed up by little theory or empirical evidence. It would seem safe to assume that we will see little in the way of a trend towards this form of interaction in the next ten years. Before it happens, if it ever does, it is likely that the role of computers and offices will have seen dramatic transformation.

The future

Clearly, there are no simple answers to the choice of selection and input devices: each case must be judged on its merits. It is not just a matter of choosing the device which is most compatible with human cognitive abilities and processes (even this would be highly task-dependent) — there are also very great overlaps with the physical demands of the various devices, the relevance to the background and skill level of the operators, the cost, the social, cultural and political implications, and many other factors.

Output technology

The problems and issues surrounding visual displays and speech as output media are seemingly less complex, in human terms, than those which surround input technologies. However, this does not mean that the problems are easier to solve or that the issues are any the less important.

Transient visual displays

Visual displays are now of a generally high quality. However, as the limits of the technology are pushed forward, old usage issues (for example, quality, character size, speed) are giving way to new ones which reflect the improvements. For example, concerns about the dot matrix size of the individual characters have faded as more manufacturers have become aware of the issues, and the addressability and resolution of displays have risen. The issues now centre on concerns over the best ways to utilize colour, integrate annotated voice messages, utilize graphics capability, and so forth. The trend is that issues which were once intimately related to the quality of the display itself, are being largely superseded by issues which increasingly relate to the cognitive aspects of using display technology in various applications. The perceptual issues associated with displays (for example, quality, size, speed), whilst still important, are now rapidly assuming a back seat.

Far from being a bad thing, this trend is actually a fair and good reflection of the importance of the issues. Display capability and performance is fast approaching a level, and a cost, where it is less of a limitation on information display than are the cognitive capabilities of the people who will use such displays. Soon displays will not be the important constraint; that constraint will be imposed by our own human limitations and imagination for their use.

Cathode ray tube devices (CRT) have served well for many years and will continue to do so for the foreseeable future. They are robust, relatively inexpensive and can be made to produce high quality images, displaying an almost infinite variety of colours. It has been well demonstrated by several researchers that reading and search performance on visual display units (VDUs) improves with higher resolution (for example, Harpster and Freivalds, 1984). There is still some debate as to whether hard copy is better than a CRT display but there is no doubt that this is highly task-dependent and that the advantages of one medium over another must be measured in many terms, not just performance on discrete simplified and controlled tasks. Askwall (1985), for instance, demonstrated that reading speed and accuracy of judgement were unaffected by presentation medium (VDU or paper), but there were differences in regard to searching for information. In the computerized situation, subjects took almost twice as long to complete the search and searched only about half as much information as they did in the non-computerized situation.

This kind of evidence indicates that, for higher-level cognitive tasks, paper-based information systems are at present more effective than screen-based ones. As displays get better, however, and methods for input and for information presentation and structure improve, it is likely that screen-based systems will come to rival and then perhaps overtake paper-based systems for these direct performance measures. In terms of many other aspects of utility, they may already be ahead and for many tasks outside the office domain, such as software engineering, they already confer performance advantages.

 One of the main problems with the CRT has stemmed from the amount of room it requires on the desk. It is a relatively old and clumsy technology in many respects. It is bulky and complex; it consumes large amounts of power; and even successive design improvements have not significantly overcome these problems. New display technologies do, however, offer hope and variety of choice for future applications.

One output technology that is already extant is the liquid crystal display (LCD). The promise of reasonable performance and resolution coupled with near flat-panel topography is just starting to be realized in this technology and there is little doubt that refinements and improvements will yield displays which offer advantages over the CRT for many applications. For portable computer systems, LCDs have already captured a significant market share. Current LCD systems offer a quality which is comparable with many CRTs at a similar high price. But LCD prices and quality are both expected to improve. Bucher and Kesch (1985) state that 1984 was a very interesting period, with the introduction of at least 30 LCD models into the personal and home computer market. Nearly all leading personal computer manufacturers now offer a portable version with LCD. The advantages of LCD for portables are obvious from their low power consumption, low volume and potential low cost. Not so easy to see are their advantages in other market sectors.

Future display terminals for commercial and consumer usage are likely to be based on low cost, high resolution flat panel technology. At present there are several technologies which offer this possibility. However, the two technologies most likely to succeed are those based on liquid crystals and electroluminescence. Electroluminescent displays are available in larger screen sizes than LCDs but they are usually expensive because they require high voltage drivers. Most have a higher power consumption and are not as visible as LCDs in bright light. LCDs themselves suffer from low contrast ratio problems at present, making them harder to read than CRTs. Recent advances in LCD technology offer the potential for larger screens, but many technical problems (such a response time) remain.

It does seem that, over the next few years, these new technologies may come to match and out-perform conventional CRT technology at least in some respects. However, for some applications there seem to be no foreseeable, viable alternatives to CRTs. The most important of these is in colour displays. It is not clear that useful colour presentation will be achieved with electroluminescent displays, whilst with LCDs true colour display is not yet a reality and various 'fixes' are currently used to provide colour, usually at the expense of degraded resolution (such as colour filters over pixels or fast colour shutters).

Another technology that has received a lot of publicity is that of plasma displays. These are now a reality but are normally expensive and hampered by low luminescence. They can provide very large format flat displays, however. So far they have only found serious application in limited settings. They would not seem poised to take over in the office for a few years yet and are also likely to find colour display a problem.

On the basis of this evidence it seems unlikley that the CRT will be superseded in office environments for some time to come. It is true that new display technologies may hold out price or performance advantages for particular applications, but these will remain limited. We must also remember that CRT technology is developing all the time, and larger, flatter, simpler, cheaper and higher quality CRTs are being introduced almost daily.

This emerging picture of the future office market in transient displays holds few surprises. In terms of cognitive psychological aspects, perhaps the most significant development might be if LCD and electroluminescent technology begins to impact on many current office applications before it can offer display quality compatible with the CRT display for those applications. For instance, it is not yet possible to make the 'desktop' metaphor appear as convincing in LCDs as on a CRT. Pressing emergent technologies too far too soon may mean that some applications aimed at increasing human–machine cognitive compatibility actually lead to a backward step in compatibility.

Hardcopy

Though this is an important technology in the modern office, it is not a major concern of this chapter. Printers and other methods of taking or producing hardcopy are improving all the time. The general trend with devices like laser printers is that the printer should be capable of reproducing exactly the images and the quality that can be displayed on screen-based systems. The terminology for this capability has become embodied in the phrase 'What you see is what you get' (WYSIWYG). As screen-based displays are getting better and are coming down in price, those applications where output is provided only in hardcopy form are likely to diminish. This also indicates that people will spend a greater proportion of their time looking at screens.

Auditory output

For the purpose of this chapter, we will only give consideration to speech output systems and not alarms, music, or other kinds of auditory outputs.

People have long been fascinated with the prospect of talking machines and as early as 1791 Wolfgang von Kempelen (see Dudley and Tarnoczy, 1950) made an attempt at dynamically controlled synthesis using a manually operated system of bellows, reeds and resonators to produce sounds. Though they still have their uses for research into human speech production, these acoustic models gave way to electrical methods in the 1930s. Early speech synthesizers like the Voder and Vocoder (developed at Bell Labs by Dudley around 1936) were primitive and rather difficult to operate but did spawn interest in several areas of research. The most relevant area, as far as we are concerned, was in terms of machine-to-human communication by playback or by direct synthesis. With the advent of microprocessor technology the dream of the talking machine has become a reality.

Although we now understand quite a lot about the behaviour of the human vocal system, virtually nothing is known about the formulation of the speech message in humans, and it is not clear which approaches will yield an insight. There is a complex relationship with speech perception and understanding and the total picture will remain unclear until we known more about both sides of the speech coin.

Current speech synthesis systems are capable of very high quality speech production. Digitized voice playback systems offer better quality at present but require larger amounts of storage. Rule-based, direct synthesis systems are improving rapidly and offer attractive advantages in terms of flexibility since any desired message can be generated from text. In reality it is likely that there will be a place for both these technologies in the office, since digitized voice is useful for quick annotations (for example, of a drawing or document and for voice messaging), whilst direct synthesis can output, in verbal form, any alphanumeric information. The main drawback with rule-based systems is that because they generate speech from stored phonemes or allophones, they require that text messages be prepared phonetically to assist in spoken reproduction. This means that an operator is required to spell messages phonetically and to insert prosodic features manually to clarify the spoken output. This is a subjective and time-consuming process.

From the cognitive psychology research considered in earlier chapters we known that human memory for spoken messages has a limited capacity and that spoken messages which are not directly relevant to the task in hand tend to impair recall. This suggests that the use of speech output in office situations will be best restricted to messages which are short and which require immediate action or supply relevant information with respect to the user's task. We are also aware that the probability of recalling the last two or three items in a sequence is greater if the items were spoken or heard at the time they were presented, than if they were simply read or seen at the time of storage, and this suggests one kind of useful application for speech output.

Apart from these limited applications, it is suggested that speech output will not become a dominant output medium for the majority of office tasks and functions. It is slow to set up, expensive on computer memory, and is not suited to outputting great amounts of information because of human limitations with respect to this medium and because of the difficulty of scanning spoken information. There is, after all, no comparable, practical auditory equivalent to leafing through a book or glancing at a diagram. In the office domain, voice messaging systems, spoken commands or warnings, multimodal presentation of critical chunks of information and multimedia documents, would seem to be the most likely applications. Added to the other problems, of course, are those associated with the likely annoyance and task interference that speech output could cause amongst office workers engaged on other tasks in close proximity. All of these factors will limit the utility of spoken output and will ensure that the screen remains the primary output medium for the foreseeable future in terms of office applications.

The future

The overwhelming message from the output technology arena would seem to be — 'expect no surprises'. A variety of technologies are improving rapidly, but as far as the majority of office applications is concerned, there would appear to be no serious rival to the CRT screen-based display. Speech output will find some useful applications, but there is a danger that it will be used for its own sake and not because it increases compatibility between the user and the system.

MAJOR DIALOGUE ELEMENTS AND DEVELOPMENTS

The following sections explore screen-based dialogues from three overlapping but distinctive points of view. First, we look briefly at the presentation of information by electronic office systems. This then leads naturally to discussion about the current status and future potential of graphical display as an interactive medium. Lastly, various levels and types of dialogue are explored.

Information presentation

Two areas are covered here: the layout of screen-based information and the use of colour in visual displays.

Layout

The layout and formatting of screen-based information can be an important determinant of human performance with a computer system. However, there is very little systematic understanding of the interaction between the display and the user's ability to perform cognitive tasks (cf. Card, Pavel and Farrell, 1984)

From the review of key cognitive psychology research findings presented in earlier chapters, we may note that preserving a useful understanding of any given system is helped if continuity in the dialogue is preserved. This can be achieved by providing information relating a current screen to past screens and possible future screens, or the consequences of future actions. Also, the comprehensibility of a screen, and hence of the dialogue as a whole, depends on how the objects, images, text, commands, etc., present on a given screen, relate to one another. If they are related within a logical, coherent framework, then it is easier for users to understand where they are in a system, and what the system can do. In this respect unrelated items, or those items which are not immediately relevant to the task in hand (are redundant) are generally better removed to another screen. Much of this kind of information is interpreted more practically in the human factors literature (see, for example, Bailey, 1982).

From all this we can see that the limitations on display size with existing equipment and work practices, and also on people's abilities to deal with large complex displays of information, are very constraining to the efficiency of human–machine interaction as a whole. Until recently, the trend in screen formatting and layout has been derived from the move to larger and faster display devices. At the same time that these improvements have allowed more information to be displayed in more interactive fashion, a trend towards better addressability and resolution has allowed some of the potential of graphics to be realized.

However, no real advantages in compatibility between the cognitive abilities of users and the technology of displaying information occurred before the comparatively recent advent of display 'windowing' (dividing the display space into independent windows where information may be displayed from one context simultaneously with that from another).

Windowing represents a great advance in cognitive terms since it has the potential to provide users with a more effective utilization of display area which is, at the same time, more consistent with the ways people need to deal with information. Card, Pavel and Farrell (1984) have listed seven major ways in which display windowing can assist human performance. More information can be displayed whilst providing access to multiple sources of information or allowing sources to be combined. For the programmer there is the advantage of independent control of multiple programs. Windows are good as *reminders* since they can function as external memory stores that do not interfere with other displayed information (for example, providing pop-up menus or showing a clock or providing a command history). Another great advantage is that different windows can be used to provide different representations of the *same* task. Many tasks can benefit enormously from this — design tasks, for example. But perhaps the greatest advantage for windows lies in the fact that they can provide *contexts* for interaction. Thus the commands available in one window can differ from those that can be selected in another. These essentially different modes can be usefully differentiated by different appearance, behaviour, cursor type, size, etc., taking account of suggestions made in previous chapters that where one context cannot be consistently maintained throughout a system then discrete perceptual, cognitive and physical boundaries should be maintained to help the user differentiate and apply the relevant part of his or her mental model to the performance of the task at hand.

It is evident that there is much room for abuse of windows. Either the interface designer could be guilty of utilizing them in an inconsistent manner which overloads a user and causes confusion, or the users themselves may try to display too much unrelated information at once, failing to tidy up the display area and thereby reducing their working efficiency without even realizing it. One challenge for future research may be to ascertain the conditions for optimal use of diverse sources of information, so that designers can hope to be able to create windowing systems that engender good human performance. As yet, there is little empirical data on which to base design decisions.

Given that windows are an attractive proposition for displaying information, this does not actually alter the fact that poor formatting of that information can still reduce its value immensely (cf. Streveler and Wasserman, 1984).

Streveler and Wasserman argue that the instructions which designers have received on how to improve screen layouts have typically been either too nebulous or too specific (see also Chapter 2, which discusses this topic at length). They suggest that, 'What is needed is a set of measures which can be explicitly stated, validated through experimentation, and then used to objectively evaluate a screen design or compare the relative merits of alternative designs.'

This philosophy is very close to that of the automated design aids discussed elsewhere in this book (Chapter 10; see also Chapter 2). Streveler and Wasserman have been able to propose some basic analytical techniques (boxing analysis, hot-spot analysis and alignment analysis) which such design aids might be able to use. They have also been able to demonstrate how those different types of analysis might be used to provide indices for different screen designs. With such indices, there is the possibility of making statements about which designs are better, provided, of course, that a clear relationship with human performance is demonstrated. This particular avenue might provide a rich development context for further research, both in academic and in applied terms.

Colour

Many cognitive issues are raised by utilization of colour displays. Do the colours used convey the expected meanings? Does the number of colours overload human memory capacity and contribute to mental loading? Are the colours causing confusion or contributing to the effectiveness of the interaction? These are just a few of the questions which we might wish to ask of a prospective designer when assessing the design for cognitive compatibility with the intended users. A solid theoretical and empirical basis from which to make design recommendations on the use of colour is beginning to emerge (see Smith, in preparation).

Colour is a useful and powerful dimension for attracting attention, assigning priorities, coding information, adding redundancy, assisting recognition, enhancing subjective appeal, providing pictorial authenticity, etc., and as such its unique properties should not be squandered by the overzealous designer. Until the necessary systematic research is available, however, it will very probably continue to be squandered.

The use and popularity of colour is increasing all the time. Unfortunately, at present, it is often used excessively and inappropriately, perhaps in an attempt to justify a high investment and to fully utilize the computer terminal's facilities (Long, 1984).

The issue of colour becomes even more important when placed in the context in which it is not most commonly found — colour graphics. The power which this medium has, in human information-processing and cognitive terms, warrants close attention in the design process. Up to now this has been lacking. We suggest that the applied field offers rich opportunities to those who wish to study the complex field of sensory coding and its effects on information processing, within a realistic environment. We turn now to look more closely at the issue of graphical interaction in its own right.

Graphical interaction

One of the greatest shortcomings of most present office systems is the paucity of graphics. When a picture is worth a thousand words (or at least some of them may be), this becomes an unviable situation with respect to the efficiency of person-to-person and person-to-computer interaction. The absence of graphics constrains the type of interaction that can take place and impoverishes the office systems environment. In the words of Foley and van Dam (1982), 'Our well-developed two- and three-dimensionally-oriented eye-brain pattern recognition mechanism allows us to perceive and process many types of data very rapidly and efficiently if the data are presented pictorially. In fact, in many design, implementation and construction processes, pictures are virtually indispensable for visualising and communicating.'

Any interactive graphics system must allow for the simple creation and reproduction of meaningful pictures and will probably make use of colour. According to Foley and van Dam, interactive graphics will increasingly become the normal mode of interaction. Jankel and Morton (1984) reinforce this view: 'Images in one way or another generated by computer are being ever more commonly seen, are performing a greater diversity of functions and are starting to change the way we live. Computers are powerful tools. Vision is a powerful medium. The union of the two is a revolutionary means of communication: computer graphics.'

Office work is often a highly skilled process requiring well-educated and well-paid personnel, from senior managers down to the most humble secretary. As computers pervade the office, so the effectiveness of the communication between people and computers becomes an increasingly critical determinant of the effectiveness of the whole business enterprise. Interactive graphics capabilities would seem to offer an almost unrivalled opportunity to enhance and extend the scope of the human–machine dialogue, making it very much more efficient and effective.

A variety of applications could benefit from this treatment rendering access to, and control of, information a much easier task, more compatible with the cognitive abilities of human beings. Animated computer graphics would, for instance, confer recall advantages on information to which they are applied. This follows from the discussion presented in the earlier, theoretical chapters of this book, which includes the finding that recall is better for dynamically interacting items than for items stored in isolation, and also that recall is better if items are presented pictorially, or are easily visualizable as pictures, rather than if they are presented as words and these are not visualizable. There is a *caveat* though: memory for visual abstract patterns is disrupted by even small amounts of distraction. This implies that graphical interaction in a business context would not benefit from the inclusion of abstract embellishments.

Clearly there are many advantages to graphical interaction and despite some of the obstacles which have to be surmounted (such as heavy processing and computer memory demands, preparation time, displays and languages capable of graphics worth the name, etc.) nothing is likely to ultimately prevent the impact of graphics on human–machine communication.

There are far-reaching implications from these conclusions for the definition of future systematic applied research programmes in many fields of study, including cognitive psychology. Work on the automated design aids discussed in this book (see Chapter 10) requires the development and enhancement of formal description techniques that allow description of such specialized types of interaction. Recent work from Bournique and Treu (1985) is encouraging in this regard, suggesting that one can develop a software tool for the specification and construction of graphical interfaces in a standardized yet tailorable way. In this context, cognitive psychology research can be applied in at least two possible ways: as a guiding principle behind the software tool that specifies and constructs the graphical interface or, separately, using the same types of input, in the context of a software evaluation tool such as the cognitive design aid outlined in Chapters 2 and 10. Again, the field would appear to offer rich picking to whoever is interested in researching it.

Dialogue level

The level at which the dialogue is conducted, between the human user and the electronic system, has been closely related to the power of machines and the languages in which they are programmed or which they support. The coming of the microelectronic circuit in the 1960s paved the way for truly interactive communications and heralded the birth of human–computer interaction studies. For the first time there could be a conversation between users and systems which did not require detailed specialist knowledge or the need for the human expert intermediary. As high-level languages have been introduced and refined, so the user environments they support have tended to become richer and friendlier.

Today we have dialogues of a variety of types. The choice and use of dialogues is partly determined by what Kiss (1983) has called the power versus generality tradeoff in human–machine interaction. This is put forward as a general law of information processing which, in relation to interfaces, maintains that the user is always in a tradeoff between having a highly specialized and powerful interface, which allows him or her to do a limited number of things very well, or a general-purpose interface which can do many things but none very well. The power of generality of the human—computer interaction is thus largely determined by the dialogue type or hybrid combinations which are used.

Kidd (1982) identifies four main modes of interaction: (1) direct mode, (2) menu mode, (3) form-filling mode and (4) natural language dialogue. It can be argued that there are other modes but these probably represent the most common in terms of office systems. Because each style of interaction has a different power, complexity and flexibility, it makes different demands on the user. Choosing the dialogue style for an interface is therefore dependent to a large degree on user abilities and the demands of the task environment.

The level at which the dialogue is conducted is usually the most influential determinant of the user's view of a system. Command-driven interaction (direct mode) puts a great deal of emphasis on deep and detailed knowledge of the system and on frequent use. It is likely to be unsuitable for people who are not experts since it requires extensive training. Menu-driven interaction puts little stress on the cognitive processes of the user population and therefore is likely to provide a reasonably effective interaction mode for any user, coupled with less chance of error. However, menus tend to slow down and constrain the interaction that can take place or which may be desirable at certain times.

There are a number of alternatives which have been proposed to combat the problems of user match to dialogue style. For instance, there has recently been a tendency towards graphical interaction (as we have noted) and this has led to the development of an increasing number of object-based interactive dialogues where the user initiates system actions by selecting icons which represent real-world objects. Unfortunately this only works well for representations of concrete, visualizable objects and not for abstract concepts or patterns. Representing commands as objects is particularly difficult and, in addition, understanding of, and memory for, icons which do this tends to be poor. All these factors — and others covered in the theoretical chapters of this book — argue that the effective application domain for purely iconic dialogues should remain fairly well circumscribed, possibly to accessing specific services or applications. The interesting question for interested researchers must now be to discover suitable hybrid dialogues, based on sound information-processing principles, which allow users to utilize the iconic base to best advantage.

Let us now turn to a brief consideration of key developments in a number of areas of human—computer interaction at the dialogue level, which may serve at least as a launching pad for further development.

Direct mode

Direct mode is taken here to mean command languages with constrained grammar, that is, where the dialogue is lexically and syntactically constrained.

They offer advantages to the experienced user because they are fast, precise and allow the user both initiative and control. Hallam and Stammers (1983) have noted that command languages are usually reflected in dialogues specific to certain applications such as bibliographic retrieval systems.

The implications which are evident from the research reported in earlier chapters of this book, are that command languages impose a high memory load on the user and require extensive training as well as frequent use.

Kidd (1982) sums up a major problem with command languages thus: 'Unfortunately, this dialogue method has been used more frequently than it should have been and has been a significant source of errors and system rejection by relatively unsophisticated users.'

Performance with command languages can be facilitated by applying a number of rules, for example, short consistent commands and rules for their application, provision and defaults, attention to the demands of the input strings and task, provision of mnemonic names, etc. Thus it is possible to enhance a command language considerably, but this does not alter the fact that they are basically unsuitable for a variety of applications and incompatible with the cognitive capabilities of many potential users of office systems.

Prompted dialogues

A number of techniques are in common use for prompting the user. They include menu selection, form-filling and 'question and answer'. Whilst these are not the well-defined categories that the distinct names would imply, it is nevertheless useful to think in these terms. They are characteristically different from a direct mode of interaction in that the dialogue is initiated, to varying degrees, by the computer and not solely by the user. The user is not required to learn a command language but is *guided* through the interaction. Syntactic and semantic problems are removed or considerably reduced. As a consequence, errors are usually reduced, the training requirement is not as great and interaction with the computer tends to *support* the job rather than *being* the job.

Menus are considered to be just about the best method of communication for the naïve or infrequent user. It is true that in large hierarchical information retrieval systems such as videotex, users can become lost or fail to find their way to the appropriate information, and experienced users often find such systems rather tedious. For most simple cases, however, menus offer users the advantage of reduced memory and typing loads and present less opportunity for mistakes to be make. As for all modes of prompted dialogue, steps can be taken to ensure that the dialogue is optimized. For instance, Perlman (1984) found that it took longer to search large menus and that ordered options were better. Each element or 'button' (after Coutaz, 1985) should be named by its first letter (rather than a–b–c–d, etc.).

In the case of form-filling, the user is presented with a familiar concept and the required format of interaction is fairly explicit.

Question and answer mode is potentially simpler than menu selection or form-filling, and it can be a highly practical technique, for instance

— if the situation demands simple prompting and choices;
— where it may be advantageous to make following questions dependent on the answer to the last one;
— where interaction is over a constrained medium, such as the telephone.

This makes the fundamental point that there really are no clear-cut solutions to selection of dialogue style. The main determinants of the optimum interaction mode(s) are once again the type(s) of user, the specific requirements of the task(s) and the capabilities of the technology. It is unlikely that any one mode of interaction will suffice for any but the simplest of dialogues. Even the now familiar bank cash dispensers make use of relatively sophisticated hybrid modes of dialogue, with the user selecting from menus, answering questions and entering parameters.

Natural language

Natural language dialogues are defined as being less syntactically and lexically constrained, approximating closely to spoken human discourse. Until relatively recently it would have been difficult to conceive of how this type of interaction could have been realized. However, recent theoretical developments in the domain of artificial intelligence have altered the situation. Many of the problems which are inherent in a natural language dialogue (for example, assumed world knowledge of the listener, complex sentence parsing, ambiguities, etc.) are now seen as within the predicted capabilities of the next generation of machines.

The advantages of natural language communication for users are potentially enormous. The demand to learn how to use the computer disappears (theoretically at least, although it is likely that current problems in this area might give way to ones which are not clearly foreseen at present) and the user gains, in a nutshell — power, freedom and flexibility. Provided that the technical difficulties can be overcome, the disadvantages of natural language dialogues stem from their imprecision and lack of suitability for some tasks. Depending on the context, it is likely that many tasks would actually be harder to carry out effectively through a natural language dialogue. (A paper by Hill, 1972, illustrates this very well.) Finally, it is unfortunately true that a natural language dialogue can cause the user inappropriately to ascribe intelligence to the machine. One can imagine the situation where a system capable of natural language dialogue via the medium of digitized speech output (where an accent may be convincingly preserved) and speech recognition could be a potential source of enormous problems for the unsuspecting user.

The advent of natural language dialogues provides a particularly challenging research context. Moves are currently being made in a number of institutions in the general direction of implementing in software computational models of human–human dialogue parsing. One could envisage this particular approach to application of cognitive psychology research having advantages over the more pragmatic approaches described elsewhere in this book. Hence, rather than, for example, checking that a particular dialogue meets the dictates of cognitive psychology principles, the approach is rather to make sure that the dialogue is *generated* within those principles — in other words, to reduce the potential for deviation from optimal parameters. How far this particular approach can potentially go, and how soon it will become more commonly used is a question to which no answer can immediately be foreseen.

Object-based interaction

It has already been mentioned that object-based interaction, as typified by the current boom in iconic dialogue modes, is extremely powerful for interactions where objects are clearly recognizable, concrete, nameable entities. As representations are required for entities which are increasingly abstract, random, non-nameable concepts, the effectiveness of iconic representation is reduced to a negative status in comparison with other ways of introducing the concepts in the dialogue. Thus it is very difficult to represent generic commands in an unambiguous way by the use of icons.

Almost all of the problems and rules which apply to selection of pictograms and messages which are used to convey information in the material world (for example, on items of equipment, on information displays, etc.) are relevant to the design of icons and other objects for screen-based dialogues. The use of object-based interaction is still at an embryonic stage in human–computer interaction and it is suggested that it is not too late for some standardization to take place with respect to essential generic objects and the way they can be represented.

There is as yet little empirical evidence on which to base a discussion of object-oriented interaction. Specific conclusions are therefore better left to speculation. A general inference, which fits in well with the rest of the discussion about dialogues, is that object-oriented interaction has much to offer depending on the context but that few dialogues will, or should want to make use of this technique in isolation.

The future

It is obvious from the preceding discussion that no one type of dialogue is a panacea. Dialogues must be crafted from a number of styles and techniques in order to support specific users carrying out specific tasks in particular contexts. Already we have noted that most dialogues are tending toward a complex hybridization of components and that this trend will continue. Since these hybrid dialogues are difficult to construct well, and may have a profound impact on the effectiveness of human–computer interaction, it is increasingly necessary to ensure that they are performing as intended. This is at the moment accomplished in part — if at all — by the input of human factors expertise in the design process. However, as the number and complexity of interacting factors that need to be considered increases, it is becoming difficult to be certain that a dialogue has been optimized within all constraints. The only effective insurance is empirical testing and interactive design. Since this is a time-consuming and expensive process (as discussed in Chapter 2), any help that can be conveyed to the designer outside the immediate face-to-face contact with a human factors expert is valuable. It is in this respect that application media such as those described in Chapter 10 come into their own. However, they need to be backed up by the appropriate theoretical basis, developed in suitably complex and naturalistic environments. Application media which are themselves technologically based — such as the cognitive design aid mentioned in Chapter 2 — need furthermore to advance in tandem with the technology they are meant to evaluate. They represent the combination of technology and theory and, while not intended to replace the human expert, can provide considerable benefits in other, more fundamental areas of the design process.

TRENDS IN OFFICE APPLICATIONS

We have already touched upon the range of applications of office technology. Basically, there are systems which facilitate the creation and formatting of information, systems which allow information to be communicated, systems which facilitate the filing, retrieval and manipulation of information, and systems which organize and present information for the purposes of decision making, problem-solving and planning. Until now we have witnessed fairly limited functionality, usability and integration in these systems. There has also been little in the way of standardization. These issues are the major pointers to the trends which have emerged.

A trend towards integration: super-interfaces

We have begun to see closer integration of some functions in current office systems and a number of vendors have been very successful at selling integrated packages. But we have not yet seen serious attempts to integrate the entire office environment in a coherent context. When this happens we might expect the advent of the super-interface which provides a consistent, customized environment to mediate between the user and the entire gamut of office functions and perhaps beyond into other domains.

As applications are integrated the issue is raised of potential increased complexity for the user. Instead of a nice, neat, dedicated system, the user may face an applications jungle. Interfaces which provide access to all the added functionality implied by increased integration are going to have to be very well designed.

There are some issues of significant import to the whole domain of applying cognitive psychology to system design, which are presented by the development of super-interfaces. For example, there is the issue of sheer size. Super-interfaces will be vast. If one adopts the automated design aid approach to applying cognitive psychology, for example, (see Chapters 2 and 10) it becomes necessary to hone down to a fine art the process of providing the evaluation tool with the necessary evaluating information. Current developments in rapid prototyping tools are encouraging in this respect. They do imply, however, that designers of technologically-based design and evaluation tools need to keep an eye on this rapidly developing field, to ensure, as far as is possible, that evaluation and design tools can be interfaced. If the process of evaluating an interface electronically is an *additional* burden on the designer, and if the size of the interface is large, then designers will very likely soon be put off the task altogether, relying on less time-consuming, and less accurate, methods of giving their interfaces the human factors 'seal of approval'. Similarly, both electronic aids and paper-based design guidelines need to be able to accommodate the different levels at which vast interfaces can be defined: overall guidelines are needed as much as more specific ones, and both need to be based on sound, 'ecologically valid' research. A 'gestaltist' view of what the interface allows the user to do, at any one time, may be beneficial. This may help define the scope and use of non-human human factors inputs: humans are very good at intuiting an overall view of a situation. This is less easy to do in the electronic or the paper-based domain. These and other issues in the provision of an adequate 'design support environment' are dicusssed at length in Chapter 10.

Organizational interfaces

There is evidence that the challenges of coping with super-interfaces may be even bigger than has so far been suggested here. The potential domain of cognitive issues in human–computer interaction could be far larger than is yet generally realized. In a recent paper, Malone (1985) proposes that the traditional emphasis of designing interfaces for individual users will have to change to accommodate a growing need for the analysis and design of what might be called 'organizational interfaces' for groups of users. He defines the traditional concept of the user interface as, 'the parts of a computer program that connect a human user to the capabilities provided by the computer'. An organizational interface is defined as, 'the parts of a computer system that connect human users to each other and to the capabilities provided by computers'.

Wilson (1984), Wilson *et al.* (1984), Maude *et al.* (1984) and Marshall (1985) have also discussed concepts that match Malone's 'organizational interface'. Implicit within these papers is the conclusion that organizational interfaces will not only determine the nature and shape of the organization, they will *become* the organization.

Clearly the implications for the disciplinary domains involved in applied psychology are enormous. The principles that govern the design of organizational interfaces will not be drawn solely from cognitive psychology, or cognitive science, or artificial intelligence — they must come also from theories of organizational behaviour and management, from group dynamics, from economics, etc. Any medium for application of research findings to interface design needs to take these factors into account. One might suggest, for example, that in addition to the cognitive design aids described in Chapter 10, one might have 'organizational design aids' in the automated toolkit supplied to designers as part of a design support environment. But the necessary integration tools then need to be developed, which implies that necessary research on the parameters of relevance needs to be done.

TRENDS IN HUMAN—COMPUTER COMPATIBILITY

Drawing on the findings reported in the earlier, theoretical chapters of this book, on the preceding discussion about technological trends, and on other current research, it is now possible to consider some emerging trends in human—computer compatibility. The motivation behind this particular section is to highlight areas where research, both pure and applied, needs to provide the designer with essential information. Some of the trends discussed have already been touched on in earlier sections, whilst others are introduced here for the first time.

Adaptiveness

Systems which are dedicated to one task and a limited user group, whose requirements do not change, are not particularly common. What is more, they represent the least of worries in a field where human—computer interaction is predominantly with more complex systems. For complex systems, like those encountered in the electronic office, user requirements and skills change with time. Practice or changing task demands can have much to do with this. This naturally means that it is rare to encounter a situation of perfect symbiosis between a system and any given user. There exist dynamic changes in human (and sometimes system) variables with time. If we had available now a simple index for human—computer compatibility, then even with a very well-designed system we would expect to see this index change with time and circumstances. At certain times the interface would be less than compatible with the performance, attributes or capabilities of a specific user or user-group.

Given that this is the case, it is sensible to seek ways of reducing such incompatibilities or removing them altogther. The obvious course of action is to build adaptability into the system architecture. Thus, in the most simple case (an adaptable interface), the system designer might provide possibilities for the user to select between a simple or novice interface, or a more complex, more powerful interface aimed at the expert. Expanding this approach would provide a number of levels at which the user can interact and which the user selects depending on how his or her performance would benefit. Taking this approach to its logical conclusion, it might make sense, using the techniques of artificial intelligence perhaps, to have the interface monitor individual users and adjust its configuration automatically in order to optimize the compatibility with its user at all times. It is not the purpose of this chapter to consider the exact mechanisms by which this can be achieved, its relative merits or demerits in a broader context, or indeed the socio-legal problems involved. There is little doubt that it is feasible; indeed, some working examples already exist.

The challenge, if adaptive interfaces are to be properly implemented, is to make sure that research and application go hand-in-hand with technological development, and are made available to designers in a suitable format. This format can vary depending on the domain being analysed: it ranges from direct inputs from a human factors expert, through paper-based guidelines, to atuomated implementation of evaluation principles and metrics. The correct apportioning of responsibility must itself also be made within a realistic and well thought-out framework, to ensure that timely transfer of knowledge to the applied domain (see Chapter 2 and 10 for detailed discussions of this topic). It may be that at the initial stages of any new research milestone the human intermediary is all that one can rely on. One would hope that gradually at least some of the expertise might be condensable and condensed into other, more 'portable' and generic media, such as paper-based design guidelines or software design aids. This is a challenging process. It is, nevertheless, necessary if cognitive psychology is to make a significant contribution to the inception of new ideas, rather than its more traditional *reactive* contribution.

High-level interaction

Current systems are, of necessity, built up in such a way that interaction with the system involves the user in specifying every action in the dialogue in low-level detail if (s)he is to achieve a goal. This imposes many demands on the user, not least the need to remember and plan actions in detailed fashion to achieve what might sometimes only amount to minor subgoals. How much better it would be if the user could work by specifying the goal in mind so that the system could assist in rapid attainment of that goal, perhaps even to the extreme of carrying out a particular routine task for the user without the need for human intervention. This trend is a natural extension of that followed in computer language design. Languages are increasingly higher-level and remove the need for most programmers to be adept in assembler or microcode. While this confers the advantage of more power and greater productivity it also costs something in terms of flexibility and machine performance. But there are great gains from such a trend (witness the universal acceptance of high-level languages) and for the user this is now being embodied in the ability, which many systems allow, for the user to define his or her own macros for frequently executed tasks. However, there are limitations inherent in such an approach where, for instance, a user may require a slight deviation or where specialist knowledge is required for the necessary configurations.

The trend towards higher-level interaction will become much more important as the trends towards greater machine intelligence and adaptiveness gather pace. Thus, in a system of the future we may see the user being able to treat the computer as a flexible, intelligent slave which, when its master orders breakfast, does not require a series of instructions as to how to prepare fresh orange marmalade or how to brew a pot of tea. In this kind of context Gaines and Facey (1976) made the following observation: 'It is helpful to envisage the computer system in the role of a (Dickensian) servant, courteously guiding and helping, quick to answer requests for information, often appearing more alert than the master and yet ultimately knowing its place.'

As the notion of subgoals and goals might come under some scrutiny in a system which promotes high-level interaction, so the designer needs to have the relevant information to ascertain the right sorts of facilities and flexibility to allow. A change in the orientation of evaluation tools may also be justified: evaluation may need to concentrate on the human performance engendered by an interface as well as, or instead of, evaluation in terms of the building blocks which support that performance. This in turn touches on questions of required usability, social and organizational psychology guidelines, and the determination of the features of the average user's more likely goals and subgoals in a given situation. Multidisciplinary integration becomes a requirement of the application of research findings to higher-level interaction.

Shared-initiative dialogues and agency

With the trend towards greater machine intelligence, the notion of agency becomes more important. With future systems the user will not be the only agent capable of initiating actions — the computer will have degrees of autonomy in this area also. What authority the system has, or authorizations it needs, will be highly user-dependent and context-dependent. For example, a particular user may be prepared to assign most of the agency for taking initiatives on filing over to the system. Only where major goals need authorization might this system seek initiatives from its user. The user may be able to deal increasingly in terms of principles which define operational constraints for the system within which it is largely free to determine how goals and subgoals should be achieved.

The implications of this particular trend are much as those for high-level interaction, discussed above. An additional requirement the designer will have will be some yardstick against which to measure the optimal locus of control and agency in a system, so that (s)he can ensure that the balance is right or can be set right for a given system and situation.

User models

Implicit within all the scenarios presented so far is the assumption that the system builds and maintains a dynamic model of its user(s) from which it is able to draw knowledge about how to proceed in given contexts. At any given point in an interactive session, the system would therefore 'know' how much initiative to take in order to optimize the interaction and achieve goals efficiently. Future developments in the psychological basis for such user models can have a lot to offer the design of adaptive, mixed-initiative interfaces.

Intelligence

Another assumption which is implicit within the aforementioned concepts is that of increased machine intelligence. Enough has been said about this already so it is only necessary to mention its possible contribution here. Without entering the 'great debate' on the nature of intelligence, it is sufficient to point out the consequences of increasing the amount of intelligence within a computer system. Just as natural animal intelligence tends to confer a genetic advantage on certain species, thereby ensuring a higher probability of survival, there is an analogous situation for machines. Those which possess more intelligence, or are capable of acting in an intelligent manner, will supersede their more 'dumb' contemporaries for an increasing number of applications. Dumb systems will be relegated to the 'working class' of systems who are only qualified for more menial labours. Intelligence will quickly become a common trait as the cost of building intelligent systems declines.

Multimodal and multimedia interaction

There is little and limited integration of media like voice, image, text and data and of tactile, verbal or visual input and output modalities in current interfaces. Humans do, however, have the capacity to operate in several sensory and motor modalities in rapid succession and in parallel, allowing them to deal with a variety of media. Theoretically, multimodal and multimedia interfaces have the potential to enhance human–computer interaction in terms of minimized processing time, optimised information exchange, improved training, etc. The human issues in terms of increasing modalities and media are extremely complex.

At present there is no coherent model which can drive the development of multimodal and multimedia interfaces in a way which is consistent and compatible with human performance. In this sense, introducing another modality, for instance, might easily cause more problems for the user than would otherwise have been the case. More basic research is needed which can provide designers and applied psychologists with the necessary information for developing suitably well-founded interfaces, and for carrying out further, applied research on coherent modelling in this area. However, there is little doubt that system interfaces will continue to provide more media for more applications and that interaction with these media will require more modalities (and combinations of modalities) to be available across the user interface.

Functional separation and user-interface management systems (UIMS)

A number of researchers have suggested that there could be serious advantages to functionally separating the user interface from underlying applications. Such benefits would be that the host machine could be optimized for running the application without the overheads that user interfaces impose; the user interface could similarly be optimized for high performance and user compatibility. In addition, there would be an advantage in terms of modular design where the effects of changing the interface could be largely isolated from the rest of the system. And because protocols between the interface module and other applications would have to be well specified, this would assist in a more rigorous and logical design process, lifting interface design beyond an artform. Also, a functionally separate interface could more easily provide a more consistent environment for users between the applications it dealt with. There are several other advantages for such an approach but these represent the most significant in system design terms.

The notion of functional separation and the arguments presented above lead to the conclusion that it might be best to handle the whole concept of the user interface in similar fashion to the way computer science is handling displays, databases, etc. That is, by providing systems which assist in the *management* of these functions. Taken in this context, there is a small but growing consensus of opinion that what is needed for handling the interface between users and complex computer systems are user-interface management systems. Quite clearly, such systems would contain elements to facilitate the testing and 'debugging' of the user–system interface software from the point of view of enhancing usability. They would become, in a way, intermediaries between the user and the machine, providing a two-way translation system aimed at making the interface understand the inputs from the user, and the user understand the feedback from the system.

Some preliminary work is already going on in implementing these management 'front-ends' to electronic systems. Some of that work relies heavily on notions and research findings from a number of areas of psychology work, including cognitive psychology research. It requires that a coherent model exist of the key functions and processing requirements entailed in a given task or tasks. The model also needs to be specified at a level where computational implementation is possible. Here is, therefore, one area to which cognitive psychologists interested in the applied domain may like to direct their efforts: from small, self-contained models tested and applied in this fashion may come the more wide-ranging 'super-models' at which cognitive psychology has aimed for almost 30 years now.

Standards for human–computer interaction

Without dwelling on the complexities which it is possible to encounter in this area, in terms of what ought to be standardized and how, it is sufficient that we observe the trend towards specifying standards for the ergonomic design of the user interface. A number of physical, perceptual and environmental aspects have already received the attention of the relevant standards bodies, but the latest trend is that the cognitive interface should receive the same treatment. Deutsches Institut für Normung (DIN) draft release 66234 (Part 8) is a first (though much criticized) move in this direction.

The main point to make is that, strewn with problems though it is, this trend in standardization will continue. Hence, there will be important implications for the design of any human–computer interface as the constraints on system designers are tightened. This poses two significant problems. The first is to do with ensuring that whatever standards are implemented truly reflect the underlying theory — in fact, ensuring that standards are based on theory to begin with! This implies, from the research psychologists, a willingness to accept that standards will come, and it is in their interests to ensure they are the right ones. It also entails from applied psychologists taking seriously the not inconsiderable brief to take academic research to the relevant standardization bodies.

The second problem is possibly more pragmatic: How do we tell designers about such 'esoteric' matters as cognitive standards? A possible candidate might be some kind of automated control over interface design, which incorporates the relevant information about standards. Automated design aids, such as those described in the next chapter, might be one such vehicle. This, of course, entails some form of commitment to ensure that the design aids themselves are both up-to-date and accessible. Human factors experts are also likely candidates — provided they are involved in the design process from a sufficiently early stage.

Whatever the vehicle, behind the solutions to both of the problems highlighted above is the development of a structured and effective communications network amongst the research and application domains, the industry domain, and the relevant standardization bodies. Satisfying these requirements will, in itself, be a major enterprise — but it will need to be done, and the sooner the better.

In summary

The above trends in human–computer compatibility by no means constitute an exhaustive set. They are the major emerging trends at this time which seem to have most relevance to the question of applying cognitive psychology research to user-interface design. They cover a sufficiently wide field to give an indication of the scale and diversity of the questions that need to be addressed if cognitive psychology, singly or in combination with other disciplines, is to make in user-interface design the kind of impact it ought to make.

The need is beginning to be apparent for some form of structured approach to the whole question of applying any kind of academic discipline to interface design. Attention needs to be given to such disparate factors as selecting an appropriate medium for transferring the knowledge that already exists and is likely to exist in the future; the kinds of general research approaches and areas that are likely to be particularly fruitful in ensuring orderly and adequate development of the interface of the future; the approaches to ensuring that research findings are applied in suitable form, either as standards or in more creative, individual ways.

CONCLUSION

This chapter has provided a broad overview of emerging trends in the technologies and techniques of human–computer interaction which relate specifically to human cognitive capabilities. It has also identified a number of trends in human–computer compatibility and discussed the importance of these for the shape and timing of applying cognitive research to user-interface design. The following paragraphs attempt to give a summary of the main points emerging from the discussion above.

Interface technologies, including input and output devices, will continue to evolve and mature. However, no foreseeable advances are likely to have much impact in the input/output bottleneck in the short to medium term. True, there will be a slow widening of the bottleneck as displays get larger, as multimodal and multimedia interaction develops in more interfaces and as operational performance limits of existing devices are explored. But this is unlikely to have a significant impact because concomitant with any marginal improvements will be the increasing amounts and complexities of information which have to cross the input/output bottleneck of advanced computer systems.

The alternative to device improvement is to concentrate effort on technology (in the software sense) for information management. Two approaches are evident. The first is to make actions easier, the second is to make actions carry more meaning. If actions carry more meaning, fewer actions are required. Such improvements in the compactness of the interface language are rich with promise for improvements to interface design over the next ten years. In this respect, many of the issues discussed under the sections on major dialogue elements and developments and trends in human–computer compatibility will assume increasing importance for cognitive aspects of interface design, and thus for the kinds of basic and applied research which are likely to be necessary, and for the form of their application.

Trends in graphical and object-based interaction, in hybrid dialogues and natural language, in mixed-initiative and adaptive, intelligent dialogues, goal-oriented interaction, functional separation, etc. will significantly alter the flavour of human–computer interfaces in the near future. Some of these trends will pose very interesting problems for the design and evaluation of human–computer interfaces which are effective and good to use, and for the fundamental research that is likely to be needed.

THE NEXT CHAPTER

This chapter concludes the presentation a 'case' for the application of cognitive psychology research to user-interface design, including brief discussions, where appropriate, concerning the format that such an application process should take. The need to provide a suitably well engineered 'design support environment' to designers of information technology products follows naturally from the issues raised above and in Chapters 2 and 8. The next chapter considers in detail the requirements of such a design environment, and how these might be satisfied within the constraints of transferring to the design team appropriate knowledge about human cognitive capabilities and limitations.

It is also the case that application of a discipline — whatever the discipline — cannot be treated as a one-off process, which simply gathers what is available and sees what can be done with it. Application and the application methodology also have implications for how strands within the discipline should develop, which areas should be researched further and how. With this in mind, in our concluding chapter, we will also address in more detail the implications of what has been said so far in terms of future work and methodological considerations in cognitive psychology.

PART FOUR:
APPLICATION AND RESEARCH PRIORITIES

Bruce Christie and Margaret M. Gardiner

OVERVIEW OF PREVIOUS CHAPTERS

In previous chapters we considered research findings from mainstream cognitive psychology, their possible application to the derivation of design guidelines, and the implications of current trends in the technologies and techniques of human–computer interaction. In addition, we cast the application of cognitive psychology into the prevailing design context, and considered the existing routes for channelling to the design team knowledge about human cognition. In particular, we discussed current design processes, and looked at the impact that applied cognitive psychology has had on those processes.

Perhaps disappointingly, it was noted that cognitive psychology — along with human factors knowledge in general — does not appear to have had as much of an impact as the value of its contribution would warrant. A number of factors are involved. Two stand out as particularly important: organizational constraints on the design team, including the advertising of and budgeting for the human factors resource; and the packaging of human factors knowledge, so that it is 'user-friendly' to the design team. Given our brief — to explore the applicability and potential value of cognitive psychology research for interface design — we shall only touch briefly here on the first of those factors, following on from the discussion in Chapter 2. We shall consider the second factor in more detail, offering specific suggestions and comments and, where appropriate, highlighting the implications of the approach we suggest to the organizational determinants of applied cognitive psychology work.

PACKAGING COGNITIVE PSYCHOLOGY

Among the reasons given in Chapter 2 for the relative lack of impact of human factors guidelines on interface design work is that finding relevant information is often a time-consuming exercise and that, even then, the information obtained is often pitched either at too general or too precise a level. Allied with this is the notion that designers have no very clear idea of the potential scope of the human factors contribution, and tend to develop their own mini-models of the user which restrict the types of information they are likely to seek.

Implied in what has been said above is the realization that human factors expertise needs to be advertised more widely and more effectively than it is at present, and that means need to be devised for making human factors advice more 'user-friendly' to the designer.

In order to gain the respect and interest of design teams, applied cognitive psychology needs to show that it is a serious discipline which can produce visible improvements to interface designs and user–system compatibility (as reflected, for example, in user attitudes and sales figures), and can deliver these within the tight timescales that apply in the design process. We discussed in Chapter 2 a number of ways in which this could be done, for example through the provision of guidelines, generic designs, training courses, newsletters and other publications; through participation in the design process as a member of, or consultant to the design team, and so on. However, to date not many of these application routes have been developed in a harmonious and coherent manner. By and large, their use, and the proportion of their contribution to the design process, are swayed by organizational factors which may be largely divorced from the requirements of the task at hand. They also rely on designers knowing what they can obtain as human factors help, and how. We feel the time is now ripe to approach the application of cognitive psychology to the design process in a much more systematic manner, just as we recommended a more systematic and structured derivation process for guideline development.

A coherent, systematic design process that takes full benefit from its contributing disciplines needs to take into account a number of very different factors. Obviously, the amount of time available is a pressing constraint. Also important is the optimal allocation of tasks to people and the optimal subdivision of the design tasks. Similarly, systematic consideration of user populations and adoption of an iterative design process are key in determining the optimal matching of interface to user. We shall now consider each of these in more detail.

Timing

If the design team is to make full use of available human factors knowledge, including that based on cognitive psychology, it needs to have fast access to that information, and to obtain advice in the most time-effective manner. This implies the need to provide guidance in a format which is directly applicable to the design task. The 'allowable' amount of interpretation and extrapolation of advice received (for example guidelines information) to the requirements of the current context depends to a large extent on the composition of the design team: what would take a human factors expert a day to translate and apply to the current design problem, may take a non-psychologist many days of work to interpret. Clearly, timing constraints are related to both team composition and task allocation within the team, as well as to the format in which information is made available,

Task–expert match

In order to reap maximum benefit from team work, one needs to ensure that team members are employed fruitfully, on those tasks to which they are best suited. This saves time and improves the quality of the eventual output. It also helps to reinforce the role of the different experts in the team, increasing the likelihood that the relevant knowledge or advice will be sought. The onus is largely on the cognitive psychologist in the design team to ensure that his or her role is suitably well-defined so that other team members know what they can ask for. This obviously also involves being able to deliver when asked to, and being prepared to make decisions based on best judgement, as other team members are required to do.

Expert–media match

Optimal use of a person's knowledge depends on providing that person with appropriate tools to do the job. In the case of human factors experts, one needs to take into account a number of different factors which will contribute to optimum use being made of the expert's time and knowledge. For example, we mentioned in Chapter 9 that for the 'super-interface' of the future, there will be a need to step back and take a global view of the interface; we also saw that with actions carrying more meaning, and with systems taking some of the initiative in the accomplishment of tasks, there will be more of a need to consider the interaction as a whole, as well as the building blocks which lead to the achievement of the end result. Humans are particularly good at adopting this global, 'gestaltist' view. They are also creative, and have a wealth of knowledge and experience upon which they can call. To use a human factors expert simply to put out fires, or deal with very routine, mechanical tweaking of low-level features of an interface is hence potentially to squander a very rare and valuable resource. Clearly, tools need to be developed that take some of this low-level routine work away from the expert and free him or her to do what (s)he is best at. Guidelines were initially meant to take on this role. They have a number of shortcomings, as we saw. Other tools need to be developed as well.

Iterative design

With appropriate tools and a well-understood structure to the design team, iterative design may in fact not overly tax the design process, as is often the case today. But in order to work effectively, iterative design needs to have both the support of the organization concerned, and the commitment of the individuals involved. Good design tools will go some way towards satisfying this second requirement. Hopefully, the effect of their use will tend to wear away any initial organizational resistance there may be.

We have now reviewed a number of key requirements for a productive, efficient design process which makes effective use of the human factors resource. In the next section, we turn to more specific suggestions for implementing such a process, in the context of a 'design support environment' (more specifically, a cognitive psychology user-interface design support environment). It is important to note that when we describe the design support environment, we are describing a set of tools, and their integration to produce an appropriate source of information and advice to the design team. The intention is not to solve all the problems of the design process, rather to demonstrate how some of these can be eased. Hopefully, reduction in the more critical design problems will feed into the other aspects of the design process which we considered earlier and which are not specific to cognitive psychology but apply more generally to the application of human factors to user-interface design.

TOWARDS A DESIGN SUPPORT ENVIRONMENT

We noted earlier (Chapter 2) that there are a number of routes to the application of cognitive psychology to interface design. Amongst these are human factors tools such as guidelines, principles, generic designs, tutorials, etc. Automated design aids were also briefly discussed. These are software-based tools which take relevant knowledge and apply it in any of several possible ways to the design of user interfaces. Gardiner and Christie (1985) outline one such design aid — a cognitive design aid — currently being developed within the ESPRIT programme. This type of automated design aid is based on the application of appropriate metrics to formal interface descriptions to produce evaluations of the interface from a number of different viewpoints. Automated aids of this kind have proved useful in other fields of human factors (see Pulat and Grice, 1985). The attractiveness of this type of tool lies in the fact that it does not necessarily require expert knowledge to use, yet it makes such expert knowledge available in the context of iterative evaluations at different stages of interface development; the results of one evaluation can be fed back to the interface description as modifications, and the revised description can be evaluated all over again.

The potential for using information technology as a means of improving information technology products is enormous. It provides flexibility, automatization of routine and other aspects of iterative design — hence freeing the expert for more creative and productive work — and, importantly, it provides a uniform, coherent environment in which a design team can work. It does not solve *all* the problems the team may have, but it contributes to taking advantage of sources of information which until now have not been used effectively. Also, within such an environment, it is possible to get a better view of the separate aspects of the whole design process — human factors inputs included — so that budgeting for these may be facilitated.

In the next few sections we discuss in more detail the objectives and development of a technologically-based design support environment which combines many of the existing human factors tools mentioned above.

The support environment described addresses specifically the application of *cognitive psychology* research, since this is the brief of this book. In principle, however, it could also entail application of research from other disciplines — and this may indeed be very desirable in future. Within the current domain, we see the effects of applying cognitive psychology to interface design as contributing to a better match between the interface under development and its potential users. This we refer to as improving 'human–machine cognitive compatibility', using the term given to such a mapping in the ESPRIT programme.

OBJECTIVES OF A DESIGN SUPPORT ENVIRONMENT

We are specifically concerned here with a cognitive psychology user-interface design environment. The aim of such an environment is twofold:

— to help the design team to assess the degree of human–machine cognitive compatibility of particular user-interface designs; and
— to provide information, advice or other assistance of value in improving user-interface designs in regard to their degree of human–machine cognitive compatibility.

In addition to these principal objectives, there is a third objective which is desirable in terms of helping to achieve the two principal aims within the practical context of the design process. The third objective is to provide a means for achieving the two principal aims without slowing down the design process. Specifically, this third objective is:

— to couple the cognitive tools provided within the support environment to a software generator so that designs developed by the design team with support from the tools can be automatically translated into runnable software; in other words, the specification and the coding become part of the same process, with cognitive psychology aspects being treated as an integral part of the specification process.

The tools provided within the support environment are not intended to replace the expert judgements of the design team. Their purpose is to contribute to the design process by providing the design team with:

— some (though not all) of the information the team might find useful in deciding on the degree of human–machine cognitive compatibility achieved by a particular design, and areas where the design might be particularly weak in this regard;
— help in making appropriate design decisions, both during the initial stages of developing a design and in modifying the design to take account of weaknesses or to make enhancements; and
— a means of generating software directly and automatically from the specification developed.

Each of these will now be considered in turn.

ASSESSMENT OF COGNITIVE COMPATIBILITY

The first objective is to provide an assessment of user-interface designs in terms of human–machine cognitive compatibility. Key aspects of the necessary cognitive psychology research basis for this have been considered in Part Two. The need here is to consider how a method of assessment can be built upon that research base, which is amenable to translation into software. Basically, this refers to developing a software tool which is capable of taking the information provided in the theoretical chapters, and applying it in a systematic manner, to produce evaluations of interface descriptions. The following are some key factors that need to be considered in this regard.

A multivariate versus a univariate view of human–machine cognitive compatibility

The first question to address is whether to conceive of human–machine cognitive compatibility in univariate or multivariate terms. In principle, either a univariate or a multivariate view can be adopted. A univariate view would have the benefit of simplicity of presentation. It would provide a broad indication of overall compatibility. On the other hand, it would have two major weaknesses. First, any single index attempting to reflect overall compatibility could be affected very significantly as new research findings needed to be taken into account in calculating it, or additional areas of cognitive psychology were included in the assessment procedures leading to the index. Second, as an overall index, it would hide the more detailed picture — the more specific indices that could in principle be provided to reflect different aspects of the design (for example, load on short-term memory, coherence, probability of automatized responding) — two different designs could achieve a similar moderate level of compatibility with quite different patterns of relative strengths and weaknesses.

A multivariate view would present not a single index but a profile of indices reflecting a number of different aspects of the design which affect compatibility.

Such a profile would need interpretation. An ideal user-interface design would result in good compatibility indices for all the variables assessed, but this situation would rarely if ever be achieved in practice. In normal circumstances tradeoffs would need to be made between different indices, and the design team would need to make design decisions reflecting the desired tradeoffs.

The kind of tradeoffs that would need to be made are the same as those that are made routinely in the design process today. The difference would be that the profile of compatibility indices provided by the cognitive assessment tools would contribute to the background information the design team would have available when making the necessary design decisions; the decisions would be better informed. The tools would in this way help to make explicit some of what is currently done intuitively. They would have benefits in supplementing the design team's intuitions with systematic information based on calculations that might be too time-consuming or tedious for the design team to perform manually. The aim of this aspect of the design support environment should therefore be to provide the design team with some information of potential value in making design decisions, not to remove any decision-making from the design team.

It is also not necessarily the intention that the interpretation of the indices of cognitive compatibility produced by the evaluation tool should be left entirely to non-experts. The tool could simply remove from the cognitive psychologist or the human factors expert the need to perform manually certain types of interface evaluation work. Interpretation of the output and subsequent modification of the interface could still be very much the province of the human factors expert. Indeed, given the current state of development of cognitive psychology, and the absence of a coherent overall model of cognitive processing (as evidenced by the theoretical chapters) this would have to be the case initially, to ensure appropriate interpretation and use of the indices produced.

Developing an appropriate architecture for the assessment tools

The architecture of the assessment tools needs to facilitate coverage of all the relevant areas of cognitive psychology that can be applied to the assessment process.

One way in principle of achieving this would be to parallel the structure of the human mind. All the relevant aspects of human cognitive psychology would then certainly be covered. This is not possible at the present stage of development of cognitive psychology, because no such 'plan of the mind' at a sufficient level of detail has been agreed by researchers in this field. Indeed, as we have seen from the discussion in earlier chapters, there has been a movement away from grand theories attempting to cover all aspects of cognition towards smaller theories treating particular areas in more depth.

Even if it were possible, careful consideration would need to be given to whether this would be the optimum way of proceeding. In this connection, it is important to consider a second criterion. As well as covering all the relevant areas, the tools need to be capable of being updated and modified easily in the light of new research. It is possible that an alternative structure would serve this purpose better whilst still meeting the criterion of adequate coverage.

An approach which has been found useful in other areas of software development emphasizes a high degree of modularity in the overall design. This approach helps to keep the software development task manageable, and it facilitates revisions to the software. One can envisage a modular structure to the assessment tools within the design support environment providing similar advantages.

A modular approach acknowledges that something of relevance to human–machine cognitive compatibility is known by cognitive psychologists working in different areas, especially those areas considered in the previous chapters, but it does not constrain the assessment tools to use an integrated, uniform approach across all areas. It allows a set of conceptual modules to be defined which can examine a user-interface design from several different points of view. Each module can take its own required information as inputs, perform its own particular kind of processing on those inputs, and produce its own indices relevant to cognitive compatibility.

The different modules could be closely matched to particular areas of cognitive psychology research, such as working memory, or automaticity; or they could cut across different areas and look instead at user 'states', such as mental load levels, expert interaction, etc. The number of modules and their structure would depend on the available knowledge. As we saw in the theoretical chapters, certain areas of cognitive psychology research (for example, skill acquisition) appear to lend themselves to more computational kinds of usage and interpretation, whereas others (such as, thinking) are more descriptive. The information required by the modules, in order to carry out their evaluation of the interface would also vary. For example, the factors that lead to automaticity (for example, frequency of action, feedback latency) are different from those that lead to increased working memory load (number of items to be held in memory, task structure, etc.). Each module would therefore have its own requirements from the interface description concerned.

Clearly, though, one should not have just an assortment of different modules, looking at an interface from completely different aspects in isolation. The interrelationships amongst the evaluations by the different modules should be at least as instructive as each of the individual indices. For example, expertise might change the importance of a high working memory load, or inconsistencies at the level of commands might be written off by a particularly good mapping between a user's model of a task and its electronic implementation. At present, it is difficult to see how such interrelationships could be taken care of exclusively in software. However, they could serve as a basis for directing user trials, or for supporting and shaping decisions by the cognitive psychologist or human factors expert in the design team. As theory develops — possibly also spurred by the results of utilizing an evaluation tool of this kind — so more of the necessary information could be built into the evaluation tool, to automatically adjust the results of the different modular evaluations.

In considering the structure proposed it is important to bear in mind the criteria of adequate coverage of different areas, capability to update the tools easily in the light of new research, and flexibility in the way different areas are treated. It is also important to recognize that the assessment tools are *not* intended to embody a complete 'theory of the mind' but to be practical tools within the overall design support environment. A further criterion is important in this respect. If it *were* possible to incorporate a complete and perfect theory of cognition in the assessment tools, it might still not be useful to do so. The reason for this is that the amount of information that would need to be provided about the user-interface designs concerned in order to apply the theory in all its details would probably be so great as to make the disadvantages of the effort and time involved outweigh any advantage of getting systematic feedback rather than relying on intuition.

The assessment tools, then, need to be useful — based on whatever cognitive psychological theory exists that can be applied with minimal practical costs, but not necessarily reflecting every last detail, for instance every detail of every possible interaction between different aspects of cognition; they can be approximate. All that is important is that they help the design team, on average, to do better than would be done in the absence of the tools, with an acceptable cost in terms of any extra design effort or time that might be involved.

SUPPORT FOR DESIGN DECISIONS

The second function of the design support environment would be to provide the design team with support in making decisions about particular designs — both during the initial development of the designs and during subsequent iterations when the designs are added to or modified to take account of human–machine cognitive compatibility or other factors.

This type of decision support in principle can be provided at several levels. The profile of compatibility indices produced by the evaluation tools itself provides some support by helping to identify those aspects of a design that are especially weak in some respects (or especially strong). Beyond this, the following are among the kinds of support that can be provided, from general to specific:

— links to materials presenting relevant aspects of cognitive psychology in an educational or informative style;
— design guidelines, and/or advice based on such guidelines; and
— examples of good designs.

These will now each be considered briefly in more detail.

Links to cognitive psychology

The initiative for establishing a link could in principle be taken by either the individual designer or the decision support tools, or a mixture of the two depending upon particular circumstances. In either case, the objective of this kind of support is to provide the individual designer with appropriate opportunities conveniently to 'bone up' on aspects of cognitive psychology that are especially pertinent in the context of the designs currently being worked on. The kind of support provided under this heading could be more or less specific, depending upon the inclinations of the individual designer and other circumstances. We are not concerned here with questions of how to design an effective and acceptable user interface to this part of the design support environment, simply with identifying the kinds of support that might be provided. These include:

— online mini-tutorials covering specific aspects of human–machine cognitive compatibility;
— references to the relevant cognitive psychological and human factors literature, possibly with some of this available online with the design support environment acting as a 'gateway';
— information on current training courses being run in particular areas, probably including in-house courses as well as more public courses; and
— ancillary information such as previous products the company has worked on which seem to have involved similar design problems, and associated information (for example, names of individuals within the company who might be able to offer specialist advice based on previous experience with the type of problem involved).

Guidelines and advice

The aim of this aspect of the support environment is to provide more directly applicable guidance concerning particular design decisions. The feasibility of developing design guidelines based on cognitive psychology principles has been demonstrated in Chapter 8. Building upon this, two kinds of support are envisaged:

— Online access to appropriate guidelines at key decision points in the design process. These could be presented as and when specifically requested by the individual designer actively seeking guidance. Alternatively, they could be linked to the assessment tools so that the support environment could take more of an initiative in identifying relevant guidelines and perhaps prompting the designer when the assessment profile indicates that this might be helpful.

— An expert system consultation service. Using this service within the overall support environment, the individual designer or design team could review aspects of the particular user-interface design concerned with an expert system whose knowledge base would stem from the design guidelines. The key advantage of this type of support is that it is more interactive and dynamic than the raw guidelines, and better able to take account of the interrelationships between different guidelines. The need to take account of this kind of complexity has been discussed in Chapter 8.

These two approaches are not seen as being mutually exclusive, but as two different levels of support. Which is appropriate depends upon the particular circumstances. In some instances, a designer may be fairly familiar with the area covered but wish to consult a specific guideline to refresh his or her memory about some particular point. In other instances, a more in-depth exploration of the design problem and the relevant guidelines might be more appropriate.

In either case, this kind of support would not be offered in isolation of the rest of the support environment but would connect with other aspects of the environment, including the linkages to cognitive psychology. In this way, the individual designer could choose to pursue a particular design problem to whatever depth seems appropriate in the circumstances, the aim being to *support* rather than *automate* the designer.

Examples of good designs

The concept of 'generic designs' has been discussed in Chapter 2. These are designs which illustrate particular cognitive psychology principles (or, in other contexts, other principles). They are examples of 'good designs'. Other, more specific designs may also be 'good designs' even if they have been developed to meet the needs of a very particular design problem. In either case, the design support environment would provide the design team with access to such designs. The key concepts involved in this aspect of the support environment are:

— a database of designs, built up continuously over a period of time, and including 'generic designs' as well as more specific but still 'good' designs, including 'company standards' (for example, helping to ensure consistency in house style);
— a sophisticated information retrieval system, probably utilizing artificial intelligence techniques, for accessing appropriate designs — either in response to direct requests from the design team or in response to requests from other parts of the support environment — for example, the expert system consultation service or the mini-tutorial service; and

— a means of copying, editing and otherwise using the designs in the user interface currently being developed.

The idea would be to allow the design team to build on previous work. For example, if a lot of effort was invested in the development of a particular solution to a design problem in one context, it would be wasteful to simply start from scratch again in another situation which might benefit from a *modified* version of that solution. The ability to port to the current environment work previously done, to modify it as required and, if need be, to run it through the evaluation tool again might save time in the long run.

LINKAGE TO SOFTWARE PRODUCTION

The third high-level objective of the cognitive psychology design support environment is to facilitate the application of cognitive psychology within the design process without significantly slowing the design cycle. The need for this has been discussed in Chapter 2. A key element in achieving it is to provide a means of producing code directly and automatically from the specifications produced using the various tools within the support environment.

The feasibility of this has been demonstrated in systems such as RAPID/USE (see Wasserman, 1985) and SET (from PA Technology) which already exist. These systems allow the designer to specify the design of a user interface using a very high-level language which can then be used automatically to produce either an interactive mock-up of the interface (both RAPID/USE and SET do this) or final code (SET).

The purpose of this aspect of the design support environment in the present context would be twofold:

— to provide a means of rapid prototyping, so that — if time permits — user tests (see Chapter 2) can be conducted on critical aspects of the design; and
— to produce final code as efficiently as possible in order to meet the time and cost constraints that normally apply (see Chapter 2).

RESEARCH PRIORITIES

We have outlined a design support environment incorporating human factors tools based on cognitive psychology research. This is an electronic support environment, containing software-based versions of traditional human factors tools (for example, guidelines) as well as other, less well-known means of packaging cognitive psychology (for example, automated evaluation tools). The intention is to make available to the design team, in a 'user-friendly' and time-effective format, within a coherent environment, a number of aids to decision-making.

Obviously, the effectiveness of such a design environment is critically dependent on the methodological and theoretical soundness of its cognitive psychological underpinnings, as well as the soundness and availability of appropriate techniques and models which are implicated directly in the implementation of the design support environment. We now review some of these issues.

Methodological points concerning the cognitive psychology base

A need for ecological validity

The majority of work in cognitive psychology has followed the traditional experimental approach of most areas of mainstream psychology — it has been based on controlled laboratory experiments in which the behaviour of subjects (very often psychology undergraduates) has been observed in highly contrived, very simple situations. In terms of statistical sampling theory, neither the subjects nor the situations examined can very often be said to have been representative of the world at large. Without denying the achievements of this approach, it would seem to be the case that this type of work has so far largely failed to provide a basis for generalizable principles having theoretical and/or practical utility in a variety of real-world situations.

This problem was foreseen by Brunswick and others as early as 30 years ago (see Brunswick, 1956), and attention was drawn to it again more recently in an influential paper by Neisser (1984).

According to one school of thought, the problem is not with the methodology but with the timescale of the research in relation to the problems that need to be addressed. The argument goes that cognitive psychology is simply too young for too much to be expected from it, and in another 30 years we can expect to see the fruits of what is in progress now.

An alternative view argues that for practical purposes it is not time that is the limiting factor on what can be achieved with the traditional type of experiment but the method itself, and that at least in some areas the traditional approach needs to be replaced or augmented with more ecologically-valid research.

In the present context, the earlier chapters suggest that one need not go to either extreme — abandoning traditional experiments completely, or sticking with that approach exclusively. It is clear from the discussions in Part Two that many of the findings from relatively simple, controlled experiments in cognitive psychology have practical implications for the design of user interfaces (Chapter 8 bears witness to this). At the same time, many of the potential links between mainstream cognitive psychology and the applied world could be developed significantly by more attention being given to the complexity of situations in which user-system interaction actually occurs.

The problems that currently exist in applying the results of cognitive psychology research will become worse as the technology develops, unless new research methods are adopted. The technology is developing so fast that research findings based on the highly simplified situations of traditional laboratory experiments are likely to lag further and further behind the questions that are of importance to the designer of user interfaces to modern office systems. Similarly, research carried out on the simple technologies of the recent past may not generalize well to the problems of the technology of the present and, more importantly, the future.

We would argue that a move towards more ecologically-valid research would be of benefit not just to the applied field but to cognitive psychology in general — that some of the most significant developments in theory will come not from studying behaviour in highly simplified, unrealistic situations, but from studying behaviour in the kinds of environments in which it normally occurs.

A need for longitudinal research

A limitation on the conclusions that can be drawn from much previous research stems from the two related facts that: (a) the experiments concerned have been based on observations of subjects who were unfamiliar with the experimental tasks and were observed for a relatively short period, in other words, during the early part of any learning that might have been taking place; and (b) cognitive changes due to learning are the rule rather than the exception, even in relatively simple situations as well as the complex situations typical of user–system interaction.

Key aspects of the learning which characterizes user–system interaction have been identified in Part Two. These include especially: changes in users' schemata as a result of experience with the system, in the degree of automatization of skilled sequences of behaviour, and in effective memory capacity as a result of 'chunking'.

An understanding of these changes is especially important in relation to the design of user interfaces that accommodate changes in the level of users' expertise.

Applying cognitive psychology within a design support environment

We discussed above the benefits that might accrue from formalizing key aspects of the application of cognitive psychology research within a design support environment. In particular, we mentioned the use of evaluation tools which would allow certain aspects of the human factors expert's work to be automated. Development of such automated tools itself poses some demands on theory and methodology development, for example to do with the formal description of user-interface designs and user tasks, and with the development of metrics that reflect the cognitive psychology theory. We will now consider each of these issues in turn.

A need for formal methods of user-interface description

Recent years have seen increasing interest in describing the user interface in formal terms (see, for example, Chi, 1985; Wasserman, 1985). This has been stimulated in large part by a need to facilitate communication between the team producing the high-level design specification and the programming team who need to code the software that runs the interface. The feasibility of producing formal descriptions has been demonstrated convincingly by the incorporation of such methods into automated design tools that produce software (mock-ups or final software) from specifications produced by the designer. Examples of such interface generators are RAPID/USE (see Wasserman, 1985) and SET (from PA Technology).

The description methods developed so far have largely been concerned with facilitating the coding of software from formal specifications. They have not been concerned with questions of human–machine cognitive compatibility. A research need remains to develop methods of formal description that include information about the interface that is directly relevant to cognitive compatibility.

This is essential in order to build the kind of design support environment discussed above, and it has important spinoff benefits for pure research in terms of ecological validity.

Spinoff benefits for pure research   A great advantage of the traditional laboratory experiment was that it was easy to describe the environment in which the behaviour was occurring. Indeed, this was the essence of the approach — to describe accurately every important aspect of the environment, and how behaviour varied as critical features of the environment were adjusted.

A similar need obtains when studying behaviour in more complex, real-life situations — it is necessary to describe the key features of the situation accurately and in sufficient detail that changes in behaviour can be interpreted appropriately as key features of the situation are adjusted.

In doing research on user behaviour in relation to complex, realistic user interfaces, it is necessary to be able to describe the user interface concerned in sufficient and appropriate detail — in other words, there is a need for formal description.

Descriptions based on such methods would provide a powerful tool for research on human–machine cognitive compatibility, allowing the researcher to assess effects on user behaviour as key aspects of the interface are varied.

A need for formal methods of task description

The need to consider the nature of the task has been a recurrent theme in the earlier discussions. The user of an office system does not respond mechanically to the various prompts produced by the system. Rather, the user actively chooses a route through the available dialogue in order to achieve certain purposes. Two key aspects of this need to be distinguished, which may be called analysis of:

— the objective task;
— the subjective task.

The objective task   This is the task as specified by the designer of the system. In principle, it may be based on an analysis of how the intended users of the system 'naturally' see the task concerned, or it may be based entirely on the designer's own, perhaps very idiosyncratic view of the task. What is important here is that it is independent of any particular user of the system, and in that sense it is 'objective'. It can be regarded as a description of the task as the designer intended the task to be carried out (whether or not that would correspond to how users would prefer to do the task).

Any user-interface design reflects an objective task analysis — either explicitly (if documented separately) or implicitly (if not). In the absence of such an analysis, the dialogue involved in using the interface would be bound to be nonsensical — just a 'random' or arbitrary arrangement of possible interactions between human and machine, lacking any purpose. Any real interface design embodies notions of 'what the user should be trying to achieve', 'what the user needs to do now' and 'what the user needs to do next'. It reflects a logic that is intended to lead the user towards particular goals that the system is intended to make possible (for example, creating a document, filing a document, creating a project plan, retrieving a drawing, sending a message).

A number of methods exist for developing an objective task analysis. One method is based on the GOMS model of Card, Moran and Newell (1983). Card, Moran and Newell present examples of how, using this model, tasks can be broken down hierarchically into subtasks which can then be used as a basis for comparing different user-interface designs in terms of user performance (for example, times taken to complete the various subtasks, numbers of keystrokes involved, and so forth).

The GOMS model is based on the notion of any task being describable in terms of a hierarchy of goals. In using the analysis to compare the user interfaces of different systems, it is assumed that key goals and subgoals can be identified which are common to usage of the different systems involved. Comparisons between the systems in terms of the model are meaningless unless this can be done.

This kind of analysis is concerned with *what* needs to be done (in the GOMS model, described as a hierarchy of goals), not *how* it is done. For example, a very low-level goal in the hierarchy might be to position the cursor in a particular box on the screen. How this is achieved — for example, by using cursor keys or a mouse — is not a concern of the task analysis.

This, however, is a simplification. If even lower-level goals are defined, then the distinction between the *what* and the *how* breaks down. For example, if very low-level goals such as 'press the rightward cursor key', or 'slide the mouse rightward' are defined then they may effectively specify the 'how' (for example, pressing the rightward cursor key only applies if pressing the cursor keys is the means by which the user achieves the higher-level goal of positioning the cursor). Under these circumstances the distinction between the 'what' and the 'how' becomes meaningless or arbitrary.

Research is needed on effective methods for describing the objective task, and on how the description of the objective task relates to the description of the dialogue by which the task intended is to be achieved. At a theoretical level, it may be that the two overlap or can be considered as two formally equivalent ways of describing the same thing. Even if this turns out to be the case, the research is of practical importance in developing tools to support the design of user interfaces. In developing such tools, it is necessary to come to a decision about what to include in the description of the 'what' (the objective task) and what to include in the 'how' (the dialogue by which the task can be achieved). The decision may turn out to be arbitrary in theoretical terms, but it is likely that some arrangements will be more effective than others in practice.

The subjective task This is the task as perceived by and planned by the individual user. It varies according to the user, not the particular user interface (whereas the objective task description varies according to the user interface and not the particular user). Two different users attempting to achieve the same objective task using the same user interface may be working within the contexts of two different subjective tasks. They may have different (perhaps inaccurate) beliefs about how the system operates, and they may plan their work differently to accord with their beliefs. Various models have been proposed for describing what is involved in this, and some have been considered in Chapter 2. It is still an area where research is needed.

Relationship to mental models The concept of mental models has been discussed in Chapter 4. The relevance of the concept in this context is in terms of the degree of match or mismatch between the subjective task of the individual user and the objective task embodied in the design of the user interface concerned. One way of reducing the mismatch is to base the objective task description on the subjective descriptions of a representative sample of the intended users. (Dzida and Valder, 1984, discuss the value of taking users' perceptions and natural ways of structuring tasks into account in deciding how a task should be represented in an electronic system.) It is also the case, as discussed in Chapter 4, that users modify their views of how to accomplish tasks using a system as they gain more experience with the system. There is also the question of when it might be appropiate to design an interface so that it adapts (or can be adapted) to fit in more closely with the way an individual user perceives the task and how to do it using the system concerned and, when they are appropriate, how best to design such interfaces.

All of these considerations point to a need for research on optimal ways of structuring tasks (objectively) within electronic systems to fit in with the intended users, and for describing that structure — not just to the team responsible for trans-lating the design specifications into a working user interface, but also to the users of that interface so as to facilitate the development of appropriate mental models.

A need for metrics

The previous chapters have shown how it is possible to take findings from mainstream cognitive psychology, extract general cognitive principles, and use these as a basis for developing design guidelines. Such guidelines are only one form in which the knowledge can be embodied. In applying the research findings to formal descriptions of user-interface designs and objective tasks, it is necessary to interpret them not into the guidelines (which have their own use in the design support environment, as discussed above) but into metrics that can be applied routinely to the descriptions to yield indices of compatibility.

The development of metrics is essential for the development of the type of design support environment discussed above, and is a key area for applied research in this context. It also has potentially important spinoff benefits for pure research.

Spinoff benefits for pure research   The development of metrics for the design support environment provides a vehicle for the operationalization of hypotheses concerning the cognitive aspects of user–system interaction. Being software-based, the metrics require that the researcher be specific about what is meant. Terms need to be defined precisely, relationships between key concepts need to be made absolutely clear, and so forth. This is a defining characteristic of true science in any area, not just cognitive psychology, but when the vehicle for communication with others is text it can be extraordinarily difficult to ensure rigorous application of that scientific principle.

The problem is brought into sharp focus when the requirement is to communi-cate what is meant to a programmer whose task is to translate what is said into code that runs and, in running, does what the researcher meant it to do. In order to work, it means that the researcher has to think much more clearly in terms of what Johnson-Laird (1983) has termed 'effective procedures'.

As an example of the level of clarity that is needed, consider the following general principle of short-term memory: that it will become overloaded once a critical number of items to be remembered has been exceeded. In principle, this overload could take a number of different forms, of which the following are just a few possibilities: the first item could be lost as the new one is entered into memory; the last item entered before the critical number was reached could be lost; the item in the middle of the sequence could be lost; all items, including the new one, could be held in store but with some memory impairment of each (for example, longer time to retrieve each of them from store, or some distortion of each); all items could be retained but with a reduced probability of being retrieved; and so on.

In developing applicable models, details such as these need to be made explicit.

A need for more coherent models of the user

Modern cognitive psychology has become somewhat fragmented. Research interests have often focused on rather narrow areas, each of which has been researched in depth, with relatively little consideration of the linkages and relationships between the different areas. This makes it difficult to produce an overall view of the cognitive functioning of the user of an electronic system. Coverage is very uneven. There are small islands of relatively detailed knowledge about the mechanisms involved, with largely uncharted waters between.

In contrast, the user of an electronic office system normally acts as a coherent system, not an isolated fragment of a system. A key characteristic of systems is that they have 'emergent properties' — the whole is greater than the sum of its parts.

Some effort devoted to developing an overall framework for relating models in different areas of cognitive psychology more clearly could have some advantages in terms of helping to capture the 'systems' aspect of the user of office systems, and for guiding applied research more systematically.

CONCLUSIONS

Cognitive psychology is a young subdiscipline of a young discipline — psychology — and it covers a much broader domain than user–system interaction. It is encouraging, in the light of this, that it has as much to offer in the present context as it would seem to have from the research considered in the earlier chapters of this book.

Industry has been taking an increasing interest in what cognitive psychology might have to offer to the design of user interfaces to modern office systems, and so the invitation is open to cognitive psychologists to apply their knowledge to real-world problems in this context, if they wish to do so.

In this book, we have considered some of the key constraints under which design teams operate, and some of the ways in which cognitive psychology might be most usefully incorporated into the design process. A key message is that the rules of the design game are tough, for the game is played in a highly competitive world where the stakes are high and time can be a v ry great deal of money. Products are needed today, and cannot make use of advice that may be available in another 30 years time. If they wish to be part of the game, cognitive psychologists, like other specialists involved in the design process, must be willing to make positive contributions on the basis of what is known now, whilst also contributing to research on key issues that will pay dividends in the future.

The effectiveness of the research methods used will have a key bearing on the viability of applied cognitive psychology over the next 20 years. There is an urgent need to review the match between what can be achieved using traditional methods and what is needed by the applied domain. Traditional laboratory experiments in particular are relatively time-comsuming and some would argue that they are inherently limited in terms of what they can achieve. Developments in information technology may offer possibilities for faster, more effective research — the potential is there but it demands imagination to be fully realized in practice.

References

Abelson, R.P. (1981). Psychological status of the script concept. *American Psychologist*, **36**, 715–729.

Adelson, B. (1984). When novices surpass experts: the difficulty of a task may increase with expertise. *Journal of Experimental Psychology: Learning, Memory and Cognition*, **10**, 483–495.

Aitkenhead, A.M. and Slack, J.M. (1985). Introduction. In: A.M. Aitkenhead and J.M. Slack (eds.), *Issues in Cognitive Modeling*. London: Lawrence Erlbaum Associates.

Alba, J.W. and Hasher, L. (1983). Is memory schematic? *Psychological Bulletin*, **93**, 203–231.

Allen, R.B. and Scerbo, M.W. (1983). Details of command-language keystrokes. *ACM Transactions on Office Information Systems*, **1**, 159–178.

Anderson, J.R. (1976). *Language, Memory and Thought*. Hillsdale, NJ: Lawrence Erlbaum Associates.

Anderson, J.R. (1980). *Cognitive Psychology and its Implications*. San Francisco: W.H. Freeman and Co.

Anderson, J.R. (1982). Acquisition of cognitive skill. *Psychological Review*, **89**, 396–406.

Anderson, J.R. (1983a). Retrieval of information from long-term memory. *Science*, **220**, 25–30.

Anderson, J.R. (1983b). *The Architecture of Cognition*. Cambridge, Mass.: Harvard University Press.

Anderson, J.R. (1984). Cognitive psychology. *Artificial Intelligence*, **23**, 1–11.

Anderson, J.R. and Bower, G.H. (1973). *Human Associative Memory*. Washington, DC: V.H. Winston and Sons.

Anderson, J.R., Farrell, R., and Sauers, R. (1984). Learning to program in LISP. *Cognitive Science*, **8**, 87–129.

Ashcraft, M.H. (1978). Property dominance and typicality effects in property statement verification. *Journal of Verbal Learning and Verbal Behavior*, **17**, 155–164.

Askwall, S. (1985). Computer supported reading versus reading text on paper: A comparison of two reading situations. *International Journal of Man–Machine Studies*, **22**, 425–439.

Atkinson, R.C. and Shiffrin, R.M. (1971). The control of short-term memory. *Scientific American*, **225**, 82–90.

Austin, J.L. (1962). *How to Do Things with Words*. Oxford: Oxford University Press.

Baddeley, A.D. (1968). How does acoustic similarity influence short-term memory? *Quarterly Journal of Experimental Psychology*, **20**, 249–264.

Baddeley, A.D. (1976). *Human Memory*. New York: Basic Books.

Baddeley, A.D. (1982). Domains of recollection. *Psychological Review*, **89**, 708–729.

Baddeley, A.D. (1983). Working memory. *Philosophical Transactions of the Royal Society London B*, **302**, 311–324.

Baddeley, A.D. and Hitch, G.J. (1974). Working memory. In: G.H. Bower (ed.), *The Psychology of Learning and Motivation, vol. 8*. New York: Academic Press.

Baddeley, A.D. and Hitch, G.J. (1977). Recency re-examined. In S. Dornic (ed.), *Attention and Performance, vol. 6*. Hillsdale, NJ: Lawrence Erlbaum Associates.

Baddeley, A.D. and Lewis, V.J. (1981). Inner active processes in reading: the inner voice, the inner ear and the inner eye. In: A.M. Lesgold and C.A. Perfetti (eds.), *Interactive Processes in Reading*. Hillsdale, NJ: Lawrence Erblaum Associates.

Baddeley, A.D., Eldridge, M., and Lewis, V.J. (1981). The role of subvocalisation in reading. *Quarterly Journal of Experimental Psychology*, **33**, 439–454.

Baddeley, A.D. and Woodhead, M.M. (1982). Depth of processing, context of face recognition. *Canadian Journal of Psychology*, **36**, 148–164.

Baddeley, A.D., Thomson, N., and Buchanan, M. (1975). Word length and the structure of short-term memory. *Journal of Verbal Learning and Verbal Behavior*, **14**, 575–589.

Baddeley, A.D., Lewis, V., Eldridge, M., and Thomson, N. (1984). Attention and retrieval from long-term memory. *Journal of Experimental Psychology: General*, **113**, 518–540.

Bailey, R.W. (1982). *Human Performance Engineering: A Guide for System Designers*. Englewood Cliffs, NJ: Prentice Hall.

Baker, C.A. and Eason, K.D. (1981). An observational study of man–computer interaction using an online bibliographic information retrieval system. *On-Line Review*, **5**, 122–132.

Bannon, L., Cypher, A., Greenspan, S., and Monty, M. (1983). Evaluation and analysis of users' activity organization. In *Proceedings of CHI '83: Human Factors in Computing Systems*, Boston, December 1983. New York: ACM.

Barnard, P.J. (1983a). Experiments on learning interactive dialogues: problems and prospects. In M.J. Elphick (ed.), *Man–Machine Interaction: Proceedings of the Joint IBM/University of Newcastle Seminar*.

Barnard, P.J. (1983b). Applying the products of research on interactive dialogues. In M.J. Elphick (ed.), *Man–Machine Interaction: Proceedings of the Joint IBM/University of Newcastle Seminar*.

Barnard, P.J. and Hammond, N.V. (1982). Usability and its multiple determination for the occasional user of interactive systems. In: M.B. Williams (ed.), *Pathways to the Information Society. Sixth International Conference on Computer Communication*. Amsterdam: North-Holland.

Barnard, P.J., Hammond, N.V., MacLean, A., and Morton, J. (1982). Learning and remembering interactive commands in a text-editing task. *Behaviour and Information Technology*, **1**, 347–358.

Barsalou, L.W. (1983). *Ad hoc* categories. *Memory and Cognition*, **11**, 211–227.

Barsalou, L.W. (1984). The instability of graded structure: implications for the nature of concepts. Paper presented at a conference on The Ecological and Intellectual Bases of Categories at Emory University, October 1984. To appear in U. Neisser (ed.), *Concepts Reconsidered: The Ecological and Intellectual Bases of Categories*. Cambridge: Cambridge University Press.

Barsalou, L.W. and Sewell, D.R. (1984). Constructing representations of categories from different points of view. *Emory Cognition Project Report #4*.

Bartlett, F.C. (1932). *Remembering*. Cambridge: Cambridge University Press.

Belbin, E. (1979). Applicable psychology and some national problems. *Bulletin of the British Psychological Society*, **32**, 241–244.

Bennett, J.L. (1979). The commercial impact of usability in interactive systems. In *Infotech*

State of the Art Report on Man/Computer Communication (2 volumes). Maidenhead, Berks.: Infotech International Ltd.

Berlin, B. and Kay, P. (1969). *Basic Color Terms: Their Universality and Evolution.* Berkeley and Los Angeles: University of California Press.

Beth, E.W. and Piaget, J. (1966). *Mathematical Epistemology and Psychology.* Dordrecht: Reidel.

Bjørn-Andersen, N. and Rasmussen, L.B. (1980). Sociological implications of computer systems. In: H.T. Smith and T.R.G. Green (eds.), *Human Interaction with Computers.* London: Academic Press.

Blackburn, J.M. (1936). Acquisition of skills: an analysis of learning curves. *Industrial Health Research Body Report,* **73**, London: HMSO.

Bolinger, D.L. (1975). *Aspects of Language,* 2nd ed. New York: Harcourt Brace Jovanovich Inc.

Bott, R. (1979). A study of complex learning: theory and methodology. *CHIP Report 82,* Center for Human Information Processing, UCSD, La Jolla, Cal.

Botterill, J.H. (1982). The design rationale of the System 38 user interface. *IBM Systems Journal,* **21**, 384–423.

Bournique, R. and Treu, S. (1985). Specification and generation of variable personalised graphical interfaces. *International Journal of Man–Machine Studies,* **22**, 663–684.

Bower, G.H. (1970). Imagery as a relational organizer in associative learning. *Journal of Verbal Learning and Verbal Behavior,* **9**, 529–533.

Bower, G.H. and Winzenz, D. (1970). Comparison of associative learning strategies. *Psychonomic Science,* **20**, 119–120.

Bower, G.H., Karlin, M.B., and Dueck, A. (1975). Comprehension and memory for pictures. *Memory and Cognition,* **3**, 216–220.

Boyle, J., Ogden, W., Uhlir, S., and Wilson, P. (1984). QMF usability: how it really happened. In: B. Schackel (ed.), *Interact '84: First IFIP Conference on Human Computer Interaction.* Amsterdam: IFIP, North-Holland.

Bransford, J.D. and Johnson, M.K. (1972). Contextual prerequisites for understanding: some investigations of comprehension and recall. *Journal of Verbal Learning and Verbal Behavior,* **11**, 717–726.

Brewer, W.F. and Treyens, J.C. (1981). Role of schemata in memory for places. *Cognitive Psychology,* **13**, 207–230.

Broadbent, D.E. (1958). *Perception and Communication.* London: Pergamon Press.

Broadbent, D.E. (1973). *In Defence of Empirical Psychology.* London: Methuen.

Broadbent, D.E. (1984). The Maltese Cross: a new simplistic model of memory. *The Behavioural and Brain Sciences,* **7**, 55–94.

Broadbent, D.E. and Broadbent, M.H.P. (1981a). Articulatory suppression and the grouping of successive stimuli. *Psychological Review,* **43**, 57–67.

Broadbent, D.E. and Broadbent, M.H.P. (1981b). Recency effects of visual memory. *Quarterly Journal of Experimental Psychology,* **33A**, 1–15.

Brown, J. (1958). Some tests of the decay theory of immediate memory. *Quarterly Journal of Experimental Psychology,* **10**, 12–21.

Brown, R.W. (1956). Language and categories. Appendix to J.S. Bruner, J.L. Goodnow and G.A. Austin, *A Study of Thinking.* New York: John Wiley and Sons.

Brown, R.W. and Lenneberg, E.H. (1954). A study in language and cognition. *Journal of Abnormal and Social Psychology,* **49**, 454–462.

Bruner, J.S., Goodnow, J.L., and Austin, G.A. (1956). *A Study of Thinking.* New York: John Wiley and Sons.

Brunswick, E. (1956). *Perception and the Representative Design of Psychological Experiments.* Berkeley: University of California Press.

Bryan, W.L. and Harter, N. (1899). Studies of the telegraphic language. The acquisition of a hierarchy of habits. *Psychological Review*, **6**, 345–375.

Bucher, R. and Kesch, J. (1985). *The Liquid Crystal Display Market 1985–1989*. Green Book No. 7, F. Hoffman-La Roche.

Byrne, B. and Arnold, L. (1981). Dissociation of the recency effect and immediate memory span: evidence from beginning readers. *British Journal of Psychology*, **72**, 371–376.

Card, S.K., English, W.K., and Burr, B.J. (1978). Evaluation of mouse, rate-controlled isometric joystick, step keys, and text keys for text selection on a CRT. *Ergonomics*, **21**, 601–613.

Card, S.K., Moran, T.P., and Newell, A. (1983). *The Psychology of Human–Computer Interaction*. Hillsdale, NJ: Lawrence Erlbaum Assoicates.

Card, S.K., Pavel, M., and Farrel, J.E. (1984). Window-based computer dialogues. In B. Schackel (ed.), *Interact '84: First IFIP Conference on Human Computer Interaction*. Amsterdam: IFIP, North-Holland.

Carroll, J.M. (1984a). Mental models and software human factors: an overview. (To appear in the *Proceedings of the National Academy of Sciences*).

Carroll, J.M. (1984b). Minimalist design for active users. In: B. Schackel (ed.), *Interact '84: First IFIP Conference on Human Computer Interaction*. Amsterdam: IFIP, North-Holland.

Carroll, J.M. and Carrithers, C. (1984a). Training wheels in a user interface. *Communications of the Association for Computing Machinery*, **27**, 800–806.

Carroll, J.M. and Carrithers, C. (1984b). Blocking learner error states in a training-wheels system. *Human Factors*, **26**, 377–391.

Carroll, J.M. and Kay, D.S. (1985). Prompting, feedback and error correction in the design of a scenario machine. In: L. Borman and B. Curtis (eds.), *Proceedings of CHI '85: Human Factors in Computing Systems*, San Francisco, April. New York: ACM.

Carroll, J.M. and Mazur, S.A. (1984). Learning to use an office system with an on-line tutorial. *RC 10644*: IBM Watson Research Center, Yorktown Heights, NY.

Carroll, J.M. and Rosson, M.B. (1984). Usability specifications as a tool in iterative development. In: H.R. Hartson (ed.), *Advances in Human–Computer Interaction*. Norwoord, NY: Ablex Publishing.

Carroll, J.M. and Thomas, J.C. (1982). Metaphor and the cognitive representation of computing systems. *IEEE Transactions on Systems, Man, and Cybernetics*, **12**, 107–116.

Carroll, J.M., Thomas, J.C. and Malhotra, A. (1979). Clinical-experimental analysis of design problem solving. *Design Studies*, **1**, 84–92.

Carroll, J.M., Thomas, J.C., and Malhotra, A. (1980). Presentation and representation in design problem solving. *British Journal of Psychology*, **71**, 143–153.

Carroll, J.M., Mack, R.L., Lewis, C.H., Grischkowsky, N.L., and Robertson, S.R. (1984). Learning to use a word processor by guided exploration *RC 10428*: IBM Watson Reserch Center, Yorktown Heights, NY.

Cermak, L.S. and Craik, F.I.M. (1978). *Levels of Processing in Human Memory*. Hillsdale, NJ: Lawrence Erlbaum Associates.

Chapanis, A., Garner, W.R., and Morgan, C.T. (1949). *Applied Experimental Psychology*. New York: John Wiley and Sons.

Chase, W.G. and Ericsson, K.A. (1981). Skilled memory. In: J.R. Anderson (ed.), *Cognitive Skills and their Acquisition*. Hillsdale, NJ: Lawrence Erlbaum Associates.

Chase, W.G. and Ericsson, K.A. (1982). Skill and working memory. In G.H. Bower (ed.), *The Psychology of Learning and Motivation, vol. 16*. New York: Academic Press.

Chi, U.H. (1985). Formal specification of user interfaces: a comparison and evaluation of four axiomatic approaches. *IEEE Transactions on Software Engineering*, **SE-11**(8), 671–685.

Chomsky, N. (1957a). *Syntactic Structures*. The Hague: Mouton.

Chomsky, N. (1957b). Review of *Verbal Behaviour* by B.F. Skinner. *Language*, **35**, 26–58.

Chomsky, N. (1965). *Aspects of the Theory of Syntax*. Cambridge, Mass.: MIT Press.

Chomsky, N. (1968). *Language and Mind*. New York: Harcourt Brace Jovanovich, Inc.

Chrostowski, J.J. and Griggs, R.A. (1985). The effects of problem content, instructions, and verbalization procedure on Wason's selection task. *Current Psychological Research and Reviews*, in press.

Clark, E.V. (1973). What's in a word? On the child's acquisition of semantics in his first language. In: T.E. Moore (ed.), *Cognitive Development and the Acquisition of Language*. New York: Academic Press.

Clark, E.V. (1979). Responding to indirect speech acts. *Cognitive Psychology*, **11**, 430–477.

Clark, E.V. and Hecht, B.V. (1982). Learning to coin agent and instrument nouns. *Cognition*, **12**, 1–24.

Clark, H.H. (1983). Language use and language users. In: G. Lindzey and E. Aranson (eds.), *Handbook of Social Psychology* (3rd ed.). Reading, Mass.: Addison-Wesley.

Clark, H.H. and Clark, E.V. (1977). *Psychology and Language: An Introduction to Psycholinguistics*. New York: Harcourt Brace Jovanovich, Inc.

Clark, H.H. and Haviland, S.E. (1977). Comprehension and the given-new contract. In: R.O. Freedle (ed.), *Discourse Production and Comprehension*. Norwood, NJ: Ablex Publishing.

Clark, H.H. and Wilkes-Gibbs, D. (in press) Referring as a collaborative process. *Cognition*.

Clark, J.A. and Hillen, J.R.C. (1985). Spare the rod and improve the child: Some anomalous observations in the computer-based training of novice users. *Dept. MACS Occasional Paper 85—5*. Sunderland Polytechnic.

Collins, A.M. and Loftus, E.F. (1975). A spreading activation theory of semantic processing. *Psychological Review*, **82**, 407–428.

Collins, A.M. and Quillian, M.R. (1972). How to make a language user. In: E. Tulving and W. Donaldson (eds.), *Organization of Memory*. New York: Academic Press.

Conrad, R. (1964). Acoustic confusion and immedite memory. *British Journal of Psychology*, **55**, 75–84.

Coutaz, J. (1985). Abstractions for user interface design. *Computer*, **September**, 21–34.

Craik, F.I.M. (1977) Age differences in human memory. In: J.E. Birren and K.W. Schaie (eds), *Handbook of the Psychology of Ageing*. New York: Van Nostrand Reinhold.

Craik, F.I.M. (1983). On the transfer of information from temporary to permanent memory. *Philosophical Transactions of the Royal Society of London, B*, **302**, 341–359.

Craik, F.I.M. and Byrd, M. (1982). Aging and cognitive deficits: the role of attentional resources. In: F.I.M. Craik and S. Trehub (eds.), *Aging and Cognitive Processes*. New York: Plenum Press.

Craik, F.I.M. and Jacoby, L.L. (1979). Elaboration and distinctiveness in episodic memory. In: L.G. Nilssen (ed.), *Perspectives on Memory Research*. Hillsdale, NJ: Lawrence Erlbaum Associates.

Craik, F.I.M. and Lockhart, R.S. (1972). Levels of processing: a framework for memory research. *Journal of Verbal Learning and Verbal Behavior*, **11**, 671–684.

Craik, F.I.M. and Tulving, E. (1975). Depth of processing and the retention of words in episodic memory. *Journal of Experimental Psychology: General*, **104**, 268–294.

Crossman, E.R.F.W. (1959). A theory of the acquisition of speed-skill. *Ergonomics*, **2**, 153–166.

Crowder, R.G. (1982). The demise of short-term memory. *Acta Psychologica*, **50**, 291–323.

Dagwell, R. and Weber, R. (1983). System designers' user models: a comparative study and methodological critique. *Communications of the ACM*, **26**, 987–997.

Damper, R.I., Lambourne, A.D., and Guy, D.P. (1984). Speech input as an adjunct to keyboard entry in television subtitling. In: B. Schackel (ed.), *Interact '84: First IFIP Conference on Human Computer Interaction*. Amsterdam: IFIP, North-Holland.

Daneman, M. and Carpenter, P.A. (1980). Individual differences in working memory and reading. *Journal of Verbal Learning and Verbal Behaviour*, **19**, 450–466.

Danserau, D.F. (1969). An information processing model of mental multiplication. (Doctoral dissertation, Carnegie-Mellon University). *Dissertation Abstracts*, **30**, 1916B. (University microfilms no. 69–15, 746.)

Dean, S.J. and Martin, R.B. (1966). Reported mediation as a function of degree of learning. *Psychonomic Science*, **4**, 231–232.

Dickinson, A. (1980). *Contemporary Animal Learning Theory*. Cambridge: Cambridge University Press.

diSessa, A.A. (1985). A principled design for an integrated computational environment. *Human–Computer Interaction*, **1**, 1–47.

Dix, A. and Runciman, C. (1985). Abstract models of interactive systems. In: P. Johnson and S. Cook (eds.), *People and Computers: Designing the Interface*. Cambridge: Cambridge University Press.

Douglas, S.A. and Moran, T.P. (1983). Learning text editor semantics by analogy. In *Proceedings of CHI '83: Human Factors in Computing Systems*, Boston, December 1983. New York: ACM.

Draper, S.W. (1984). The nature of expertise in UNIX. In: B. Schackel (ed.), *Interact '84: First IFIP Conference on Human Computer Interaction*. Amsterdam: IFIP, North-Holland.

Dreyfus, H. (1953). *Designing for People*. New York: Simon and Schuster.

Du Boulay, B., O'Shea, T., and Monk, J. (1981). The black box inside the glass box: presenting computing concepts to novices. *International Journal of Man–Machine Studies*, **14**, 237–249.

Dudley, H. and Tarnoczy, T. (1950). The speaking machine of Wolfgang von Kempelen. *Journal of the Acoustics Society of America*, **22**, 151–166.

Duncker, K. (1945). On problem solving. *Psychological Monographs*, **58**, 1–113.

Dzida, W. and Valder, W. (1984). Application domain modelling by knowledge engineering techniques. In: B. Schackel (ed.), *Interact '84; First IFIP Conference on Human Computer Interaction*. Amsterdam: IFIP, North-Holland.

Eason, K.D. (1982). The process of introducing information technology. *Behaviour and Information Technology*, **1**, 197–213.

Eccles, J.C. (1977). *The Understanding of the Brain* (2nd ed.). New York: McGraw-Hill.

Ericsson, K.A. and Simon, H.A. (1980). Verbal reports as data. *Psychological Review*, **87**, 215–251.

Ericsson, K.A. and Simon, H.A. (1984). *Protocol Analysis: Verbal Reports as Data*. Cambridge, MA: MIT Press.

Evans, J. St B. T. (1977). Toward a statistical theory of reasoning. *Quarterly Journal of Experimental Psychology*, **29**, 151–166.

Evans, J. St B. T. (1982). *The Psychology of Deductive Reasoning*. London: Routledge and Kegan Paul.

Evans. J. St B. T. (1984). Heuristic and analytic processes in reasoning. *British Journal of Psychology*, **75**, 451–468.

Evans, J. St B. T. and Lynch, J.S. (1973). Matching bias in the selection task. *British Journal of Psychology*, **64**, 391–397.

Evans, J. St B. T. and Wason, P.C. (1976). Rationalisation in a reasoning task. *British Journal of Psychology*, **67**, 479–486.

Eysenck, M.W. (1983). Individual differences in human memory. In: A.R. Mayes (ed.), *Memory in Animals and Humans*. Wokingham: Van Nostrand.

Eysenck, M.W. (1984). *A Handbook of Cognitive Psychology*. London: Lawrence Erlbaum Associates.

Fechner, G.T. (1860). Elemente der Psychophysik. (H.E. Adler, Trans., *Elements of Psychophysics*. New York: Holt Rinehart and Winston, 1966).

Festinger, G.T. (1957). *A Theory of Cognitive Dissonance*. Evanston, Ill.: Row and Peterson.

Fisher, R.P. and Craik, F.I.M. (1977). The interaction between encoding and retrieval processes in cued recall. *Journal of Experimental Psychology: Human Learning and Memory*, **3**, 701–711.

Fitts, P.M. (1964). Perceptual-motor skill learning. In: A.W. Melton (ed.), *Categories of Human Learning*. New York: Academic Press.

Fitts, P.M. and Posner, M.I. (1967). *Human Performance*. Belmont, California: Brooks-Cole.

Fitts, P.M. and Seeger, C.M. (1953). SR compatibility: Spatial characteristics of stimulus and response codes. *Journal of Experimental Psychology*, **46**, 199–210.

Foley, J.D. and van Dam, A. (1982). *Fundamentals of Interactive Computer Graphics*. New York: Addison-Wesley.

Gaines, B.R. and Facey, P.V. (1976). Programming interactive dialogues. In: A. Parkin (ed.), *Proceedings of a Conference on Computing and People*, Leicester, UK.

Gardiner, J.M. and Gregg, V.H. (1979). When auditory memory is not overwritten. *Journal of Verbal Learning and Verbal Behavior*, **18**, 705–719.

Gardiner, J.M., Gregg, V.H., and Gardiner, M.M. (1984). Concerning some more evidence of an auditory advantage in prerecency as well as recency recall. *American Journal of Psychology*, **97**, 593–604.

Gardiner, M.M. (1983). *Tests of the generality of the cue-overload principle*. PhD thesis, The City University, London.

Gardiner, M.M. and Christie, B. (1985). Packaging cognitive psychology for user-interface design. In *Proceedings of the 9th Congress of the International Ergonomics Association*. Bournemouth, 2–5 September.

Geiselman, R.E. and Bjork, R.A. (1980). Primary versus secondary rehearsal in imagined voices: differential effects on recognition. *Cognitive Psychology*. **12**, 188–205.

Gibbs, R.W., Jr. (1981). Your wish is my command: convention and context in interpreting indirect requests. *Journal of Verbal Learning and Verbal Behavior*, **20**, 431–444.

Gibbs, S. and Tsichritzis, D. (1983). A data modeling approach for office information systems. *ACM Transactions on Office Information Systems*, **1**, 299–319.

Gilhooly, K.J. (1982). *Thinking: Directed, Undirected and Creative*. London: Academic Press.

Glanzer, M. (1972). Storage mechanisms in recall. In: G.H. Bower (ed.), *The Psychology of Learning and Motivation*, vol. 5. New York: Academic Press.

Glanzer, M. and Razel, M. (1974). The size of the unit in short-term storage. *Journal of Verbal Learning and Verbal Behavior*, **13**, 114–131.

Golding, E. (1981). *The effect of past experience on problem-solving*. Paper presented at the annual conference of the British Psychological Society.

Goodwin, N.C. (1975). Cursor positioning on an electronic display using lightpen, lightgun, or keyboard for three basic taks. *Human Factors*, **17**, 289–295.

Gould, J.D. (1965). Differential visual feedback of component motions. *Journal of Experimental Psychology*, **69**, 263–268.

Gould, J.D. and Boies, S.J. (1983). Human factors challenges in creating a principal support office system — the speech filing system approach. *ACM Transactions in Office Automation Systems*, **1**, 254–271.

Gould, J.D. and Lewis, C. (1985). Designing for usability: key principles and what designers think. *Communications of the ACM*, **28**, 300–311.

Gould, J.D., Conti, J., and Hovanyecz, T. (1983). Composing letters with a simulated listening typewriter. *Communications of the ACM*, **26**, 295–308.

Granda, R.E. (1980). Man/machine design guidelines for the use of screen display terminals. In *Proceedings of the Human Factors Society 24th Annual Meeting*.

Green, T.R.G., Payne, S.J., Gilmore, D.J., and Mepham, M. (1984). Predicting expert slips. In: B. Schackel (ed.), *Interact '84: First IFIP Conference on Human Computer Interaction*. Amsterdam: IFIP, North-Holland.

Grice, H.P. (1975). Logic and conversation. In: P. Cole and J.L. Morgan (eds.), *Studies in Syntax. Vol. 3: Speech Acts*. New York: Academic Press.

Griggs, R.A. (1983). The role of problem content in the selection task and THOG problem. In J. St B. T. Evans (ed.), *Thinking and Reasoning: Psychological Approaches*. London: Routledge and Kegan Paul.

Griggs, R.A. and Cox, J.R. (1982). The elusive thematic-materials effect in Wason's selection task. *British Journal of Psychology*, **75**, 407–420.

Gross, T.F. (1985). *Cognitive Development*. Belmont, California: Brooks-Cole.

Halasz, F. and Moran, T.P. (1982). Analogy considered harmful. In *Proceedings of Conference on Human Factors in Computer Systems*, Gaithersburg, March. New York: ACM.

Hallam, J. and Stammers, R.B. (1983). *Man–Computer Dialogues Within Future Systems*. MOD Contract No. 2097/046 AMTE(T). University of Aston, UK.

Haller, R., Mutschler, H., and Voss, M. (1984). Comparison of input devices for correction of typing errors in office systems. In: B. Schackel (ed.), *Interact '84: First IFIP Conference on Human Computer Interaction*. Amsterdam: IFIP, North-Holland.

Hamilton, P., Hockey, G.R.J., and Rejman, M. (1977). The place of the concept of activation in human information processing theory: an integrative approach. In: S. Dornic (ed.), *Attention and Performance*, vol. 6. Hillsdale, NJ: Lawrence Erlbaum Associates.

Hammond, N.V. and Barnard, P.J. (1984). Dialogue design: characteristics of user knowledge. In A.F. Monk (ed.), *Fundamentals of Human–Computer Interaction*. London: Academic Press.

Hammond, N.V., Hinton, G., Barnard, P.J., MacLean, A., Long, J.B., and Whitefield, A. (1984). Evaluating the interface of a document processor: a comparison of expert judgement and user observation. In: B. Schackel (ed.), *Interact '84: First IFIP Conference on Human Computer Interaction*. Amsterdam: IFIP, North-Holland.

Hammond, N.V., Jørgensen, A.H., MacLean, A., Barnard, P.J., and Long, J.B. (1983a). Design practice and interface usability: evidence from interviews with designers. In *Proceedings of CHI '83: Human Factors in Computing Systems*, Boston, December 1983. New York: ACM.

Hammond, N.V., MacLean, A., Hinton, G., Long, J.B., Barnard, P.J., and Clark, I.A. (1983b). Novice use of an interactive graph-plotting system. *Human Factors Report HF083*: IBM Laboratories, Hursley Park.

Hammond, N.V., Morton, J., MacLean, A., and Barnard, P.J. (1983c). Fragments and signposts: Users' models of the system. In *Proceedings of the Tenth International Symposium on Human Factors in Telecommunications*, Helsinki.

Hammond, N.V., Morton, J., Barnard, P.J., Long, J.B., and Clark, I.A. (in press). Characterising user performance in interactive dialogue. *Behaviour and Information Technology.*

Hampson, S. (1985). *The principles of breadth and hierarchical structure in personality: conceptual analyses of internal data.* Paper presented to the British Psychological Society, London Conference, December 1985.

Hampton, J.A. (1979). Polymorphous concepts in semantic memory. *Journal of Verbal Learning and Verbal Behavior,* **18**, 441–461.

Hampton, J.A. (1981). An investigation of the nature of abstract concepts. *Memory and Cognition,* **9**, 149–156.

Hampton, J.A. (1982). A demonstration of intransitivity in natural categories. *Cognition,* **12**, 151–164.

Hampton, J.A. (1985a). *Combination of natural concepts.* Paper presented at the Annual Convention of the Psychonomics Society, Boston, November 1985.

Hampton, J.A. (1985b). *Inheritance of features in natural concept conjunctions.* Paper presented to the British Psychological Society, London Conference, December 1985.

Hampton, J.A. and Gardiner, M.M. (1983). Measures of internal category structure: a correlational analysis of normative data. *British Journal of Psychology,* **74**, 491–516.

Harpster, J.L. and Freivalds, A. (1984). VDT screen resolution and operator performance. In: B. Schackel (ed.), *Interact '84: First IFIP Conference on Human Computer Interaction.* Amsterdam: IFIP, North-Holland.

Harrison, M. and Thimbleby, H, (1985). Formalising guidelines for the design of interactive systems. [Norwich conference]

Harrison, N. (1983). Touching on screens. *Systems International,* **September**, 101–102.

Hayes, J.R. (1985). Three problems in teaching general skills. In: J. Segal, S. Chipman, and R. Glaser (eds.), *Thinking and Learning, Volume 2,* Hillsdale, NJ: Lawrence Erlbaum Associates.

Healy, A.F. and Nairne, J.S. (1985). Short-term memory processes in counting. *Cognitive Psychology,* **17**, 417–444.

Hedberg, B. and Mumford, E. (1975). The design of computer systems: man's vision of man as an integral part of the system design process. In: E. Mumford and H. Sackman (eds.), *Human Choice and Computers.* Amsterdam: North-Holland.

Henle, M. (1968). On the relation between logic and thinking. In: P.C. Wason and P.N. Johnson-Laird (eds.), *Thinking and Reasoning.* Harmondsworth: Penguin.

Herrigel, E. (1953). *Zen in the Art of Archery.* London: Routledge and Kegan Paul.

Higgins, C.A. and Whitrow, R.J. (1984). On-line cursive script recognition. In: B. Schackel (ed.), *Interact '84: First IFIP Conference on Human Computer Interaction.* Amsterdam: IFIP, North-Holland.

Hill, I.D. (1972). Wouldn't it be nice if we could write computer programs in ordinary English — or would it? *Honeywell Computer Journal,* **6**, 76–83.

Hirst, W., Spelke, E.S., Reaves, C.C., Caharack, G., and Neisser, U. (1980). Dividing attention without alternation or automaticity. *Journal of Experimental Psychology: General,* **109**, 98–117.

Hitch, G.J. (1978). The role of short-term working storage in mental arithmetic. *Cognitive Psychology,* **10**, 302–323.

Hitch, G.J. (1980). Developing the concept of working memory. In: G. Claxton (ed.), *Cognitive Psychology: New Directions.* London: Routledge and Kegan Paul.

Hitch, G.J. and Baddeley, A.D. (1976). Verbal reasoning and working memory. *Quarterly Journal of Experimental Psychology,* **28**, 603–621.

Hoch, S.J. and Tschirgi, J.E. (1983). Cue redundancy and extra logical inferences in a deductive reasoning task. *Memory and Cognition,* **11**, 200–209.

Houston, T. (1983). The allegory of software: beyond, behind, and beneath the electronic desk. *Byte*, **December**, 210–214.

Hunt, M. (1981). *The Universe Within*. Hassocks, Sussex: Harvester Press.

Hyde, T.S. and Jenkins, J.J. (1973). Recall for words as a function of semantic, graphic and syntactic orienting tasks. *Journal of Verbal Learning and Verbal Behavior*, **12**, 471–480.

Ingalls, D.H. (1981). Design principles behind Smalltalk. *Byte*, **August**, 286–298.

Inhelder, B. and Piaget, J. (1958). *The Growth of Logical Thinking*. New York: Basic Books.

Jacob, R.J.K. (1983). Executable specifications for a human–computer interface. In: *Proceedings of CHI '83: Human Factors in Computing Systems*, Boston, December 1983. New York: ACM.

James, W. (1890). *The Principles of Psychology*. New York: Holt, Rinehart and Winston.

Janis, I.L. and Frick, F. (1943). The relationship between attitudes towards conclusions and errors in judging logical validity of syllogisms. *Journal of Experimental Psychology*, **33**, 73–77.

Jankel, A. and Morton, R. (1984). *Creative Computer Graphics*. Cambridge: Cambridge University Press.

Johnson, P. (1985). Towards a task model of messaging: an example of the application of TAKD to user interface design. In: P. Johnson and S. Cook (eds.), *People and Computers: Designing the Interface*. Cambridge: Cambridge University Press.

Johnson, P., Diaper, D., and Long, J. (1984). Task, skills and knowledge: task analysis for knowledge based descriptions. In: B. Schackel (ed.), *Interact '84: First IFIP Conference on Human Computer Interaction*. Amsterdam: IFIP, North-Holland.

Johnson-Laird, P.N. (1983). *Mental Models*. London: Cambridge University Press.

Johnson-Laird, P.N. and Bara, B. (1982). *The Figural Effect in Syllogistic Reasoning*. Mimeo, Laboratory of Experimental Psychology, Sussex.

Johnson-Laird, P.N. and Steedman, M.J. (1978). The psychology of syllogisms. *Cognitive Psychology*, **10**, 64–99.

Johnson-Laird, P.N. and Wason, P.C. (1970a). A theoretical analysis of insight into a reasoning task. *Cognitive Psychology*, **1**, 134–148.

Johnson-Laird, P.N. and Wason, P.C. (1970b). Insight into a logical relation. *Quarterly Journal of Experimental Psychology*, **22**, 49–61.

Johnson-Laird, P.N. and Wason, P.C. (1977). A theoretical analysis of insight into a reasoning task: postscript. In: P.N. Johnson-Laird and P.C. Wason (eds), *Thinking: Readings in Cognitive Science*. London: Cambridge University Press.

Johnson-Laird, P.N., Legrenzi, P., and Legrenzi, M.S. (1972). Reasoning and a sense of reality. *British Journal of Psychology*, **63**, 395–400.

Jolicoeur, P., Gluck, M., and Kosslyn, S. (1984). Pictures and names: making the connection. *Cognitive Psychology*, **16**, 243–275.

Jørgensen, A.H., Barnard, P.J., Hammond, N.V., and Clark, I.A. (1983). Naming commands: an analysis of designers' naming behaviour. In T.R.G. Green, S.J. Payne, and G.C. van der Veer (eds.), *The Psychology of Computer Use*. London: Academic Press.

Kahneman, D., Slovic, P., and Tversky, A. (1982). *Judgement under Uncertainty: Heuristics and Biases*. London: Cambridge University Press.

Karat, J., McDonald, J.E., and Anderson, M. (1984). A comparison of selection techniques: touch panel, mouse and keyboard. In: B. Schackel (ed.), *Interact '84: First IFIP Conference on Human Computer Interaction*. Amsterdam: IFIP, North-Holland.

Keele, S.W. (1973). *Attention and Human Performance*. Pacific Palisades: Goodyear.

Keil, F.C. (1986). On the acquisition of natural kind and artifact terms. In: W. Demopolous (ed.), *Conceptual Change*. Norwood, NJ: Ablex Publishing.

Keller, D. and Kellas, G. (1978). Typicality as a dimension of encoding. *Journal of Experimental Psychology: Human Learning and Memory*, **4**, 78–85.

Keller, F.S. (1958). The phantom plateau. *Journal of Experimental Analysis of Behaviour*, **1**, 1–13.

Keppel, G. and Underwood, B.J. (1962). Proactive inhibition in short-term retention of single items. *Journal of Verbal Learning and Verbal Behavior*, **1**, 153–161.

Kidd, A.L. (1982). Man–machine dialogue design. *British Telecom Research Laboratory*, Martlesham Consultancy, vol. 1, Study 1, April.

Kieras, D.E. and Polson, P.G. (1985). An approach to the formal analysis of user complexity. *International Journal of Man–Machine Studies*, **22**, 365–394.

Kiss, G. (1983). *Power versus generality: theoretical constraints in man–machine interaction*. Paper presented at the Leicester Polytechnic Conference on the Ergonomics of the User–System Interface.

Klatzky, R.L. (1984). *Memory and Awareness: An Information-Processing Perspective*. New York: W.H. Freeman and Co.

Klemmer, E.T. (1962). Communication and human performance. *Human Factors*, **4**, 75–79.

Kohler, W. and Wallach, H. (1944). Figural after effects: an investigation of visual processes. *Proceedings of the American Philosophical Society*, **88**, 269–357.

Kolers, P.A. (1975). Memorial consequences of automatized encoding. *Journal of Experimental Psychology: Human Learning and Memory*, **1**, 689–701.

Kuhn, T.S. (1970). *The Structure of Scientific Revolutions*, 2nd ed. Chicago: University of Chicago Press.

Kuhn, T.S. (1977). A function for thought experiments. In: P.N. Johnson-Laird and P.C. Wason (eds.), *Thinking: Readings in Cognitive Science*. Cambridge: Cambridge University Press.

LaBerge, D. and Samuels, S.J. (1974). Towards a theory of automatic information processing in reading. *Cognitive Psychology*, **6**, 293–323.

Lamb, M. and Buckley, V. (1984). New techniques for gesture-based dialogue. In: B. Schackel (ed.), *Interact '84: First IFIP Conference on Human Computer Interaction*. Amsterdam: IFIP, North-Holland.

Landauer, T., Galotti, K., and Hartwell, S. (1983). Natural command names and initial learning: a study of text-editing terms. *Communications of the ACM*, **26**, 495–503.

Larkin, J., McDermott, J., Simon, D., and Simon, H. (1980). Expert and novice performance in solving physics problems. *Science*, **208**, 1335–1342.

Leahey, T.H. (1980). *A History of Psychology*. Englewood Cliffs, NJ: Prentice Hall Inc.

Ledgard, H., Whiteside, J.A., Singer, A., and Seymour, W. (1980). The natural language of interactive systems. *Communications of the ACM*, **23**, 556–563.

Legrenzi, P. (1971). Discovery as a means to understanding. *Quarterly Journal of Experimental Psychology*, **23**, 417–422.

Lenneberg, E.H. (1967). *Biological Foundations of Language*. New York: John Wiley and Sons.

Lesgold, A.M. (1984). Human skill in a computerized society: complex skills and their acquisition. *Behavioural Research Methods and Instrumentation*, **16**, 79–87.

Lewis, C.H. and Mack, R.L. (1982). *The role of abduction in learning to use text processing systems*. Paper presented at the annual meeting of the American Education Research Association, New York City.

Lockhart, R.S., Craik, F.I.M., and Jacoby, L.L. (1976). Depth of processing, recognition and recall. In: J. Brown (ed.), *Recall and Recognition*. New York: John Wiley and Sons.

Logan, G.D. (1982). On the ability to inhibit complex movements: a stop-signal study of typewriting. *Journal of Experimental Psychology: Human Perception and Performance*, **8**, 189–207.

Logan, G.D. (1985). Skill and automaticity: relations, implications, and future directions. *Canadian Journal of Psychology*, **39**, 367–386.

Long, J., Hammond, N.V., Barnard, P., Morton, J., and Clark, I. (1983). Introducing the interactive computer at work: the users' views. *Behaviour and Information Technology*, **2**, 39–106.

Long, T. (1984). Human factors principles for the design of computer colour graphics displays. *British Telecom Journal*, **2**, 10–15.

Luchins, A.S. (1951). The *Einstellung* test of rigidity. Its relation to concreteness of thinking. *Journal of Consulting Psychology*, **15**, 303–310.

Lunzer, E.A., Harrison, C., and Davey, M. (1972). The four-card problem and the generality of formal reasoning. *Quarterly Journal of Experimental Psychology*, **24**, 326–339.

Mack, R., Lewis, C., and Carroll, J. (1983) Learning to use word processors: problems and prospects. *ACM Transactions on Office Information Systems*, **1**, 254–271.

MacGuire, M. (1982). An evaluation of published recommendations on the design of man–computer dialogues. *International Journal of Man–Machine Studies*, **16**, 237–261.

MacKay, D.G. (1982). The problems of flexibility, fluency, and speed-accuracy trade-off in skilled behaviour. *Psychological Review*, **89**, 483–506.

MacLean, A., Barnard, P.J., and Wilson, M.D. (1985a). A comparison between performance and preference tradeoffs in a data entry task. In *Proceedings of the 11th International Symposium on Human Factors in Telecommunications*. Cesson Sevigne, France, September.

MacLean, A., Barnard, P.J., and Wilson, M.D. (1985b). Evaluating the human interface on a data entry system: user choice and performance measures yield different tradeoff situations. In: P. Johnson and S. Cook (eds.), *People and Computers: Designing the Interface*. Cambridge: Cambridge University Press.

Malhotra, A., Thomas, J.C., Carroll, J.M., and Miller, L.A. (1980). Cognitive processes in design. *International Journal of Man–Machine Studies*, **12**, 119–140.

Malone, T.W. (1983). How do people organize their desks? Implications for the design of office information systems. *ACM Transactions on Office Information Systems*, **1**, 99–112.

Malone, T.W. (1985). Designing organisational interfaces. In: L. Borman and B. Curtis (eds.), *Proceedings of CHI '85: Human Factors in Computing Systems*, San Francisco, April. New York: ACM.

Malt, L.G. (1977). Keyboard design for the electronic era. *PIRA-Developments in Data Capture and Photocomposition*.

Mandler, G. (1985). *Cognitive Psychology: An Essay in Cognitive Science*. Hillsdale, NJ: Lawrence Erlbaum Associates.

Mani, K. and Johnson-Laird, P.N. (1982). The mental representation of spatial descriptions. *Memory and Cognition*, **10**, 181–187.

Manktelow, K.I. (1981). Recent developments in research on Wason's selection task. *Current Psychological Reviews*, **1**, 257–268.

Manktelow, K.I. and Evans, J. St B. T. (1979). Facilitation of reasoning by realism: effect or non-effect? *British Journal of Psychology*, **70**, 477–488.

Marcus, M.P. (1980). *A Theory of Syntactic Recognition for Natural Language*. London: MIT Press.

Marshall, C.J. (1982). *The intelligibility of synthetic speech for machine to man communication*. Unpublished dissertation. Loughborough University.

Marshall, C.J. (1985). More bite for mailbox users. In: N. Bevan and D. Murray (eds.), *Infotech State of the Art Report 13: 1. Man–Machine Integration*. London: Pergamon Press.

Martin, M. (1978). Memory span as a measure of individual differences in memory capacity. *Memory and Cognition*, **6**, 194–198.

Massengil, D.P., Gordan, M.E., and Henry, H.G. (1975). Studies in typewriter modification. II. Effects of amount of change, finger load and copy content of accuracy and speed. *Journal of Applied Psychology*, **60**, 227–230.

Maude, T.I., Heaton, N.O., Gilbert, G.N., Wilson, P.A., and Marshall, C.J. (1984). An experiment in group working on mailbox systems. In: B. Schackel (ed.), *Interact '84: First IFIP Conference on Human Computer Interaction*. Amsterdam: IFIP, North-Holland.

Mayer, R.E. (1981). *The Promise of Cognitive Psychology*. San Francisco: W.H. Freeman and Co.

Mazur, J. and Hastie, R. (1978). Learning as accumulation: a re-examination of the learning curve. *Psychological Bulletin*, **85**, 1256–1274.

McCloskey, M. and Glucksberg, S. (1979). Decision processes in verifying category membership statements: implications for models of semantic memory. *Cognitive Psychology*, **11**, 1–37.

McElroy, L.A. and Slamecka, N.J. (1982). Memorial consequences of generating non-words: implications for semantic-memory interpretations of the generation effect. *Journal of Verbal Learning and Verbal Behavior*, **21**, 249–259.

Melton, A.W. (1963). Implications of short-term memory for a general theory of memory. *Journal of Verbal Learning and Verbal Behavior*, **2**, 1–21.

Mervis, C.B., Catlin, J., and Rosch, E. (1976). Relationships among goodness-of-example, category norms, and word frequency. *Bulletin of the Psychonomic Society*, **7**, 283–284.

Meyer, D.E. (1970). On the representation and retrieval of stored semantic information. *Cognitive Psychology*, **1**, 242–300.

Michaels, S.E. (1971). QWERTY versus alphabetic keyboards as a function of typing skills. *Human Factors*, **13**, 419–426.

Miller, G.A. (1956). The magical number seven plus or minus two: some limits on our capacity for processing information. *Psychological Review*, **63**, 81–97.

Miller, G.A. (1969). A psychological method to investigate verbal concepts. *Journal of Mathematical Psychology*, **6**, 169–191.

Miller, G.A. (1981). Trends and debates in cognitive psychology. *Cognition*, **10**, 215–225.

Miller, G.A., Galanter, E., and Pribram, K.H. (1960). *Plans and the Structure of Behaviour*. New York: Holt, Rinehart and Winston.

Monk, A.F. (1986). Mode errors: a user-centred analysis and some preventative measures using keying-contingent sound. Manuscript submitted to *International Journal of Man–Machine Studies*.

Monsell, S. (1984). Components of working memory underlying verbal skills: A 'distributed capacities' view — a tutorial review. In: H. Bouma and D.G. Bouwhuis (eds.), *Attention and Performance, vol. 10*. Hillsdale, NJ: Lawrence Erlbaum Associates.

Moran, T.P. (1980). Compiling cognitive skill. *AIP Memo 150*, Xerox Parc.

Moran, T.P. (1981). The Command Language Grammar: a representation for the user interface of interactive computer systems. *International Journal of Man–Machine Studies*, **15**, 3–50.

Moran, T.P. (1983). Getting into a system: external–internal task mapping analysis. In *Proceedings of CHI '83: Human Factors in Computing Systems*, Boston, December 1983, New York: ACM.

Morgan, L., Williams, G., and Lemmons, P. (1983). An interview with Wayne Rosing, Bruce Daniels, and Larry Tesler, *Byte*, **February**, 90–114.

Morton, J. (1981). Will Cognition survive? *Cognition*, **10**, 227–234.

Morton, J., Barnard, P., Hammond, N., and Long, J.B. (1979). Interacting with the computer: a framework. In: E.J. Boutmy and A. Danthine (eds.), *Teleinformatics '79*. Amsterdam: North-Holland.

Mosier, J.N. and Smith, S.L. (1986). Application of guidelines for designing user interface software. *Behaviour and Information Technology*, **5**, 39–46.

Murdock, B.B. Jr. (1967). Recent developments in short-term memory. *British Journal of Psychology*, **58**, 421–433.

Murphy, G.L. and Medin, D.L. (1985). The role of theories in conceptual coherence. *Psychological Review*, **92**, 289–316.

Murphy, G.L. and Smith, E.E. (1982). Basic-level superiority in picture categorization. *Journal of Verbal Learning and Verbal Behavior*, **21**, 1–20.

Nairne, J.S. and Healy, A.F. (1983). Counting backwards produces systematic errors. *Journal of Experimental Psychology: General*, **112**, 37–40.

Neisser, U. (1967). *Cognitive Psychology*. New York: Prentice Hall.

Neisser, U. (1976). *Cognition and Reality: Principles and Implications of Cognitive Psychology*. San Francisco: W.H. Freeman and Co.

Neisser, U. (1984). Toward an ecologically oriented cognitive science. *Emory Cognition Project Report #1*. Emory University.

Neisser, U., Novick, R., and Lazar, R. (1963). Searching for ten targets simultaneously. *Perceptual and Motor Skills*, **17**, 955–961.

Neves, D.M. and Anderson, J.R. (1981). Knowledge compilation: mechanisms for the automatization of cognitive skills. In: J.R. Anderson (ed.), *Cognitive Skills and their Acquisition*. Hillsdale, NJ: Lawrence Erlbaum Associates.

Newell, A.F. (1984). Speech the natural modality for man–machine interaction? In: B. Schackel (ed.), *Interact '84: First IFIP Conference on Human Computer Interaction*. Amsterdam: IFIP, North-Holland.

Newell, A. and Rosenbloom, P.S. (1981). Mechanisms of skill acquisition and the law of practice. In: J.R. Anderson (ed.), *Cognitive Skills and their Acquisition*. Hillsdale, NJ: Lawrence Erlbaum Associates.

Newell, A. and Simon, H.A. (1972). *Human Problem Solving*. Englewood Cliffs, NJ: Prentice Hall.

Nisbett, R.E. and Ross, L. (1980). *Human Inference*. Englewood Cliffs, NJ: Prentice Hall.

Norman, D.A. (1981). Categorization of action slips. *Psychological Review*, **88**, 1–15.

Norman, D.A. (1982). Steps towards a cognitive engineering: design rules based on analyses of human error. In *Proceedings of Conference on Human Factors in Computer Systems*, Gaithersburg, March. New York: ACM.

Norman, D.A. (1983). Some observations on mental models. In: D. Gentner and A.L. Stevens (eds.), *Mental Models*. London: Lawrence Erlbaum Associates.

Norman, D.A. and Bobrow, D.G. (1979). Descriptions: an intermediate stage in memory retrieval. *Cognitive Psychology*, **11**, 107–123.

Norman, D.A. and Rumelhart, D.E. (1975). *Explorations in Cognition*. San Francisco: W.H. Freeman and Co.

Norman, D.A. and Shallice, T. (1980). Attention to action: willed and automatic control of behaviour. *Technical Report 99*. La Jolla, California: Center for Human Information Processing, University of California, San Diego. (UCSD).

Noyce, R.N. (1977). Microelectronics. *Scientific American*, **237**, 16–20.

Oakhill, J.V. and Johnson-Laird, P.N. (1985). Rationality, memory, and the search for counterexamples. *Cognition*, **20**, 79–94.

Ogden, W.C. and Boyle, J.M. (1982). Evaluating human–computer dialog styles: Command vs. form fill-in for report modification. *Proceedings of the Annual Meeting of the Human Factors Society*, Seattle.

Ormerod, T.C., Manktelow, K.I., Robson, E.H., and Steward, A.P. (1986). Content and representation effects with reasoning tasks in Prolog form. *Behaviour and Information Technology* (in press).

Osherson, D.N. and Smith, E.E. (1981). On the adequacy of prototpye theory as a theory of concepts. *Cognition*, **9**, 35–58.

Osherson, D.N. and Smith, E.E. (1982). Gradedness and conceptual combination. *Cognition*, **12**, 299–318.

Paivio, A. (1971). *Imagery and Verbal Processes*. New York: Holt, Rinehart and Winston.

Paivio, A. (1976). Imagery in recall and recognition. In: J. Brown (ed.), *Recall and Recognition*. New York: John Wiley and Sons.

Parkin, A.J. (1980). Levels of processing and the cue overload principle. *Quarterly Journal of Experimental Psychology*, **32**, 427–434.

Payne, S.J. (1984). Task-action grammars. In: B. Schackel (ed.), *Interact '84: First IFIP Conference on Human Computer Interaction*. Amsterdam: IFIP, North-Holland.

Peckham, J. (1983). Automatic speech recognition: a solution in search of a problem? *Proceedings of the User Interface: The Ergonomics of Interactive Computing*. Leicester Polytechnic, UK.

Perlman, G. (1984). Making the right choice with menus. In: B. Schackel (ed.), *Interact '84: First IFIP Conference on Human Computer Interaction*. Amsterdam: IFIP, North-Holland.

Peterson, L.R. and Peterson, M.J. (1959). Short-term retention of individual items. *Journal of Experimental Psychology*, **58**, 193–198.

Phillips, W.A. (1974). On the distinction between sensory storage and short-term visual memory. *Perception and Psychophysics*, **16**, 283–290.

Phillips, W.A. (1983). Short-term visual memory. *Philosophical Transactions of the Royal Society London B*, **302**, 295–309.

Piaget, J. (1977). Intellectual evaluation from adolescence to adulthood. In: P.N. Johnson-Laird and P.C. Wason (eds.), *Thinking: Readings in Cognitive Science*. Cambridge: Cambridge Univesity Press.

Pollard, P. (1982). Human reasoning: some possible effects of availability. *Cognition*, **12**, 65–96.

Pollard, P. and Gubbins, M. (1982). Content and rule manipulations on the Wason selection task. *Current Psychological Research*, **2**, 139–149.

Poller, M.F. and Garter, S.K. (1984). The effects of modes on text editing by experienced editor users. *Human Factors*, **26**, 449–462.

Posner, M.I. and Rossman, E. (1965). Effect of size and location of information transforms on short-term memory. *Journal of Experimental Psychology*, **70**, 496–505.

Pulat, B.M. and Grice, A.E. (1985). Computer aided techniques for crew station design: Work-space Organizer — WORG; Workstation Layout Generator — WOLAG. *International Journal of Man—Machine Studies*, **23**, 443–457.

Pylyshyn, Z. (1978). Computational models and empirical constraints. *Behavioural and Brain Sciences*, **1**, 93–127.

Rabbit, P.M.A. (1981). Human ageing and disturbances of memory control processes underlying 'intelligent' performance of some cognitive tasks. In: M.P. Friedman, J.P. Das, and N. O'Connor (eds.), *Intelligence and Learning*. New York: Plenum Press.

Reason, J.T. (1984a). Lapses of attention in everyday life. In R. Parasuraman and D.R. Davies (eds.), *Varieties of Attention*. New York: Academic Press.

Reason, J.T. (1984b). Absent-mindedness and cognitive control. In: J.E. Harris and P.E.

Morris (eds.), *Everyday Memory, Actions and Absent-Mindedness*. London: Academic Press.

Reason, J. and Mycielska, K. (1982). *Absent-Minded? The Psychology of Mental Lapses and Everyday Errors*. Englewood Cliffs, NJ: Prentice Hall.

Reisner, P. (1983). Formal grammars as a tool for analyzing ease of use: Some fundamental concepts. In: J.C. Thomas and M. Schneider (eds.), *Human Factors in Computing systems*. Norwood, NJ: Ablex Publishing.

Reynolds, A.G. and Flagg, P.W. (1983). *Cognitive Psychology*, 2nd ed. Boston: Little, Brown and Co.

Riley, M. and O'Malley, C. (1984). Planning nets: a framework for analyzing user-computer interactions. In: B. Schackel (ed.), *Interact '84: First IFIP Conference on Human Computer Interaction*. Amsterdam: IFIP, North-Holland.

Rips, L.J. and Marcus, S.M. (1977). Suppositions and the analysis of conditional sentences. In: M.A. Just and P.A. Carpenter (eds.), *Cognitive Processes in Comprehension*. Hillsdale, NJ: Lawrence Erlbaum Associates.

Rips, L.J., Shoben, E.J., and Smith, E.E. (1973). Semantic distance and the verification of semantic relations. *Journal of Verbal Learning and Verbal Behavior*, **12**, 1–20.

Ritchie, G.J. and Turner, J.A. (1975). Input devices for interactive graphics. *International Journal of Man–Machine Studies*, **7**, 639–660.

Roberts, T.L. and Moran, T.P. (1983). The evaluation of text editors: methodology and empirical results. *Communications of the ACM*, **26**, 265–283.

Rosch, E. (1973). On the internal structure of perceptual and semantic categories. In: T.E. Moore (ed.), *Cognitive Development and the Acquisition of Language*. New York: Academic Press.

Rosch, E. (1974a). Universals and cultural specifics in human categorization. In: R. Brislim, W. Lonner, and S. Bochner (eds.), *Cross-Cultural Perspectives on Learning*. London: Sage Press.

Rosch, E. (1974b). Linguistic relativity. In: A. Silverstein (ed.), *Human Communication: Theoretical Perspectives*, Hillsdale, NJ: Lawrence Erlbaum Associates.

Rosch, E. (1975a). Cognitive representations of semantic categories. *Journal of Experimental Psychology: General*, **104**, 192–233.

Rosch, E. (1975b). Cognitive reference points. *Cognitive Psychology*, **1**, 532–547.

Rosch, E. (1978). Principles of categorisation. In: E. Rosch and B.B. Lloyd (eds.), *Cognition and Categorization*. Hillsdale, NJ: Lawrence Erlbaum Associates.

Rosch, E. and Mervis, C.B. (1975). Family resemblances: studies in the internal structure of categories. *Cognitive Psychology*, **7**, 573–605.

Rosch, E., Simpson, C., and Miller, R.S. (1976). Structural bases of typicality effects. *Journal of Experimental Psychology: Human Perception and Performance*, **2**, 491–502.

Rosch, E., Mervis, C.B., Gray, W.D., Johnson, D.M., and Boves-Braem, P. (1976). Basic objects in natural categories. *Cognitive Psychology*, **8**, 382–439.

Rosson, M.B. (1984). Effects of experience on learning, using and evaluating a text editor. *Human Factors*, **26**, 463–476.

Roth, E.M. (1979). Facilitating insight into a reasoning task. *British Journal of Psychology*, **70**, 265–272.

Roth, E.M. and Shoben, E.J. (1983). The effect of context on the structure of categories. *Cognitive Psychology*, **15**, 346–378.

Routh, D.A. (1970). 'Trace strength', modality and the serial position curve in immediate memory. *Psychonomic Science*, **18**, 355–357.

Routh, D.A. (1976). An 'across-the-board' modality effect in immediate serial recall. *Quarterly Journal of Experimental Psychology*. **28**, 285–304.

Rumelhart, D.E. (1980). Schemata: the building blocks of cognition. In: R.J. Spiro, B.C. Bruce, and W.F. Brewer (eds), *Theoretical Issues in Reading Comprehension*. Hillsdale, NJ: Lawrences Erlbaum Associations.

Rumelhart, D.E. and Norman, D.A. (1978). Accretion, tuning, and restructuring: three modes of learning. In: J. Cotton and R. Klatzky (eds.), *Semantic Factors in Cognition*, Hillsdale, NJ: Lawrence Erlbaum Associates.

Rumelhart, D.E. and Norman, D.A. (1981). Analogical processes in learning. In: J.R. Anderson (ed.), *Cognitive Skills and their Acquisition*. Hillsdale, NJ: Lawrence Erlbaum Associates.

Rumelhart, D.E. and Norman, D.A. (1982). Simulating a skilled typist: a study of skilled cognitive-motor performance. *Cognitive Science*, **6**, 1–36.

Ryan, C. (1983). Reassessing the automaticity-control distinction: item recognition as a case paradigm. *Psychological Review*, **90**, 171–178.

Ryan, J. (1969). Grouping and short-term memory: different means and patterns of grouping. *Quarterly Journal of Experimental Psychology*, **21**, 137–147.

Savage, R.E., Habinek, J.K., and Barnhart, T.W. (1982). The design, simulation and evaluation of a menu-driven user interface. In *Proceedings of Conference on Human Factors in Computer Systems*, Gaithersburg, March. New York: ACM.

Scapin, D.L. (1981). Computer commands in restricted natural language: some aspects of memory and experience. *Human Factors*, **23**, 365–375.

Schank, R.C. (1980). Language and memory. *Cognitive Science*, **4**, 243–284.

Schank, R.C. (1982). *Dynamic Memory*. London: Cambridge University Press.

Schank, R.C. and Abelson, R.P. (1977). *Scripts, Plans, Goals, and Understanding*. Hillsdale, NJ: Lawrence Erlbaum Associates.

Schiano, D.J. and Watkins, M.J. (1981). Speech-like coding of pictures in short-term memory. *Memory and Cognition*, **9**, 110–114.

Schmidt, R.A. (1975). A schema theory of discrete motor skill learning. *Psychological Review*, **82**, 225–260.

Schneider, W. and Fisk, A.D. (1980). Context dependent automatic processing. *Report no. 8009*, Human Attention Research Laboratory, University of Illinois.

Schneider, W. and Fisk, A.D. (1982). Degree of consistent training: improvements in search performance and automatic process development. *Perception and Psychophysics*, **31**, 160–168.

Schneider, W. and Fisk, A.D. (1984). Automatic category search and its transfer. *Journal of Experimental Psychology: Learning, Memory and Cognition*, **10**, 1–15.

Schneider, W. and Shiffrin, R.M. (1977). Controlled and automatic human information processing: I. Detection, search, and attention. *Psychological Review*, **84**, 1–66.

Schneider, W., Dumais, S.T., and Shiffrin, R.M. (1984). Automatic and control processing and attention. In: R. Parasuraman and D.R. Davies (eds.), *Varieties of Attention*. New York: Academic Press.

Schofield, D. (1985). Interaction using speech. In: N. Bevan and D. Murray (eds.), *Infotech State of the Art Report 13: 1. Man–Machine Integration*. London: Pergamon Press.

Scholes, P.A. (1955). *The Oxford Companion to Music*, 9th ed. London: Oxford University Press, p. 808.

Seymour, P.H.K. (1979). *Human Visual Cognition*. London: Collier Macmillan.

Shaffer, W. and Shiffrin, R.M. (1972). Rehearsal and storage of visual information. *Journal of Experimental Psychology*, **92**, 292–296.

Shallice, T. (1979). The dominant action system: an information-processing approach to consciousness. In: J.L. Singer and K. Pope (eds.), *The Stream of Consciousness*. New York: Plenum.

Shand, M.A. and Klima, E.S. (1981). Nonauditory suffix effects in cogenitally deaf signers of American sign language, *Journal of Experimental Psychology: Human Learning and Memory*, **7**, 464–474.

Shepard, R.N. (1967). Recognition memory for words, sentences and pictures. *Journal of Verbal Learning and Verbal Behavior*, **6**, 156–163.

Shiffrin, R.M. and Dumais, S.T. (1981). The development of automatism. In: J.R. Anderson (ed.), *Cognitive Skills and their Aquisition*. Hillsdale, NJ: Lawrence Erlbaum Associates.

Shiffrin, R.M. and Schneider, W. (1977). Controlled and automatic human information processing: II. Perceptual learning, automatic attending, and a general theory. *Psychological Review*, **84**, 127–190.

Shiffrin, R.M., Dumais, S.T., and Schneider, W. (1981). Characteristics of automatism. In: J.B. Long and A.D. Baddeley (eds.), *Attention and Performance IX*. Hillsdale, NJ: Lawrence Erlbaum Associates.

Shneiderman, B. (1984). The future of interactive systems and the emergence of direct manipulation. In Y. Vassilou (ed.), *Human Factors and Interactive Computer Systems*. Norwood, NJ: Ablex Publishing.

Siebel, R. (1963). Discrimination reaction time for a 1,023 alternative task. *Journal of Experimental Psychology*, **66**, 215–226.

Simon, H. (1974). How big is a chunk? *Science*, **183**, 482–488.

Singley, M.K. and Anderson, J.R. (1985). The transfer of text-editing skill. *International Journal of Man–Machine Studies*, **22**, 403–424.

Slamecka, N.J. and Graf, P. (1978). The generation effect: delineation of a phenomenon. *Journal of Experimental Psychology: Human Learning and Memory*, **4**, 592–604.

Smedslund, J. (1970). On the circular relation between logic and understanding. *Scandinavian Journal of Psychology*, **11**, 217–219.

Smith, D.C., Irby, C., Kimball, R., Verplank, B., and Harslem, E. (1982). Designing the Star interface. *Byte*, **April**, 242–282.

Smith, E.E. and Osherson, D.N. (1984). Conceptual combination with prototype concepts. *Cognitive Science*, **8**, 337–361.

Smith, E.E., Shoben, E.J., and Rips, L.J. (1974). Structure and process in semantic memory: a featural model for semantic decisions. *Psychological Review*, **81**, 214–241.

Smith, K.U. and Smith, W.M. (1962). *Perception and Motion*. Philadelphia: Saunders.

Smith, S.L. (1986). Standards versus guidelines for designing user interface software. *Behaviour and Information Technology*, **5**, 47–61.

Smith, S.L. and Mosier, J.N. (1984a). The user interface to computer-based information systems: a survey of current software design practice. In: B. Schackel (ed.), *Interact '84: First IFIP Conference on Human Computer Interaction*. Amsterdam: IFIP, North-Holland.

Smith, S.L. and Mosier, J.N. (1984b). Design guidelines for user–system interface software. *Technical Report ESD-TR-84-190*, USAF Electronic Systems Division, Hanscom Air Force Base, Mass.

Smith, W.J. (in preparation). *Using Computer Color Effectively* (working title).

Smolensky, P., Monty, M.L., and Conway, E. (1984). Formalizing task descriptions for command specification and documentation. In: B. Schackel (ed.), *Interact '84: First IFIP Conference on Human Computer Interaction*. Amsterdam: IFIP, North-Holland.

Snoddy, G.S. (1926). Learning and stability. *Journal of Applied Psychology*, **10**, 1–36.

Standing, L., Conezio, J., and Haber, R.N. (1970). Perception and memory for pictures: single-trial learning of 2560 visual stimuli. *Psychonomic Science*, **19**, 73–74.

Stibic, V. (1980). A few practical remarks on the user-friendliness of online systems. *Journal of Information Science*, **2**, 277–283.

Streveler, D.J. and Wasserman, A.I. (1984). Quantitative measures of the spatial properties of screen designs. In: B. Schackel (ed.), *Interact '84: First IFIP Conference on Human Computer Interaction*. Amsterdam: IFIP, North-Holland.

Thimbleby, H.T. (1982). Character level ambiguity: consequences for user interface design. *International Journal of Man–Machine Studies*, **10**, 211–225.

Thimbleby, H.T. (1984). Generative user-engineering principles for user interface design. In: B. Schackel (ed.), *Interact '84: First IFIP Conference on Human Computer Interaction*. Amsterdam: IFIP, North-Holland.

Todres, A.K. and Watkins, M.J. (1981). A part-set cueing effect in recognition memory. *Journal of Experimental Psychology: Human Learning and Memory*, **7**, 91–99.

Tolman, E.C. (1948). Cognitive maps in rats and men. *Psychological Review*, **55**, 189–208.

Tschritzis, D. (1985). (ed.). *Office Automation*. Berlin: Springer-Verlag.

Tulving, E. (1972). Episodic and semantic memory. In: E. Tulving and W. Donaldson (eds.), *Organization and Memory*. New York: Academic Press.

Tulving, E. (1974). Cue-dependent forgetting. *American Scientist*, **62**, 74–82.

Tulving, E. (1983). *Elements of Episodic Memory*. New York: Oxford University Press.

Tulving, E. (1985). How many memory systems are there? 1984 APA Award Address. *American Psychologist*, **40**, 385–398.

Tulving, E. and Madigan, S.A. (1970). Memory and verbal learning. *Annual Review of Psychology*, **21**, 437–484.

Tulving, E. and Pearlstone, Z. (1966). Availability versus accessibility of information in memory for words. *Journal of Verbal Learning and Verbal Behavior*, **5**, 381–391.

Tulving, E. and Psotka, J. (1971). Retroactive inhibition in free recall: inaccessibility of information available in the memory store. *Journal of Experimental Psychology*, **87**, 1–8.

Tulving, E. and Thomson, D. M. (1973). Encoding specificity and retrieval processes in episodic memory. *Psychological Review*, **80**, 352–373.

Tversky, A. (1977). Features of similarity. *Psychological Review*, **84**, 327–352.

Tversky, A. and Hemenway, K. (1984). Objects, parts, and categories. *Journal of Experimental Psychology: General*, **113**, 169–193.

Tversky, A. and Kahneman, D. (1974). Judgement under uncertainty: heuristics and biases. *Science*, **185**, 1124–1131.

Tversky, A. and Kahneman, D. (1982). Causal schemas in judgements under uncertainty. In: D. Kahneman, P. Slovic, and A. Tversky (eds.), *Judgement under Uncertainty: Heuristics and Biases*. Cambridge: Cambridge University Press.

Tversky, A. and Kahneman, D. (1983). Extensional versus intuitive reasoning. The conjunction fallacy in probability judgement. *Psychological Review*, **90**, 293–315.

Visick, D., Johnson, P., and Long, J. (1984). The use of simple speech recognisers in industrial applications. In: B. Schackel (ed.), *Interact '84: First IFIP Conference on Human Computer Interaction*. Amsterdam: IFIP, North-Holland.

Wason, P.C. (1960). On the failure to eliminate hypotheses in a conceptual task. *Quarterly Journal of Experimental Psychology*, **12**, 129–140.

Wason, P.C. (1968). Reasoning about a rule. *Quarterly Journal of Experimental Psychology*, **20**, 273–281.

Wason, P.C. (1969). Structural simplicity and psychological complexity: some thoughts on a novel problem. *Bulletin of the British Psychological Society*, **22**, 281–284.

Wason, P.C. (1983). Realism and rationality in the selection task. In: J. St B. T. Evans (ed.), *Thinking and Reasoning: Psychological Approaches*. London: Routledge and Kegan Paul.

Wason, P.C. and Evans, J. St B. T. (1975). Dual processes in reasoning? *Cognition*, **3**, 141–154.

Wason, P.C. and Green, D.W. (1984). Reasoning and mental representation. *Quarterly Journal of Experimental Psychology*, **36A**, 597–610.

Wason, P.C. and Johnson-Laird, P.N. (1970). A conflict between selecting and evaluating information in an inferential task. *British Journal of Psychology*, **61**, 509–515.

Wason, P.C. and Johnson-Laird, P.N. (1972). *Psychology of Reasoning: Structure and Content*. London: Batsford.

Wason, P.C. and Shapiro, D.A. (1971). Natural and contrived experience in a reasoning task. *Quarterly Journal of Experimental Psychology*, **23**, 63–71.

Wasserman, A.I. (1985). Extending state transition diagrams for the specification of human–computer interaction. *IEEE Transactions on Software Engineering, vol.* **SE-11(8)**, 699–713.

Watkins, M.J. (1979). Engrams as cuegrams and forgetting as cue-overload. In: C.R. Puff (ed.), *Memory Organization and Structure*, New York: Academic Press.

Watkins, M.J. and Tulving, E. (1975). Episodic memory: when recognition fails. *Journal of Experimental Psychology: General*, **1**, 5–29.

Watkins, M.J. and Watkins, O.C. (1976). Cue-overload theory and the method of interpolated attributes. *Bulletin of the Psychonomic Society*, **7**, 289–291.

Watkins, O.C. and Watkins, M.J. (1975). Build-up of proactive inhibition as a cue-overload effect. *Journal of Experimental Psychology: Human Learning and Performance*, **104**, 442–452.

Watson, J.B. (1913). Psychology as the behaviourist views it. *Psychological Review*, **20**, 158–177.

Waugh, N.C. and Norman, D.A. (1965). Primary memory. *Psychological Review*, **72**, 89–104.

Welford, A.T. (1968). *Fundamentals of Skill*. London: Methuen.

Whiteside, J., Jones, S., Levy, P., and Dixon, D. (1985). User performance with command, menu and iconic interfaces. In: L. Borman and B. Curtis (ed), *Proceedings of CHI '85: Human Factors in Computing systems*, San Francisco, April. New York: ACM.

Whitfield, A. (1983). Pointing as an input technique for human–computer interactions. *Proceedings of an IEE Colloquium on 'Future Input Techniques for Man–machine Interactions'*, Digest No. 1983/42.

Whorf, B.L. (1956). Science and linguistics. In: J.B. Carroll (ed.), *Language, Thought and Reality: Selected Writings of Benjamin Lee Whorf*, Cambridge, Mass.: MIT Press.

Wickelgren, W.A. (1979). *Cognitive Psychology*. Englewood Cliffs, NJ: Prentice Hall.

Wickens, D.D. (1970). Encoding categories of words: an empirical approach to meaning. *Psychological Review*, **77**, 1–15.

van Wijngaarden, A. (1966). Recursive definition of syntax and semantics. In: T.B. Steel (ed.), *Formal Description Languages for Computer Programming*. Amsterdam: North-Holland.

Wilkins, M.C. (1928). The effects of changed material on the ability to do formal reasoning. *Archives of Psychology*, **16**, No. 102.

Williams, M.D. (1981). Instantiation: a data base interface for the novice user. *Xerox Palo Alto Research Center Working Paper*.

Williams, M.D. (1984). What makes RABBIT run? *International Journal of Man–Machine Studies*, **21**, 333–352.

Williams, M.D. and Hollan, J.D. (1981). The process of retrieval from very long term memory. *Cognitive Science*, **5**, 87–119.

Wilson, M.D., Barnard, P.J., and MacLean, A. (1985). Analysing the learning of command sequences in a menu system. In: P. Johnson and S. Cook (eds.), *People and Computers: Designing the Interface*. Cambridge: Cambridge University Press.

Wilson, P.A. (1984). Structures for mailbox system applications. *Proceedings of an IFIP 6.5 Conference on Computer Message Services*. Nottingham, UK, 1–4 May.

Wilson, P.A., Maude, T.I., Marshall, C.J., and Heaton, N.O. (1984). The active mailbox — your on-line secretary. *Proceedings of an IFIP 6.5 Conference on Computer Message Services*. Nottingham, UK, 1–4 May.

Winograd, T. (1975). Frame representation and the declarative-procedural controversy. In: D. Bobrow and A. Collins (eds.), *Representation and Understanding*. New York: Academic Press.

Wiser, M. and Carey, S. (1982). When heat and temperature were one. In: D. Gentner and A.L. Stevens (eds.), *Mental Models*. Hillsdale, NJ: Lawrence Erlbaum Associates, Publishers.

Wittgenstein, L. (1953). *Philosophical Investigations*. New York: Macmillan.

Wolford, G. (1971). Function of distinct associations for paired-associate performance. *Psychological Review*, **78**, 303–313.

Woodmansee, G. (1983). Visi On's interface design. *Byte*, **July**, 166–182.

Wright, P. and Bason, G. (1983). Detour routes to usability: a comparison of alternative approaches to multipurpose software design. *International Journal of Man–Machine Studies*, **10**, 391–400.

Young, R.M. and Hull, A. (1982). Cognitive aspects of the selection of Viewdata options by casual users. In: M.B. Williams (ed.), *Pathways to the Information Society: Proceedings of the Sixth International Conference on Computer Communications*. Amsterdam: North-Holland.

Yu, B., Zhang, W., Jing, Q., Peng, R., Zhang, G., and Simon, H.A. (1985). STM capacity for Chinese and English language materials. *Memory and Cognition*, **13**, 202–207.

Zadeh, L. (1965). Fuzzy sets. *Information and Control*, **8**, 338–353.

Zadeh, L. (1975). Calculus of fuzzy restrictions. In: L.A. Zadeh, K.S. Fu, K. Tanaka, and M. Shimura (eds.), *Fuzzy Sets and their Application to Cognitive and Decision Processes*. New York: Academic Press.

Zechmeister, E.B. and Nyberg, S.E. (1982). *Human Memory*. California: Brooks-Cole.

Zhang, G. and Simon, H.A. (1985). STM capacity for Chinese words and idioms: chunking and acoustical loop hypotheses. *Memory and Cognition*, **13**, 193–201.

Zipf, G.K. (1949). *Human Behavior and the Principle of Least Effort*. Cambridge, Mass.: Addison-Wesley.

Author Index

357

Subject Index

Abstract versus concrete tasks, 91
Acquisition of knowledge, 74, 111
Acquisition of skills, 9, 10, 163, 164, 287
ACT Theory, 81, 114, 151
Actions, 116, 185
Adaptation, 230, 244, 256, 262, 263, 272, 274, 305
Adaptive interfaces, 244, 306, 308
Advance organizers, 109, 114
Advanced workstation, 280
Age effects on memory, 156, 161, 234
Agency, 307
Analogy and metaphor, 109, 116, 172, 184, 228, 229, 230, 231, 250, 251, 253, 257, 258
Analysis of user tasks, 25, 37, 38
Analytic stage of thinking, 94
Analytical route from psychology to design, 30, 35
Anxiety, 132
Apple Lisa, 48, 101, 109, 228
Apple Macintosh, 48, 109, 228
Applied and applicable research, 20
Applied and scientific research, 19
Articulatory loop in working memory, 124, 125, 128, 129, 131
Artificial intelligence, 16, 17, 18, 70, 306, 308
Assessment tools, 321
Associationism, 58, 61
Associative phase in skill acquisition, 169
Attention, 10, 68, 77, 124, 128, 139, 178, 185, 249
Auditory output, 292

Automatic and controlled processing, 82, 174, 185, 186, 187, 255
Automaticity, 174, 175, 176, 177, 179, 232, 249, 254, 271
Autonomous phase in skill acquisition, 169
Availability heuristic, 93

Background information, 211, 212
Backus Normal Form (BNF) notation, 37
Basic level objects, 194, 214
Basic phenomena of memory, 145
Behaviourism, 64, 65, 66, 70, 72, 74, 75, 78, 111
Benchmarks, 33, 34, 39
Biases in thinking, 93
Brown–Peterson paradigm, 125
Budgeting, 44, 315

Calculational models of user performance, 39
Capacity
    of memory, 123
    of working memory, 103, 117, 125, 133
Capture errors, 117, 238
Categories
    and semantic memory, 138, 154, 161, 196, 213, 241
    of design guidelines, 226
Categorized materials and memory, 138, 139, 140
Category exemplars in semantic memory, 154

363